S0-AWL-356

Global Climate Change

Custom Edition prepared exclusively for San Jose State University

Ahrens/Miller/Thompson/Turk

THOMSON

*

™

WADSWORTH

Australia · Canada · Mexico · Singapore · Spain · United Kingdom · United States

Global Climate Change
Ahrens/Miller/Thompson/Turk

Custom Editor:
Marc Bove

Project Development Editor:
Lea Riddle

Marketing Coordinator:
Sara Mercurio

Production/Manufacturing Supervisor:
Donna M. Brown

Project Coordinator:
Tamara L. Sweet

Pre-Media Services Supervisor:
Dan Plofchan

Rights and Permissions Specialist:
Kalina Hintz

Senior Prepress Specialist:
Kim Fry

Cover Design:
Krista Pierson

Printer:
Cross Media

© 2006 Wadsworth, a part of the Thomson Corporation. Thomson, the Star logo and Wadsworth are trademarks used herein under license.

ALL RIGHTS RESERVED. No part of this work covered by the copyright hereon may be reproduced or used in any form or by any means — graphic, electronic, or mechanical, including photocopying, recording, taping, Web distribution or information storage and retrieval systems — without the written permission of the publisher.

Printed in the United States of America
3 4 5 6 7 8 9 10 11 12 13 14 09 08 07 06

For information about our products, contact us at:
Thomson Learning Academic Resource Center
(800) 423-0563

For permission to use material from this text or product, submit a request online at **http://www.thomsonrights.com**. Any additional questions about permissions can be submitted by email to
thomsonrights@thomson.com.

The Adaptable Courseware Program consists of products and additions to existing Wadsworth products that are produced from camera-ready copy. Peer review, class testing, and accuracy are primarily the responsibility of the author(s).

Student Edition: ISBN 0-495-14219-0

Thomson Custom Solutions
5191 Natorp Boulevard
Mason, OH 45040
www.thomsoncustom.com

Thomson Higher Education
10 Davis Drive
Belmont, CA 94002-3098
USA

Asia (Including India):
Thomson Learning
60 Albert Street, #15-01
Albert Complex
Singapore 189969
Tel 65 336-6411
Fax 65 336-7411

Australia/New Zealand:
Thomson Learning Australia
102 Dodds Street
Southbank, Victoria 3006
Australia

Latin America:
Thomson Learning
Seneca 53
Colonia Polano
11560 Mexico, D.F., Mexico
Tel (525) 281-2906
Fax (525) 281-2656

Canada:
Thomson Nelson
1120 Birchmount Road
Toronto, Ontario
Canada M1K 5G4
Tel (416) 752-9100
Fax (416) 752-8102

UK/Europe/Middle East/Africa:
Thomson Learning
High Holborn House
50-51 Bedford Row
London, WC1R 4L$
United Kingdom
Tel 44 (020) 7067-2500
Fax 44 (020) 7067-2600

Spain (Includes Portugal):
Thomson Paraninfo
Calle Magallanes 25
28015 Madrid
España
Tel 34 (0)91 446-3350
Fax 34 (0)91 445-6218

Custom Table of Contents

The Earth and Its Atmosphere

CONTENTS

well remember a brilliant red balloon which kept me completely happy for a whole afternoon, until, while I was playing, a clumsy movement allowed it to escape. Spellbound, I gazed after it as it drifted silently away, gently swaying, growing smaller and smaller until it was only a red point in a blue sky. At that moment I realized, for the first time, the vastness above us: a huge space without visible limits. It was an apparent void, full of secrets, exerting an inexplicable power over all the earth's inhabitants. I believe that many people, consciously or unconsciously, have been filled with awe by the immensity of the atmosphere. All our knowledge about the air, gathered over hundreds of years, has not diminished this feeling.

Theo Loebsack, *Our Atmosphere*

ur *atmosphere* is a delicate life-giving blanket of air that surrounds the fragile earth. In one way or another, it influences everything we see and hear—it is intimately connected to our lives. Air is with us from birth, and we cannot detach ourselves from its presence. In the open air, we can travel for many thousands of kilometers in any horizontal direction, but should we move a mere eight kilometers above the surface, we would suffocate. We may be able to survive without food for a few weeks, or without water for a few days, but, without our atmosphere, we would not survive more than a few minutes. Just as fish are confined to an environment of water, so we are confined to an ocean of air. Anywhere we go, it must go with us.

The earth without an atmosphere would have no lakes or oceans. There would be no sounds, no clouds, no red sunsets. The beautiful pageantry of the sky would be absent. It would be unimaginably cold at night and unbearably hot during the day. All things on the earth would be at the mercy of an intense sun beating down upon a planet utterly parched.

Living on the surface of the earth, we have adapted so completely to our environment of air that we sometimes forget how truly remarkable this substance is. Even though air is tasteless, odorless, and (most of the time) invisible, it protects us from the scorching rays of the sun and provides us with a mixture of gases that allows life to flourish. Because we cannot see, smell, or taste air, it may seem surprising that between your eyes and the pages of this book are trillions of air molecules. Some of these may have been in a cloud only yesterday, or over another continent last week, or perhaps part of the life-giving breath of a person who lived hundreds of years ago.

In this chapter, we will examine a number of important concepts and ideas about the earth's atmosphere, many of which will be expanded in subsequent chapters.

Overview of the Earth's Atmosphere

The universe contains billions of galaxies and each galaxy is made up of billions of stars. Stars are hot, glowing balls of gas that generate energy by converting hydrogen into helium near their centers. Our sun is an average size star situated near the edge of the Milky Way galaxy. Revolving around the sun are the earth and eight other planets (see Fig. 1.1). These planets, along with a host of other material (comets, asteroids, meteors, etc.), comprise our solar system.

Warmth for the planets is provided primarily by the sun's energy. At an average distance from the sun of nearly 150 million kilometers (km) or 93 million miles (mi), the earth intercepts only a very small fraction of the sun's total energy output. However, it is this *radiant energy (or radiation)** that drives the atmosphere into the patterns of everyday wind and weather and allows the earth to maintain an average surface temperature of about 15°C (59°F).† Although this temperature is mild, the earth experiences a wide range of temperatures, as readings can drop below −85°C (−121°F) during a frigid Antarctic night and climb, during the day, to above 50°C (122°F) on the oppressively hot subtropical desert.

The earth's **atmosphere** is a thin, gaseous envelope comprised mostly of nitrogen and oxygen, with small amounts of other gases, such as water vapor and carbon dioxide. Nested in the atmosphere are clouds of liquid water and ice crystals. Although our atmosphere extends upward for many hundreds of kilometers, almost 99 percent of the atmosphere lies within a mere 30 km (19 mi) of the earth's surface (see Fig. 1.2). In fact, if the earth were to shrink to the size of a beach ball, its inhabitable atmosphere would be thinner than a piece of paper. This thin blanket of air constantly shields the surface and its inhabitants from the sun's dangerous ultraviolet radiant energy, as well as from the onslaught of material from interplanetary space. There is no definite upper limit to the atmosphere; rather, it becomes thinner and thinner, eventually merging with empty space, which surrounds all the planets.

---

*Radiation is energy transferred in the form of waves that have electrical and magnetic properties. The light that we see is radiation, as is ultraviolet light. More on this important topic is given in Chapter 2.

†The abbreviation °C is used when measuring temperature in degrees Celsius, and °F is the abbreviation for degrees Fahrenheit. More information about temperature scales is given in Appendix A and in Chapter 2.

Figure 1.1
The relative sizes and position of the planets in our solar system. (Positions are not to scale.)

Figure 1.2
The earth's atmosphere as viewed from space during sunrise. About 90 percent of the earth's atmosphere is within the bright area and about 70 percent lies below the top of the highest cloud.

Composition of the Atmosphere   Table 1.1 shows the various gases present in a volume of air near the earth's surface. Notice that **nitrogen** (N_2) occupies about 78 percent and **oxygen** (O_2) about 21 percent of the total volume. If all the other gases are removed, these percentages for nitrogen and oxygen hold fairly constant up to an elevation of about 80 km (50 mi). (For a closer look at the composition of a breath of air at the earth's surface, read the Focus section on p. 4.)

At the surface, there is a balance between destruction (output) and production (input) of these gases. For example, nitrogen is removed from the atmosphere primarily by biological processes that involve soil bacteria. In addition, nitrogen is taken from the air by tiny ocean-dwelling plankton that convert it into nutrients that help fortify the ocean's food chain. It is returned to the atmosphere mainly through the decaying of plant and animal matter. Oxygen, on the other hand, is removed from the atmosphere when organic matter decays and when oxygen combines with other substances, producing oxides. It is also taken from the atmosphere during breathing, as the lungs take in oxygen and release carbon dioxide (CO_2). The addition of oxygen to the atmosphere occurs during photosynthesis, as plants, in the presence of sunlight, combine carbon dioxide and water to produce sugar and oxygen.

The concentration of the invisible gas **water vapor** (H_2O), however, varies greatly from place to place, and from time to time. Close to the surface in warm, steamy, tropical locations, water vapor may account for up to 4 percent of the atmospheric gases, whereas in colder arctic areas, its concentration may dwindle to a mere fraction of a percent (see Table 1.1). Water vapor molecules are, of course, invisible. They become visible only when they transform into larger liquid or solid particles, such as cloud droplets and ice crystals. The changing of water

Table 1.1	Composition of the Atmosphere Near the Earth's Surface						
PERMANENT GASES				**VARIABLE GASES**			
Gas	Symbol	Percent (by Volume) Dry Air		Gas (and Particles)	Symbol	Percent (by Volume)	Parts per Million (ppm)*
Nitrogen	N_2	78.08		Water vapor	H_2O	0 to 4	
Oxygen	O_2	20.95		Carbon dioxide	CO_2	0.037	374*
Argon	Ar	0.93		Methane	CH_4	0.00017	1.7
Neon	Ne	0.0018		Nitrous oxide	N_2O	0.00003	0.3
Helium	He	0.0005		Ozone	O_3	0.000004	0.04†
Hydrogen	H_2	0.00006		Particles (dust, soot, etc.)		0.000001	0.01–0.15
Xenon	Xe	0.000009		Chlorofluorocarbons (CFCs)		0.00000002	0.0002

*For CO_2, 374 parts per million means that out of every million air molecules, 374 are CO_2 molecules.

†Stratospheric values at altitudes between 11 km and 50 km are about 5 to 12 ppm.

Focus on A SPECIAL TOPIC

A Breath of Fresh Air

If we could examine a breath of air, we would see that air (like everything else in the universe) is composed of incredibly tiny particles called *atoms*. We cannot see atoms individually. Yet, if we could see one, we would find electrons whirling at fantastic speeds about an extremely dense center, somewhat like hummingbirds darting and circling about a flower. At this center, or nucleus, are the protons and neutrons. Almost all of the atom's mass is concentrated here, in a trillionth of the atom's entire volume. In the nucleus, the proton carries a positive charge, whereas the neutron is electrically neutral. The circling electron carries a negative charge. As long as the total number of protons in the nucleus equals the number of orbiting electrons, the atom as a whole is electrically neutral (see Fig. 1).

Most of the air particles are *molecules*, combinations of two or more atoms (such as nitrogen, N_2, and oxygen, O_2), and most of the molecules are electrically neutral. A few, however, are electrically charged, having lost or gained electrons. These charged atoms and molecules are called *ions*.

An average breath of fresh air contains a tremendous number of molecules. With every deep breath, trillions of molecules from the atmosphere enter your body. Some of these inhaled gases become a part of you, and others are exhaled.

The volume of an average size breath of air is about a liter.* Near sea level, there are roughly ten thousand million million million (10^{22})† air molecules in a liter. So,

1 breath of air $\approx 10^{22}$ molecules.

We can appreciate how large this number is when we compare it to the number of stars in the universe. Astronomers have estimated that there are about 100 billion (10^{11}) stars in an average size galaxy and that there may be as many as 10^{11} galaxies in the universe. To determine the total number of stars in the universe, we multiply the number of stars in a galaxy by the total number of galaxies and obtain

$$10^{11} \times 10^{11} = 10^{22} \text{ stars in the universe.}$$

Therefore, each breath of air contains about as many molecules as there are stars in the known universe.

In the entire atmosphere, there are nearly 10^{44} molecules. The number 10^{44} is 10^{22} squared; consequently

$$10^{22} \times 10^{22} = 10^{44} \text{ molecules in the atmosphere.}$$

We thus conclude that there are about 10^{22} breaths of air in the entire

---

*One cubic centimeter is about the size of a sugar cube, and there are a thousand cubic centimeters in a liter.
†The notation 10^{22} means the number one followed by twenty-two zeros. For a further explanation of this system of notation see Appendix A.

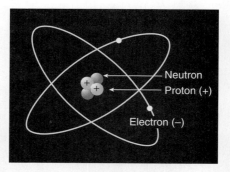

Figure 1

An atom has neutrons and protons at its center with electrons orbiting this center (or nucleus). Molecules are combinations of two or more atoms. The air we breathe is mainly molecular nitrogen (N_2) and molecular oxygen (O_2).

atmosphere. In other words, there are as many molecules in a single breath as there are breaths in the atmosphere.

Each time we breathe, the molecules we exhale enter the turbulent atmosphere. If we wait a long time, those molecules will eventually become thoroughly mixed with all of the other air molecules. If none of the molecules were consumed in other processes, eventually there would be a molecule from that single breath in every breath that is out there. So, considering the many breaths people exhale in their lifetimes, it is possible that in our lungs are molecules that were once in the lungs of people who lived hundreds or even thousands of years ago. In a very real way then, we all share the same atmosphere.

---

vapor into liquid water is called *condensation,* whereas the process of liquid water becoming water vapor is called *evaporation.* In the lower atmosphere, water is everywhere. It is the only substance that exists as a gas, a liquid, and a solid at those temperatures and pressures normally found near the earth's surface (see Fig. 1.3).

Water vapor is an *extremely* important gas in our atmosphere. Not only does it form into both liquid and solid cloud particles that grow in size and fall to earth as precipitation, but it also releases large amounts of heat—called *latent heat*—when it changes from vapor into liquid water or ice. Latent heat is an important source of atmospheric energy, especially for storms, such as thunderstorms and hurricanes. Moreover, water vapor is a potent *greenhouse gas* because it strongly absorbs a portion of the earth's outgoing radiant energy (somewhat like the glass of a greenhouse prevents the heat inside from escaping and mixing with the outside air). Thus, water vapor plays a significant role in the earth's heat-energy balance.

Carbon dioxide (CO_2), a natural component of the atmosphere, occupies a small (but important) percent of a volume of air, about 0.037 percent. Carbon dioxide enters the atmosphere mainly from the decay of vegetation, but it also comes from volcanic eruptions, the exhalations of animal life, from the burning of fossil fuels (such as coal, oil, and natural gas), and from deforestation. The removal of CO_2 from the atmosphere takes place during *photosynthesis,* as plants consume CO_2 to produce green matter. The CO_2 is then stored in roots, branches, and leaves. The oceans act as a huge reservoir for CO_2, as phytoplankton (tiny drifting plants) in surface water fix CO_2 into organic tissues. Carbon dioxide that dissolves directly into surface water mixes downward and circulates through greater depths. Estimates are that the oceans hold more than 50 times the total atmospheric CO_2 content.

Figure 1.4 reveals that the atmospheric concentration of CO_2 has risen more than 15 percent since 1958, when it was first measured at Mauna Loa Observatory in Hawaii. This increase means that CO_2 is entering the atmosphere at a greater rate than it is being removed. The increase appears to be due mainly to the burning of fossil fuels; however, deforestation also plays a role as cut timber, burned or left to rot, releases CO_2 directly into the air, perhaps accounting for about 20 percent of the observed increase. Measurements of CO_2 also come from ice cores. In Greenland and Antarctica, for example, tiny bubbles of air trapped within the ice sheets reveal that before the industrial revolution, CO_2 levels were stable at about 280 parts per million (ppm). Since the early 1800s, however, CO_2 levels have increased by as much as 25 percent. With CO_2 levels presently increasing

by about 0.4 percent annually (1.5 ppm/year), scientists now estimate that the concentration of CO_2 will likely rise from its current value of about 374 ppm to a value near 500 ppm toward the end of this century.

Carbon dioxide is another important greenhouse gas because, like water vapor, it traps a portion of the earth's outgoing energy. Consequently, with everything else being equal, as the atmospheric concentration of CO_2 increases, so should the average global surface air temperature. Mathematical model experiments that predict future atmospheric conditions estimate that increasing levels of CO_2 (and other greenhouse gases) will result in a *global warming* of surface air between 1.4°C and 5.8°C (about 2.5°F and 10.5°F) by the year 2100. Such warming (as we will learn in more detail in Chapter 19) could result in a variety of consequences, such as increasing precipitation in certain areas and reducing it in others as the global air currents that guide the major storm systems across the earth begin to shift from their "normal" paths.

Carbon dioxide and water vapor are not the only greenhouse gases. Recently, others have been gaining notoriety, primarily because they, too, are becoming more concentrated. Such gases include *methane* (CH_4), *nitrous oxide* (N_2O), and *chlorofluorocarbons* (CFCs).*

Levels of methane, for example, have been rising over the past century, increasing recently by about one-half of one percent per year (see Fig. 1.5). Most methane appears to derive from the breakdown of plant material by certain bacteria in rice paddies, wet oxygen-poor soil, the biological activity of termites, and biochemical reactions in the stomachs of cows. Just why methane should be increasing so rapidly is currently under study. Levels of nitrous oxide—commonly known as laughing gas—have been rising annually at the rate of about one-quarter

---

*Because these gases (including CO_2) occupy only a small fraction of a percent in a volume of air near the surface, they are referred to collectively as *trace gases.*

Figure 1.3
The earth's atmosphere is a rich mixture of many gases, with clouds of condensed water vapor and ice crystals. Here, water evaporates from the ocean's surface. Rising air currents then transform the invisible water vapor into many billions of tiny liquid droplets that appear as puffy cumulus clouds. If the rising air in the cloud should extend to greater heights, where air temperatures are quite low, some of the liquid droplets would freeze into minute ice crystals.

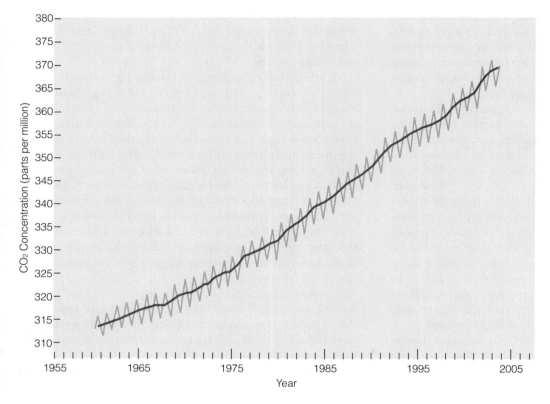

Figure 1.4
Measurements of CO_2 in parts per million (ppm) at Mauna Loa Observatory, Hawaii. Higher readings occur in winter when plants die and release CO_2 to the atmosphere. Lower readings occur in summer when more abundant vegetation absorbs CO_2 from the atmosphere. Solid line is average yearly value.

of a percent. Nitrous oxide forms in the soil through a chemical process involving bacteria and certain microbes. Ultraviolet light from the sun destroys it.

Chlorofluorocarbons (CFCs) represent a group of greenhouse gases that, up until recently, had been increasing in concentration. At one time, they were the most widely used propellants in spray cans. Today, however, they are mainly used as refrigerants, as propellants for the blowing of plastic-foam insulation, and as solvents for cleaning electronic microcircuits. Although their average concentration in a volume of air is quite small (see Table 1.1), they have an important effect on our atmosphere as they not only have the potential for raising global temperatures, they also play a part in destroying the gas ozone in the stratosphere.*

At the surface, **ozone** (O_3) is the primary ingredient of *photochemical smog*,† which irritates the eyes and throat and damages vegetation. But the majority of atmospheric ozone (about 97 percent) is found in the upper atmosphere—in the stratosphere—where it is formed naturally, as oxygen atoms combine with oxygen molecules. Here, the concentration of ozone averages less

than 0.002 percent by volume. This small quantity is important, however, because it shields plants, animals, and humans from the sun's harmful ultraviolet rays. It is ironic that ozone, which damages plant life in a polluted environment, provides a natural protective shield in the upper atmosphere so that plants on the surface may survive. We will see in Chapter 17 that when CFCs enter the stratosphere ultraviolet rays break them apart, and the CFCs release ozone-destroying chlorine. Because of this effect, ozone concentration in the stratosphere has been decreasing over

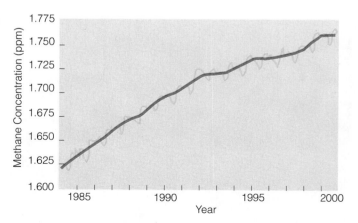

Figure 1.5
Global average concentration of atmospheric methane (CH_4).

---

*The stratosphere is located at an altitude between about 11 km and 50 km above the earth's surface.

†Originally the word *smog* meant the combining of smoke and fog. Today, however, the word usually refers to the type of smog that forms in large cities, such as Los Angeles, California. Because this type of smog forms when chemical reactions take place in the presence of sunlight, it is termed *photochemical smog*.

parts of the Northern and Southern Hemispheres. The reduction in stratospheric ozone levels over springtime Antarctica has plummeted at such an alarming rate that during September and October, there is an *ozone hole* over the region. (We will examine the ozone hole situation, as well as photochemical ozone, in Chapter 17.)

Impurities from both natural and human sources are also present in the atmosphere: Wind picks up dust and soil from the earth's surface and carries it aloft; small saltwater drops from ocean waves are swept into the air (upon evaporating, these drops leave microscopic salt particles suspended in the atmosphere); smoke from forest fires is often carried high above the earth; and volcanoes spew many tons of fine ash particles and gases into the air (see Fig. 1.6). Collectively, these tiny solid or liquid suspended particles of various composition are called **aerosols.**

Some natural impurities found in the atmosphere are quite beneficial. Small, floating particles, for instance, act as surfaces on which water vapor condenses to form clouds. However, most human-made impurities (and some natural ones) are a nuisance, as well as a health hazard. These we call **pollutants.** For example, automobile engines emit copious amounts of *nitrogen dioxide* (NO_2), *carbon monoxide* (CO), and *hydrocarbons.* In sunlight, nitrogen dioxide reacts with hydrocarbons and other gases to produce ozone. Carbon monoxide is a major pollutant of city air. Colorless and odorless, this poisonous gas forms during the incomplete combustion of carbon-containing fuel. Hence, over 75 percent of carbon monoxide in urban areas comes from road vehicles.

The burning of sulfur-containing fuels (such as coal and oil) releases the colorless gas *sulfur dioxide* (SO_2) into the air.

Weather Watch

When it rains, it rains pennies from heaven—sometimes. On July 17, 1940, a tornado reportedly picked up a treasure of over 1000 sixteenth-century silver coins, carried them into a thunderstorm, then dropped them on the village of Merchery in the Gorki region of Russia.

When the atmosphere is sufficiently moist, the SO_2 may transform into tiny dilute drops of sulfuric acid. Rain containing sulfuric acid corrodes metals and painted surfaces, and turns freshwater lakes acidic. *Acid rain* (thoroughly discussed in Chapter 17) is a major environmental problem, especially downwind from major industrial areas. In addition, high concentrations of SO_2 produce serious respiratory problems in humans, such as bronchitis and emphysema, and have an adverse effect on plant life. (More information on these and other pollutants is given in Chapter 17.)

The Early Atmosphere   The atmosphere that originally surrounded the earth was probably much different from the air we breathe today. The earth's first atmosphere (some 4.6 billion years ago) was most likely *hydrogen* and *helium*—the two most abundant gases found in the universe—as well as hydrogen compounds, such as methane and ammonia. Most scientists feel that this early atmosphere escaped into space from the earth's hot surface.

A second, more dense atmosphere, however, gradually enveloped the earth as gases from molten rock within its hot interior escaped through volcanoes and steam vents. We assume

Figure 1.6
Erupting volcanoes can send tons of particles into the atmosphere, along with vast amounts of water vapor, carbon dioxide, and sulfur dioxide.

that volcanoes spewed out the same gases then as they do today: mostly water vapor (about 80 percent), carbon dioxide (about 10 percent), and up to a few percent nitrogen. These gases (mostly water vapor and carbon dioxide) probably created the earth's second atmosphere.

As millions of years passed, the constant outpouring of gases from the hot interior—known as **outgassing**—provided a rich supply of water vapor, which formed into clouds.* Rain fell upon the earth for many thousands of years, forming the rivers, lakes, and oceans of the world. During this time, large amounts of CO_2 were dissolved in the oceans. Through chemical and biological processes, much of the CO_2 became locked up in carbonate sedimentary rocks, such as limestone. With much of the water vapor already condensed and the concentration of CO_2 dwindling, the atmosphere gradually became rich in nitrogen (N_2), which is usually not chemically active.

It appears that oxygen (O_2), the second most abundant gas in today's atmosphere, probably began an extremely slow increase in concentration as energetic rays from the sun split water vapor (H_2O) into hydrogen and oxygen during a process called *photodissociation*. The hydrogen, being lighter, probably rose and escaped into space, while the oxygen remained in the atmosphere.

This slow increase in oxygen may have provided enough of this gas for primitive plants to evolve, perhaps 2 to 3 billion years ago. Or the plants may have evolved in an almost oxygen-free (anaerobic) environment. At any rate, plant growth greatly enriched our atmosphere with oxygen. The reason for this enrichment is that, during the process of photosynthesis, plants, in the presence of sunlight, combine carbon dioxide and water to produce oxygen. Hence, after plants evolved, the atmospheric oxygen content increased more rapidly, probably reaching its present composition about several hundred million years ago.

Brief Review　Before going on to the next several sections, here is a review of some of the important concepts presented so far:

- The earth's atmosphere is a mixture of many gases. In a volume of dry air near the surface, nitrogen (N_2) occupies about 78 percent and oxygen (O_2) about 21 percent.

- Water vapor can condense into liquid cloud droplets or transform into delicate ice crystals. Water, which normally occupies less than 3 percent in a volume of air near the surface, is the only substance in our atmosphere that is found naturally as a gas (water vapor), as a liquid (water), and as a solid (ice).

- Both water vapor and carbon dioxide (CO_2) are important greenhouse gases.

- The majority of water on our planet is believed to have come from its hot interior through outgassing.

Vertical Structure of the Atmosphere

A vertical profile of the atmosphere reveals that it can be divided into a series of layers. Each layer may be defined in a number of ways: by the manner in which the air temperature varies through it, by the gases that comprise it, or even by its electrical properties. At any rate, before we examine these various atmospheric layers, we need to look at the vertical profile of two important variables: air pressure and air density.

A Brief Look at Air Pressure and Air Density　Earlier in this chapter we learned that most of our atmosphere is crowded close to the earth's surface. The reason for this fact is that air molecules (as well as everything else) are held near the earth by *gravity*. This strong invisible force pulling down on the air above squeezes (compresses) air molecules closer together, which causes their number in a given volume to increase. The more air above a level, the greater the squeezing effect or compression.

Gravity also has an effect on the weight of objects, including air. In fact, *weight* is the force acting on an object due to gravity. Weight is defined as the mass of an object times the acceleration of gravity; thus:

$$\text{Weight} = \text{mass} \times \text{gravity}.$$

An object's *mass* is the quantity of matter in the object. Consequently, the mass of air in a rigid container is the same everywhere in the universe. However, if you were to instantly travel to the moon, where the acceleration of gravity is much less than that of earth, the mass of air in the container would be the same, but its weight would decrease.

When mass is given in grams (g) or kilograms (kg), volume is given in cubic centimeters (cm^3) or cubic meters (m^3). Near sea level, air density is about 1.2 kilograms per cubic meter (nearly 1.2 ounces per cubic foot).

The **density** of air (or any substance) is determined by the masses of atoms and molecules and the amount of space between them. In other words, density tells us how much matter is in a given space (that is, volume). We can express density in a variety of ways. The molecular density of air is the number of molecules in a given volume. Most commonly, however, density is given as the mass of air in a given volume; thus:

$$\text{Density} = \frac{\text{mass}}{\text{volume}}.$$

Because there are appreciably more molecules within the same size volume of air near the earth's surface than at higher levels, air density is greatest at the surface and decreases as we move up into the atmosphere. Notice in Fig. 1.7 that, because air

---

*It is now believed that some of the earth's water may have originated from numerous collisions with small meteors and disintegrating comets when the earth was very young.

near the surface is compressed, air density normally decreases rapidly at first, then more slowly as we move farther away from the surface.

Air molecules are in constant motion. On a mild spring day near the surface, an air molecule will collide about 10 billion times each second with other air molecules. It will also bump against objects around it—houses, trees, flowers, the ground, and even people. Each time an air molecule bounces against a person, it gives a tiny push. This small force (push) divided by the area on which it pushes is called **pressure;** thus

$$\text{Pressure} = \frac{\text{force}}{\text{area}}.$$

If we weigh a column of air 1 square inch in cross section, extending from the average height of the ocean surface (sea level) to the "top" of the atmosphere, it would weigh nearly 14.7 pounds. Thus, normal atmospheric pressure near sea level is close to 14.7 pounds per square inch. If more molecules are packed into the column, it becomes more dense, the air weighs more, and the surface pressure goes up. On the other hand, when fewer molecules are in the column, the air weighs less, and the surface pressure goes down. So, the surface air pressure can be changed by changing the mass of air above the surface.

Pounds per square inch is, of course, just one way to express air pressure. Presently, the most common unit found on surface weather maps is the *millibar** (mb) although the *hectopascal* (hPa) is gradually replacing the millibar as the preferred unit of pressure on surface charts. Another unit of pressure is *inches of mercury* (Hg), which is commonly used in the field of avia-

Weather Watch

The air density in the mile-high city of Denver, Colorado, is normally about 15 percent less than the air density at sea level. As the air density decreases, the drag force on a hit baseball also decreases. Because of this fact, a baseball will travel farther when hit at Denver's Coors Field compared to one hit at sea level. Hence, a baseball hit for a 340-foot home run down the left field line on a warm, calm day at Coors Field in Denver, Colorado, would simply be a 300-foot out if hit at Camden Yards Stadium in Baltimore, Maryland.

tion and on television and radio weather broadcasts. At sea level, the *standard* value for atmospheric pressure is

1013.25 mb = 1013.25 hPa = 29.92 in. Hg.

Billions of air molecules push constantly on the human body. This force is exerted equally in all directions. We are not crushed by it because billions of molecules inside the body push outward just as hard. Even though we do not actually feel the constant bombardment of air, we can detect quick changes in it. For example, if we climb rapidly in elevation, our ears may "pop." This experience happens because air collisions outside the eardrum lessen. The popping comes about as air collisions between the inside and outside of the ear equalize. The drop in the number of collisions informs us that the pressure exerted by the air molecules decreases with height above the earth. A similar type of ear-popping occurs as we drop in elevation, and the air collisions outside the eardrum increase.

Air molecules not only take up space (freely darting, twisting, spinning, and colliding with everything around them), but—as we have seen—these same molecules have weight. In fact, air is surprisingly heavy. The weight of all the air around the earth is a staggering 5600 trillion tons or about 5.136×10^{18} kg. The weight of the air molecules acts as a force upon the earth. The amount of force exerted over an area of surface is called *atmospheric pressure* or, simply, **air pressure.**† The pressure at any level in the atmosphere may be measured in terms of the total mass of air above any point. As we climb in elevation, fewer air molecules are above us; hence, *atmospheric pressure*

---

*By definition, a *bar* is a force of 100,000 newtons (N) acting on a surface area of 1 square meter (m²). A *newton* is the amount of force required to move an object with a mass of 1 kilogram (kg) so that it increases its speed at a rate of 1 meter per second (m/sec) each second. Because the bar is a relatively large unit, and because surface pressure changes are usually small, the unit of pressure most commonly found on surface weather maps is the *millibar*, where 1 bar = 1000 mb. The unit of pressure designed by the International System (SI) of measurement is the *pascal* (Pa), where 1 pascal is the force of 1 newton acting on a surface of 1 square meter. A more common unit is the *hectopascal* (hPa), as 1 hectopascal equals 1 millibar.

†Because air pressure is measured with an instrument called a *barometer*, atmospheric pressure is often referred to as *barometric pressure.*

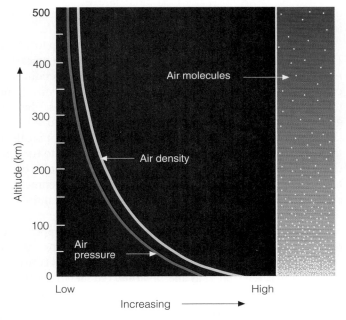

Figure 1.7
Both air pressure and air density decrease with increasing altitude.

always decreases with increasing height. Like air pressure decreases rapidly at first, then more slowly at higher levels (see Fig. 1.7).

Figure 1.8 also illustrates how rapidly air pressure decreases with height. Near sea level, atmospheric pressure is usually close to 1000 mb. Normally, just above sea level, atmospheric pressure decreases by about 10 mb for every 100 meters (m) increase in elevation—about 1 inch of mercury for every 1000 feet (ft) of rise. At higher levels, air pressure decreases much more slowly with height. With a sea-level pressure near 1000 mb, we can see in Fig. 1.8 that, at an altitude of only 5.5 km (3.5 mi), the air pressure is about 500 mb, or half of the sea-level pressure, meaning that at a mere 18,000 ft above the surface, we are above one-half of all the molecules in the atmosphere.

At an elevation approaching the summit of Mt. Everest (about 9 km or 29,000 ft—the highest mountain peak on earth), the air pressure would be about 300 mb. The summit is above nearly 70 percent of all the molecules in the atmosphere. At an altitude of about 50 km, the air pressure is about 1 mb, which means that 99.9 percent of all the molecules are below this level. Yet the atmosphere extends upwards for many hundreds of kilometers, gradually becoming thinner and thinner until it ultimately merges with outer space. (Up to now, we have concentrated on the earth's atmosphere. For a brief look at the atmospheres of the other planets, read the Focus section on p. 12.)

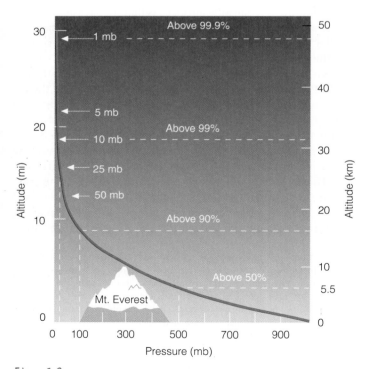

Figure 1.8
Atmospheric pressure decreases rapidly with height. Climbing to an altitude of only 5.5 km, where the pressure is 500 mb, would put you above one-half of the atmosphere's molecules.

Weather Watch

Air temperature normally decreases with increasing height above the surface; thus, if you are flying in a jet aircraft at about 9 km (30,000 ft), the air temperature just outside your window would typically be about −50°C (−58°F)—more than 60°C (108°F) colder than the air at the earth's surface, directly below you.

Layers of the Atmosphere   We have seen that both air pressure and density decrease with height above the earth—rapidly at first, then more slowly. *Air temperature,* however, has a more complicated vertical profile.*

Look closely at Fig. 1.9 and notice that air temperature normally decreases from the earth's surface up to an altitude of about 11 km, which is nearly 36,000 ft, or 7 mi. This decrease in air temperature with increasing height is due primarily to the fact (investigated further in Chapter 2) that sunlight warms the earth's surface, and the surface, in turn, warms the air above it. The rate at which the air temperature decreases with height is called the temperature **lapse rate.** The *average* (or *standard*) *lapse rate* in this region of the lower atmosphere is about 6.5°C for every 1000 m or about 3.6°F for every 1000 ft rise in elevation. Keep in mind that these values are only averages. On some days, the air becomes colder more quickly as we move upward. This would increase or steepen the lapse rate. On other days, the air temperature would decrease more slowly with height, and the lapse rate would be less. Occasionally, the air temperature may actually *increase* with height, producing a condition known as a **temperature inversion.** So the lapse rate fluctuates, varying from day to day and season to season.

The region of the atmosphere from the surface up to about 11 km contains all of the weather we are familiar with on earth. Also, this region is kept well stirred by rising and descending air currents. Here, it is common for air molecules to circulate through a depth of more than 10 km in just a few days. This region of circulating air extending upward from the earth's surface to where the air stops becoming colder with height is called the **troposphere**—from the Greek *tropein,* meaning to turn or change. The instrument used to measure the vertical profile of air temperature in the atmosphere up to an elevation sometimes exceeding 30 km (100,000 ft) is the **radiosonde.** More information on this instrument is given in the Focus section on p. 14.

Notice in Fig. 1.9 that just above 11 km the air temperature normally stops decreasing with height. Here, the lapse rate is zero. This region, where the air temperature remains constant with height, is referred to as an *isothermal* (equal temperature) zone. The bottom of this zone marks the top of the troposphere and the beginning of another layer, the **stratosphere.** The

---

Air temperature is the degree of hotness or coldness of the air and, as we will see in Chapter 2, it is also a measure of the average speed of the air molecules.

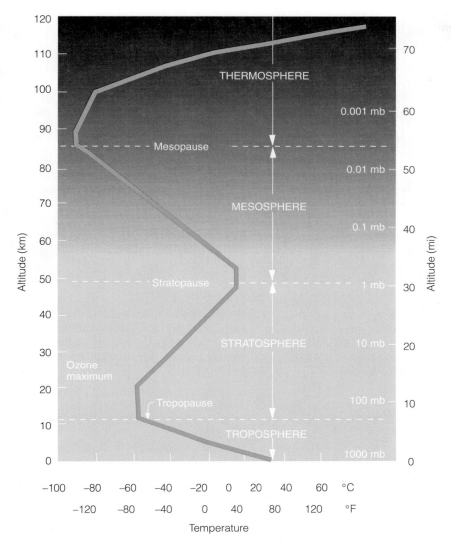

Figure 1.9
Layers of the atmosphere as related to the average profile of air temperature above the earth's surface. The heavy line illustrates how the average temperature varies in each layer.

boundary separating the troposphere from the stratosphere is called the **tropopause.** The height of the tropopause varies. It is normally found at higher elevations over equatorial regions, and it decreases in elevation as we travel poleward. Generally, the tropopause is higher in summer and lower in winter at all latitudes. In some regions, the tropopause "breaks" and is difficult to locate and, here, scientists have observed tropospheric air mixing with stratospheric air and vice versa. These breaks also mark the position of *jet streams*—high winds that meander in a narrow channel, like an old river, often at speeds exceeding 100 knots.*

From Fig. 1.9 we can see that, in the stratosphere at an altitude near 20 km (12 mi), the air temperature begins to increase with height, producing a *temperature inversion.* The inversion region, along with the lower isothermal layer, tends to

keep the vertical currents of the troposphere from spreading into the stratosphere. The inversion also tends to reduce the amount of vertical motion in the stratosphere itself; hence, it is a stratified layer.

Even though the air temperature is increasing with height, the air at an altitude of 30 km is extremely cold, averaging less than −46°C. At this level above polar latitudes, air temperatures can change dramatically from one week to the next, as a *sudden warming* can raise the temperature in one week by more than 50°C. Such a rapid warming, although not well understood, is probably due to sinking air associated with circulation changes that occur in late winter or early spring as well as with the poleward displacement of strong jet stream winds in the lower stratosphere.

The reason for the inversion in the stratosphere is that the gas ozone plays a major part in heating the air at this altitude. Recall that ozone is important because it absorbs energetic ultraviolet (UV) solar energy. Some of this absorbed energy

---

*A knot is a nautical mile per hour. One knot is equal to 1.15 miles per hour (mi/hr), or 1.9 kilometers per hour (km/hr).

Focus on A SPECIAL TOPIC

The Atmospheres of Other Planets

Earth is unique. Not only does it lie at just the right distance from the sun so that life may flourish, it also provides its inhabitants with an atmosphere rich in nitrogen and oxygen—two gases that are not abundant in the atmospheres of either Venus or Mars, our closest planetary neighbors.

The Venusian atmosphere is mainly carbon dioxide (95 percent) with minor amounts of water vapor and nitrogen. An opaque acid-cloud deck encircles the planet, hiding its surface. The atmosphere is quite turbulent, as instruments reveal twisting eddies and fierce winds in excess of 200 km/hr. This thick dense atmosphere produces a surface air pressure of about 90,000 mb, which is 90 times greater than that on earth. To experience such a pressure on earth, one would have to descend in the ocean to a depth of about 900 m (2950 ft). Moreover, this thick atmosphere of CO_2 produces a strong greenhouse effect, with a scorching hot surface temperature of 480°C (900°F).

The atmosphere of Mars, like that of Venus, is mostly carbon dioxide, with only small amounts of other gases. Unlike Venus, the Martian atmosphere is very thin, and heat escapes from the

Figure 2
A portion of Jupiter extending from the equator to the southern polar latitudes. The Great Red Spot, as well as the smaller ones, are spinning eddies similar to storms that exist in the earth's atmosphere.

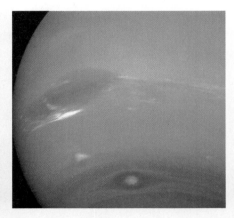

Figure 3
The Great Dark Spot on Neptune. The white wispy clouds are similar to the high wispy cirrus clouds on earth. However, on Neptune, they are probably composed of methane ice crystals.

surface rapidly. Thus, surface temperatures on Mars are much lower, averaging around −60°C (−76°F). Because of its thin cold atmosphere, there is no liquid water on Mars and virtually no cloud cover—only a barren desertlike landscape. In addition, this thin atmosphere produces an average surface air pressure of about 7 mb, which is less than one-hundredth of that experienced at the surface of the earth. Such a pressure on earth would be observed

above the surface at an altitude near 35 km (22 mi).

Occasionally, huge dust storms develop near the Martian surface. Such storms may be accompanied by winds of several hundreds of kilometers per hour. These winds carry fine dust around the entire planet. The dust gradually settles out, coating the landscape with a thin reddish veneer.

The atmosphere of the largest planet Jupiter is much different from

warms the stratosphere, which explains why there is an inversion. If ozone were not present, the air probably would become colder with height, as it does in the troposphere.*

Notice in Fig. 1.9 that the level of maximum ozone concentration is observed near 25 km (at middle latitudes), yet the stratospheric air temperature reaches a maximum near 50 km. The reason for this phenomenon is that the air at 50 km is less dense than at 25 km, and so the absorption of intense solar energy at 50 km raises the temperature of fewer molecules to a much greater degree. Moreover, much of the solar energy re-

sponsible for the heating is absorbed in the upper part of the stratosphere and, therefore, does not reach down to the level of ozone maximum. And due to the low air density, the transfer of energy downward from the upper stratosphere is quite slow.

Above the stratosphere is the **mesosphere** (middle sphere). The boundary near 50 km, which separates these layers, is called the *stratopause*. The air at this level is extremely thin and the atmospheric pressure is quite low, averaging about 1 mb, which means that only one-thousandth of all the atmosphere's molecules are above this level and 99.9 percent of the atmosphere's mass is located below it.

The percentage of nitrogen and oxygen in the mesosphere is about the same as at sea level. Given the air's low density in

---

*Recall from an earlier discussion that the concentration of stratospheric ozone is decreasing over portions of the globe as chlorofluorocarbons break apart and release ozone-destroying chlorine in the process. Again, additional material on this topic is given in Chapter 17.

Table 1   Data on Planets and the Sun

	DIAMETER	AVERAGE DISTANCE FROM SUN	AVERAGE SURFACE TEMPERATURE		MAIN ATMOSPHERIC COMPONENTS
	Kilometers	Millions of Kilometers	°C	°F	
Sun	$1,392 \times 10^3$		5,800	10,500	–
Mercury	4,880	58	260*	500	–
Venus	12,112	108	480	900	CO_2
Earth	12,742	150	15	59	N_2, O_2
Mars	6,800	228	−60	−76	CO_2
Jupiter	143,000	778	−110	−166	H_2, He
Saturn	121,000	1,427	−190	−310	H_2, He
Uranus	51,800	2,869	−215	−355	H_2, CH_4
Neptune	49,000	4,498	−225	−373	N_2, CH_4
Pluto	3,100	5,900	−235	−391	CH_4

*Sunlit side.

that of Venus and Mars. Jupiter's atmosphere is mainly hydrogen (H_2) and helium (He), with minor amounts of methane (CH_4) and ammonia (NH_3). A prominent feature on Jupiter is the Great Red Spot—a huge atmospheric storm about three times larger than earth—that spins counterclockwise in Jupiter's southern hemisphere (see Fig. 2). Large white ovals near the Great Red Spot are similar but smaller storm systems. Unlike the earth's weather machine, which is driven by the sun, Jupiter's massive swirling clouds appear to be driven by a collapsing core of hot hydrogen. Energy from this lower region rises toward the surface, then it (along with Jupiter's rapid rotation) stirs the cloud layer into more or less horizontal bands of various colors.

Swirling storms exist on other planets, too, such as on Saturn and Neptune. In fact, the large dark oval on Neptune (Fig. 3) appears to be a storm similar to Jupiter's Great Red Spot. The white wispy clouds in the photograph are probably composed of methane ice crystals. Studying the atmospheric behavior of other planets may give us added insight into the workings of our own atmosphere. (Additional information about size, surface temperature, and atmospheric composition of the other planets is given in Table 1.)

this region, however, we would not survive very long breathing here, as each breath would contain far fewer oxygen molecules than it would at sea level. Consequently, without proper breathing equipment, the brain would soon become oxygen-starved—a condition known as *hypoxia*. Pilots who fly above 3 km (10,000 ft) for too long without oxygen-breathing apparatus may experience this. With the first symptoms of hypoxia, there is usually no pain involved, just a feeling of exhaustion. Soon, visual impairment sets in and routine tasks become difficult to perform. Some people drift into an incoherent state, neither realizing nor caring what is happening to them. Of course, if this oxygen deficiency persists, a person will lapse into unconsciousness, and death may result. In fact, in the mesosphere, we would suffocate in a matter of minutes.

There are other effects besides suffocating that could be experienced in the mesosphere. Exposure to ultraviolet solar energy, for example, could cause severe burns on exposed parts of the body. Also, given the low air pressure, the blood in one's veins would begin to boil at normal body temperatures.

The air temperature in the mesosphere decreases with height, a phenomenon due, in part, to the fact that there is little ozone in the air to absorb solar radiation. Consequently, the molecules (especially those near the top of the mesosphere) are able to lose more energy than they absorb, which results in an energy deficit and cooling. So we find air in the mesosphere becoming colder with height up to an elevation near 85 km. At this altitude, the temperature of the atmosphere reaches its lowest average value, −90°C (−130°F).

Focus on AN OBSERVATION

The Radiosonde

The vertical distribution of temperature, pressure, and humidity up to an altitude of about 30 km can be obtained with an instrument called a radiosonde.* The radiosonde is a small, lightweight box equipped with weather instruments and a radio transmitter. It is attached to a cord that has a parachute and a gas-filled balloon tied tightly at the end (see Fig. 4). As the balloon rises, the attached radiosonde measures air temperature with a small electrical thermometer—a thermistor—located just outside the box. The radiosonde measures humidity electrically by sending an electric current across a carbon-coated plate. Air pressure is obtained by a small barometer located inside the box. All of this information is transmitted to the surface by radio. Here, a computer rapidly reconverts the various frequencies into values of temperature, pressure, and moisture. Special tracking equipment at the surface may also be used to provide a vertical profile of winds.† (When winds are added, the observation is called a *rawinsonde*.) When plotted on a graph, the vertical distribution of temperature, humidity, and wind is called a *sounding*. Eventually, the balloon bursts and the radiosonde returns to earth, its descent being slowed by its parachute.

At most sites, radiosondes are released twice a day, usually at the time that corresponds to midnight and noon in Greenwich, England. Releasing radiosondes is an expensive operation because many of the instruments are never retrieved, and many of those that are retrieved are often in poor working condition. To complement the radiosonde, modern geostationary satellites (using instruments that measure radiant energy) are providing scientists with vertical temperature profiles in inaccessible regions.

*A radiosonde that is dropped by parachute from an aircraft is called a *dropsonde*.
†A modern development in the radiosonde is the use of satellite Global Positioning System (GPS) equipment. Radiosondes can be equipped with a GPS device that provides more accurate position data back to the computer for wind computations.

Figure 4
The radiosonde with parachute and balloon.

The "hot layer" above the mesosphere is the **thermosphere.** The boundary that separates the lower, colder mesosphere from the warmer thermosphere is the *mesopause.* In the thermosphere, oxygen molecules (O_2) absorb energetic solar rays, warming the air. Because there are relatively few atoms and molecules in the thermosphere, the absorption of a small amount of energetic solar energy can cause a large increase in air temperature. Furthermore, because the amount of solar energy affecting this region depends strongly on solar activity, temperatures in the thermosphere vary from day to day (see Fig. 1.10). The low density of the thermosphere also means that an air molecule will move an average distance (called *mean free path*) of over one kilometer before colliding with another molecule. A similar air molecule at the earth's surface will move an average distance of less than one millionth of a centimeter before it collides with another molecule.

Because the air density in the upper thermosphere is so low, air temperatures there are not measured directly. They can, however, be determined by observing the orbital change of satellites caused by the drag of the atmosphere. Even though the air is extremely tenuous, enough air molecules strike a satellite to slow it down, making it drop into a slightly lower orbit. (For this reason, the spacecraft *Solar Max* fell to earth in December, 1989, as did the Russian space station, *Mir,* in March, 2001.) The amount of drag is related to the density of the air, and the density is related to the temperature. Therefore, by determining air density, scientists are able to construct a vertical profile of air temperature.

At the top of the thermosphere, about 500 km (300 mi) above the earth's surface, molecules can move distances of 10 km before they collide with other molecules. Here, many of the lighter, faster-moving molecules traveling in the right direction actually escape the earth's gravitational pull. The region where atoms and molecules shoot off into space is sometimes referred to as the **exosphere,** which represents the upper limit of our atmosphere.

Up to this point, we have examined the atmospheric layers based on the vertical profile of temperature. The atmosphere, however, may also be divided into layers based on its composition. For example, the composition of the atmosphere begins to slowly change in the lower part of the thermosphere. Below the thermosphere, the composition of air remains fairly uniform (78 percent nitrogen, 21 percent oxygen) by turbulent mixing. This lower, well-mixed region is known as the **homosphere** (Fig. 1.10). In the thermosphere, collisions between atoms and molecules are infrequent, and the air is unable to keep itself stirred. As a result, diffusion takes over as heavier atoms and molecules (such as oxygen and nitrogen) tend to settle to the bottom of the layer, while lighter gases (such as hydrogen and helium) float to the top. The region from about the base of the thermosphere to the top of the atmosphere is often called the **heterosphere.**

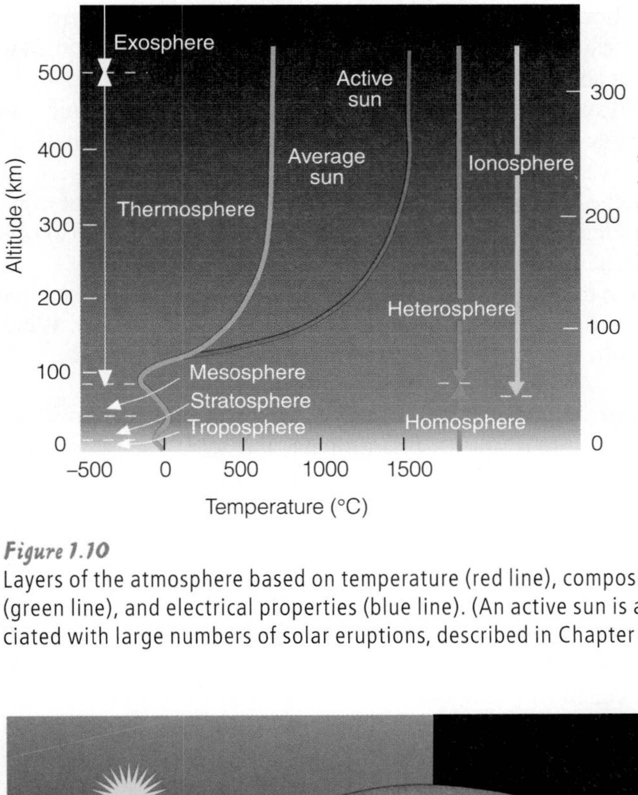

The Ionosphere   The **ionosphere** is not really a layer, but rather an electrified region within the upper atmosphere where fairly large concentrations of ions and free electrons exist. *Ions* are atoms and molecules that have lost (or gained) one or more electrons. Atoms lose electrons and become positively charged when they cannot absorb all of the energy transferred to them by a colliding energetic particle or the sun's energy.

The lower region of the ionosphere is usually about 60 km above the earth's surface. From here (60 km), the ionosphere extends upward to the top of the atmosphere. Hence, the bulk of the ionosphere is in the thermosphere (see Fig. 1.10).

The ionosphere plays a major role in radio communications. The lower part (called the D region) reflects standard AM radio waves back to earth, but at the same time it seriously weakens them through absorption. At night, though, the D region gradually disappears and AM radio waves are able to penetrate higher into the ionosphere (into the E and F regions—see Fig. 1.11), where the waves are reflected back to earth. Because there is, at night, little absorption of radio waves in the higher reaches of the ionosphere, such waves bounce repeatedly from the ionosphere to the earth's surface and back to the ionosphere again. In this way, standard AM radio waves are able to travel for many hundreds of kilometers at night.

Around sunrise and sunset, AM radio stations usually make "necessary technical adjustments" to compensate for the changing electrical characteristics of the D region. Because they can broadcast over a greater distance at night, most AM stations reduce their output near sunset. This reduction prevents two stations—both transmitting at the same frequency but hundreds of kilometers apart—from interfering with each other's radio programs. At sunrise, as the D region intensifies, the power supplied to AM radio transmitters is normally increased. FM stations do not need to make these adjustments because FM

Figure 1.10

Layers of the atmosphere based on temperature (red line), composition (green line), and electrical properties (blue line). (An active sun is associated with large numbers of solar eruptions, described in Chapter 2.)

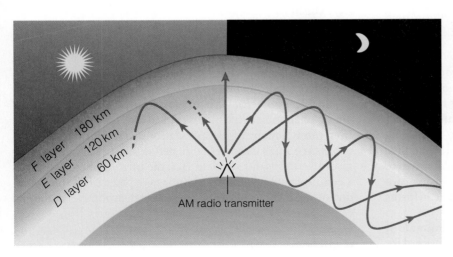

Figure 1.11

At night, the higher region of the ionosphere (*F* region) strongly reflects AM radio waves, allowing them to be sent over great distances. During the day, the lower *D* region strongly absorbs and weakens AM radio waves, preventing them from being picked up by distant receivers.

radio waves are shorter than AM waves, and are able to pene-trate through the ionosphere without being reflected.

■ *Brief Review*   We have, in the last several sections, been examining our atmosphere from a vertical perspective. A few of the main points are:

■ Atmospheric pressure at any level represents the total mass of air above that level, and atmospheric pressure always de-creases with increasing height above the surface.

■ The atmosphere may be divided into layers (or regions) ac-cording to its vertical profile of temperature, its gaseous com-position, or its electrical properties.

■ Ozone at the earth's surface is the main ingredient of pho-tochemical smog, whereas ozone in the stratosphere protects life on earth from the sun's harmful ultraviolet rays.

We will now turn our attention to weather events that take place in the lower atmosphere. As you read the remainder of this chapter, keep in mind that the content serves as a broad overview of material to come in later chapters, and that many of the concepts and ideas you encounter are designed to famil-iarize you with items you might read about in a newspaper or magazine, or see on television.

Weather and Climate

When we talk about the **weather,** we are talking about the condition of the atmosphere at any particular time and place. Weather—which is always changing—is comprised of the ele-ments of:

1. *air temperature*—the degree of hotness or coldness of the air
2. *air pressure*—the force of the air above an area
3. *humidity*—a measure of the amount of water vapor in the air
4. *clouds*—a visible mass of tiny water droplets and/or ice crys-tals that are above the earth's surface
5. *precipitation*—any form of water, either liquid or solid (rain or snow), that falls from clouds and reaches the ground
6. *visibility*—the greatest distance one can see
7. *wind*—the horizontal movement of air

If we measure and observe these **weather elements** over a specified interval of time, say, for many years, we would obtain the "average weather" or the **climate** of a particular region. Cli-mate, therefore, represents the accumulation of daily and sea-sonal weather events (the average range of weather) over a long period of time. The concept of climate is much more than this, for it also includes the extremes of weather—the heat waves of summer and the cold spells of winter—that occur in a partic-ular region. The *frequency* of these extremes is what helps us distinguish among climates that have similar averages.

If we were able to watch the earth for many thousands of years, even the climate would change. We would see rivers of ice

moving down stream-cut valleys and huge glaciers—sheets of moving snow and ice—spreading their icy fingers over large portions of North America. Advancing slowly from Canada, a single glacier might extend as far south as Kansas and Illinois, with ice several thousands of meters thick covering the region now occupied by Chicago. Over an interval of 2 million years or so, we would see the ice advance and retreat several times. Of course, for this phenomenon to happen, the average tempera-ture of North America would have to decrease and then rise in a cyclic manner.

Suppose we could photograph the earth once every thou-sand years for many hundreds of millions of years. In time-lapse film sequence, these photos would show that not only is the cli-mate altering, but the whole earth itself is changing as well: Mountains would rise up only to be torn down by erosion; isolated puffs of smoke and steam would appear as volcanoes spew hot gases and fine dust into the atmosphere; and the en-tire surface of the earth would undergo a gradual transforma-tion as some ocean basins widen and others shrink.*

In summary, the earth and its atmosphere are dynamic sys-tems that are constantly changing. While major transformations of the earth's surface are completed only after long spans of time, the state of the atmosphere can change in a matter of min-utes. Hence, a watchful eye turned skyward will be able to ob-serve many of these changes.

Up to this point, we have looked at the concepts of weather and climate without discussing the word **meteorology.** What does this term actually mean and where did it originate?

Meteorology—A Brief History   *Meteorology* is the study of the atmosphere and its phenomena. The term itself goes back to the Greek philosopher Aristotle who, about 340 B.C., wrote a book on natural philosophy entitled *Meteorologica.* This work represented the sum of knowledge on weather and climate at that time, as well as material on astronomy, geography, and chemistry. Some of the topics covered included clouds, rain, snow, wind, hail, thunder, and hurricanes. In those days, all substances that fell from the sky, and anything seen in the air, were called meteors, hence the term *meteorology,* which actu-ally comes from the Greek word *meteoros,* meaning "high in the air." Today, we differentiate between those meteors that come from extraterrestrial sources outside our atmosphere (meteoroids) and particles of water and ice observed in the at-mosphere (hydrometeors).

In *Meteorologica,* Aristotle attempted to explain atmos-pheric phenomena in a philosophical and speculative manner. Even though many of his speculations were found to be erro-neous, Aristotle's ideas were accepted without reservation for al-most two thousand years. In fact, the birth of meteorology as a genuine natural science did not take place until the inven-tion of weather instruments, such as the thermometer at the end

---

*The movement of the ocean floor and continents is explained in the widely ac-claimed theory of *plate tectonics,* formerly called the theory of continental drift.

of the sixteenth century, the barometer (for measuring air pressure) in 1643, and the hygrometer (for measuring humidity) in the late 1700s. With observations from instruments available, attempts were then made to explain certain weather phenomena employing scientific experimentation and the physical laws that were being developed at the time.

As more and better instruments were developed in the 1800s, the science of meteorology progressed. The invention of the telegraph in 1843 allowed for the transmission of routine weather observations. The understanding of the concepts of wind flow and storm movement became clearer, and in 1869 crude weather maps with *isobars* (lines of equal pressure) were drawn. Around 1920, the concepts of air masses and weather fronts were formulated in Norway. By the 1940s, daily upper-air balloon observations of temperature, humidity, and pressure gave a three-dimensional view of the atmosphere, and high-flying military aircraft discovered the existence of jet streams.

Meteorology took another step forward in the 1950s, when high-speed computers were developed to solve the mathematical equations that describe the behavior of the atmosphere. At the same time, a group of scientists in Princeton, New Jersey, developed numerical means for predicting the weather. Today, computers plot the observations, draw the lines on the map, and forecast the state of the atmosphere at some desired time in the future.

After World War II, surplus military radars became available, and many were transformed into precipitation-measuring tools. In the mid-1990s, these conventional radars were replaced by the more sophisticated *Doppler radars,* which have the ability to peer into severe thunderstorms and unveil their winds.

In 1960, the first weather satellite, *Tiros I,* was launched, ushering in space-age meteorology. Subsequent satellites provided a wide range of useful information, ranging from day and night time-lapse images of clouds and storms to pictures that depict swirling ribbons of water vapor flowing around the globe. Throughout the 1990s, and into the twenty-first century, ever more sophisticated satellites were developed to supply computers with a far greater network of data so that more accurate forecasts—perhaps up to two weeks or more—will be available in the future.

A Satellite's View of the Weather

A good view of the weather can be seen from a weather satellite. Figure 1.12 is a satellite image showing a portion of the Pacific Ocean and the North American continent. The photograph was obtained from a *geostationary satellite* situated about 36,000 km (22,300 mi) above the earth. At this elevation, the satellite travels at the same rate as the earth spins, which allows it to remain positioned above the same spot so it can continuously monitor what is taking place beneath it.

The dotted lines running from pole to pole on the satellite picture are called *meridians.* Since the zero meridian (or prime meridian) runs through Greenwich, England, the *longitude* of any place on earth is simply how far east or west, in de-

grees, it is from the prime meridian. North America is west of Great Britain and most of the United States lies between 75°W and 125°W longitude.

The dotted lines that parallel the equator are called *parallels of latitude.* The latitude of any place is how far north or south, in degrees, it is from the equator. The latitude of the equator is 0°, whereas the latitude of the North Pole is 90°N and that of the South Pole is 90°S. Most of the United States is located between latitude 30°N and 50°N, a region commonly referred to as the **middle latitudes.**

Storms of All Sizes   Probably the most dramatic spectacle in Fig. 1.12 is the whirling cloud masses of all shapes and sizes. The clouds appear white because sunlight is reflected back to space from their tops. The dark areas show where skies are clear. The largest of the organized cloud masses are the sprawling storms. One such storm shows as an extensive band of clouds, over 2000 km long, west of the Great Lakes. Superimposed on the satellite image is the storm's center (large red L) and its adjoining weather fronts in red, blue, and purple. This **middle latitude cyclonic storm** system (or *extratropical cyclone*) forms outside the tropics and, in the Northern Hemisphere, has winds spinning counterclockwise about its center, which is presently over Minnesota.

A slightly smaller but more vigorous storm is located over the Pacific Ocean near latitude 12°N and longitude 116°W. This tropical storm system, with its swirling band of rotating clouds and surface winds in excess of 64 knots* (74 mi/hr), is known as a **hurricane.** The diameter of the hurricane is about 800 km (500 mi). The tiny dot at its center is called the *eye.* In the eye, winds are light and skies are generally clear. Around the eye, however, is an extensive region where heavy rain and high surface winds are reaching peak gusts of 100 knots.

Smaller storms are seen as white spots over the Gulf of Mexico. These spots represent clusters of towering *cumulus* clouds that have grown into **thunderstorms,** that is, tall churning clouds accompanied by lightning, thunder, strong gusty winds, and heavy rain. If you look closely at Fig. 1.12, you will see similar cloud forms in many regions. There were probably thousands of thunderstorms occurring throughout the world at that very moment. Although they cannot be seen individually, there are even some thunderstorms embedded in the cloud mass west of the Great Lakes. Later in the day on which this photograph was taken, a few of these storms spawned the most violent disturbance in the atmosphere—the **tornado.**

A tornado is an intense rotating column of air that extends downward from the base of a thunderstorm. Sometimes called *twisters,* or *cyclones,* they may appear as ropes or as a large circular cylinder. The majority are less than a kilometer wide and many are smaller than a football field. Tornado winds may exceed 200 knots but most probably peak at less than 125

---

*Recall from p. 11 that 1 knot equals 1.15 miles per hour.

Figure 1.12
This satellite image (taken in visible reflected light) shows a variety of cloud patterns and storms in the earth's atmosphere.

knots. Some tornadoes never reach the ground, and often appear to hang from the base of a parent cloud as a rapidly rotating funnel. Often, they dip down then rise up before disappearing.

A Look at a Weather Map   We can obtain a better picture of the middle latitude storm system by examining a simplified surface weather map for the same day that the satellite picture was taken. The weight of the air above different regions varies and, hence, so does the atmospheric pressure. In Fig. 1.13, the letter L on the map indicates a region of low atmospheric pressure, often called a *low,* which marks the center of the middle-latitude storm. (Compare the center of the storm in Fig. 1.13 with that in Fig. 1.12.) The two letters H on the map

represent regions of high atmospheric pressure, called *highs,* or *anticyclones.* The circles on the map represent individual weather stations. The **wind** is the horizontal movement of air. The **wind direction**—the direction *from which* the wind is blowing*—is given by lines that parallel the wind and extend outward from the center of the station. The *wind speed*—the rate at which the air is moving past a stationary observer—is indicated by barbs.

Notice how the wind blows around the highs and the lows. The horizontal pressure differences create a force that starts the air moving from higher pressure toward lower pres-

---

*If you are facing north and the wind is blowing in your face, the wind would be called a "north wind."

sure. Because of the earth's rotation, the winds are deflected toward the right in the Northern Hemisphere.* This deflection causes the winds to blow *clockwise* and *outward* from the center of the highs, and *counterclockwise* and *inward* toward the center of the low.

As the surface air spins into the low, it flows together and rises, much like toothpaste does when its open tube is squeezed. The rising air cools, and the moisture in the air condenses into clouds. Notice in Fig. 1.13 that the area of precipitation (the shaded green area) in the vicinity of the low corresponds to an extensive cloudy region in the satellite image (Fig. 1.12).

Also notice by comparing Figs. 1.12 and 1.13 that, in the regions of high pressure, skies are generally clear. As the surface air flows outward away from the center of a high, air sinking from above must replace the laterally spreading air. Since sinking air does not usually produce clouds, we find generally

---
*This deflecting force, known as the *Coriolis force,* is discussed more completely in Chapter 9, as are the winds.

clear skies and fair weather associated with the regions of high pressure.

The swirling air around the areas of high and low pressure are the major weather producers for the middle latitudes. Look at the middle latitude storm and the surface temperatures in Fig. 1.13 and notice that, to the southeast of the storm, southerly winds from the Gulf of Mexico are bringing warm, humid air northward over much of the southeastern portion of the nation. On the storm's western side, cool dry northerly breezes combine with sinking air to create generally clear weather over the Rocky Mountains. The boundary that separates the warm and cool air appears as a heavy, dark line on the map—a **front,** across which there is a sharp change in temperature, humidity, and wind direction.

Where the cool air from Canada replaces the warmer air from the Gulf of Mexico, a *cold front* is drawn in blue, with arrowheads showing its general direction of movement. Where the warm Gulf air is replacing cooler air to the north, a *warm front* is drawn in red, with half circles showing its general

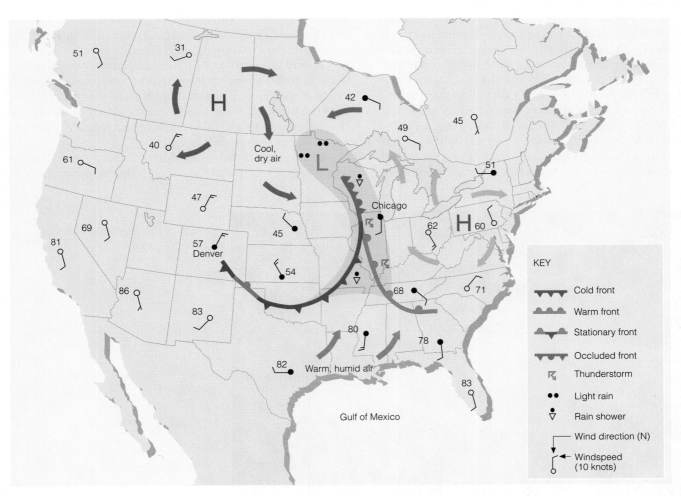

Figure 1.13
Simplified surface weather map that correlates with the satellite picture shown in Fig. 1.12. The shaded green area represents precipitation. The numbers on the map represent air temperatures in °F.

direction of movement. Where the cold front has caught up to the warm front and cold air is now replacing cool air, an *occluded front* is drawn in purple, with alternating arrowheads and half circles to show how it is moving. Along each of the fronts, warm air is rising, producing clouds and precipitation. Notice in the satellite image (Fig. 1.12) that the occluded front and the cold front appear as an elongated, curling cloud band that stretches from the low-pressure area over Minnesota into the northern part of Texas.

In Fig. 1.13 observe that the weather front is to the west of Chicago. As the westerly winds aloft push the front eastward, a person on the outskirts of Chicago might observe the approaching front as a line of towering thunderstorms similar to those in Fig. 1.14. In a few hours, Chicago should experience heavy showers with thunder, lightning, and gusty winds as the front passes. All of this, however, should give way to clearing skies and surface winds from the west or northwest after the front has moved on by.

Observing storm systems, we see that not only do they move but they constantly change. Steered by the upper-level westerly winds, the middle latitude storm in Fig. 1.13 intensifies into a larger storm, which moves eastward, carrying its clouds and weather with it. In advance of this system, a sunny day in Ohio will gradually cloud over and yield heavy showers and thunderstorms by nightfall. Behind the storm, cool dry northerly winds rushing into eastern Colorado cause an overcast sky to give way to clearing conditions. Farther south, the thunderstorms presently over the Gulf of Mexico (Fig. 1.12) expand a little, then dissipate as new storms appear over water and land areas. To the west, the hurricane over the Pacific Ocean drifts northwestward and encounters cooler water. Here, away

from its warm energy source, it loses its punch; winds taper off, and the storm soon turns into an unorganized mass of clouds and tropical moisture.

Weather and Climate in Our Lives   Weather and climate play a major role in our lives. Weather, for example, often dictates the type of clothing we wear, while climate influences the type of clothing we buy. Climate determines when to plant crops as well as what type of crops can be planted. Weather determines if these same crops will grow to maturity. Although weather and climate affect our lives in many ways, perhaps their most immediate effect is on our comfort. In order to survive the cold of winter and heat of summer, we build homes, heat them, air condition them, insulate them—only to find that when we leave our shelter, we are at the mercy of the weather elements.

Even when we are dressed for the weather properly, wind, humidity, and precipitation can change our perception of how cold or warm it feels. On a cold, windy day the effects of *wind chill* tell us that it feels much colder than it really is, and, if not properly dressed, we run the risk of *frostbite* or even *hypothermia* (the rapid, progressive mental and physical collapse that accompanies the lowering of human body temperature). On a hot, humid day we normally feel uncomfortably warm and blame it on the humidity. If we become too warm, our bodies overheat and *heat exhaustion* or *heat stroke* may result. Those most likely to suffer these maladies are the elderly with impaired circulatory systems and infants, whose heat regulatory mechanisms are not yet fully developed.

Weather affects how we feel in other ways, too. Arthritic pain is most likely to occur when rising humidity is accompa-

Figure 1.14
Thunderstorms developing along an approaching cold front.

Figure 1.15
An ice storm in January, 1998, crippled Quebec, Canada.

nied by falling pressures. In ways not well understood, weather does seem to affect our health. The incidence of heart attacks shows a statistical peak after the passage of warm fronts, when rain and wind are common, and after the passage of cold fronts, when an abrupt change takes place as showery precipitation is accompanied by cold gusty winds. Headaches are common on days when we are forced to squint, often due to hazy skies or a thin, bright overcast layer of high clouds.

For some people, a warm dry wind blowing down-slope (a *chinook wind*) adversely affects their behavior (they often become irritable and depressed). Just how and why these winds impact humans physiologically is not well understood. We will take up the question of why these winds are warm and dry in Chapter 10.

When the weather turns colder or warmer than normal, it influences the lives and pocketbooks of many people. For example, the cool summer of 1992 over the eastern two-thirds of North America saved people billions of dollars in air-conditioning costs. On the other side of the coin, the colder than normal winter of 2000–2001 over much of North America sent heating costs soaring as demand for heating fuel escalated.

Major cold spells accompanied by heavy snow and ice can play havoc by snarling commuter traffic, curtailing airport services, closing schools, and downing power lines, thereby cutting off electricity to thousands of customers (see Fig. 1.15). For example, a huge ice storm during January, 1998, in northern New England and Canada left millions of people without power and caused over a billion dollars in damages, and a devastating snow storm during March, 1993, buried parts of the East Coast with 14-foot snow drifts and left Syracuse, New York, paralyzed with a snow depth of 36 inches. When the frigid air settles into the Deep South, many millions of dollars worth of temperature-sensitive fruits and vegetables may be ruined, the eventual consequence being higher produce prices in the supermarket.

Prolonged dry spells, especially when accompanied by high temperatures, can lead to a shortage of food and, in some places, widespread starvation. Parts of Africa, for example, have periodically suffered through major droughts and famine. In 1986, the southeastern section of the United States experienced a terrible drought as searing summer temperatures wilted crops, causing losses in excess of a billion dollars. When the climate turns hot and dry, animals suffer too. Over 500,000 chickens perished in Georgia alone during a two-day period at the peak of the summer heat. Severe drought also has an effect on water reserves, often forcing communities to ration water and restrict its use. During periods of extended drought, vegetation often becomes tinder-dry and, sparked by lightning or a careless human, such a dried-up region can quickly become a raging inferno. During the summer of 1998, hundreds of thousands of acres in drought-stricken northern and central Florida were ravaged by wildfires.

Each summer, scorching *heat waves* take many lives. During the past 20 years, an annual average of more than 300 deaths in the United States were attributed to excessive heat exposure. In one particularly devastating heat wave that hit Chicago, Illinois, during July, 1995, high temperatures coupled with high humidity claimed the lives of more than 500 people.

Figure 1.16
Tornadoes annually inflict widespread damage and cause the loss of many lives.

Each year, the violent side of weather influences the lives of millions. It is amazing how many people whose family roots are in the Midwest know the story of someone who was severely injured or killed by a tornado. Tornadoes have not only taken many lives, but annually they cause damage to buildings and property totaling in the hundreds of millions of dollars, as a single large tornado can level an entire section of a town (see Fig. 1.16).

Although the gentle rains of a typical summer thunderstorm are welcome over much of North America, the heavy downpours, high winds, and hail of the *severe thunderstorms* are not. Cloudbursts from slowly moving, intense thunderstorms can provide too much rain too quickly, creating *flash floods* as small streams become raging rivers composed of mud and sand entangled with uprooted plants and trees (see Fig. 1.17). On the average, more people die in the United States from floods and flash floods than from any other natural disaster. Strong downdrafts originating inside an intense thunderstorm (a *downburst*) create turbulent winds that are capable of destroying crops and inflicting damage upon surface structures. Several airline crashes have been attributed to the turbulent *wind shear* zone within the downburst. Annually, hail damages crops worth millions of dollars, and lightning takes the lives of about eighty people in the United States and starts

Figure 1.17
Flooding during April, 1997, inundates Grand Forks, North Dakota, as flood waters of the Red River extend over much of the city.

fires that destroy many thousands of acres of valuable timber (see Fig. 1.18).

Even the quiet side of weather has its influence. When winds die down and humid air becomes more tranquil, fog may form. Heavy fog can restrict visibility at airports, causing

Figure 1.18
Estimates are that lightning strikes the earth about 100 times every second. About 25 million lightning strikes hit the United States each year. Consequently, lightning is a very common, and sometimes deadly, weather phenomenon.

Weather Watch

On the average, 146 people die each year in the United States from floods and flash floods—more than from any other natural disaster. Of those who died in flash floods during the past ten years, over half of them were in motor vehicles.

flight delays and cancellations. Every winter, deadly fog-related auto accidents occur along our busy highways and turnpikes. But fog has a positive side, too, especially during a dry spell, as fog moisture collects on tree branches and drips to the ground, where it provides water for the tree's root system.

Weather and climate have become so much a part of our lives that the first thing many of us do in the morning is to listen to the local weather forecast. For this reason, many radio and television newscasts have their own "weather person" to present weather information and give daily forecasts. More and more of these people are professionally trained in meteorology, and many stations require that the weathercaster obtain a seal of approval from the American Meteorological Society (AMS), or a certificate from the National Weather Association (NWA). To make their weather presentation as up-to-the-minute as possible, an increasing number of stations are taking advantage of the information provided by the National Weather Service (NWS), such as computerized weather forecasts, time-lapse satellite pictures, and color Doppler radar displays.

For many years now, a staff of trained professionals at "The Weather Channel" have provided weather information twenty-four hours a day on cable television. And finally, the National Oceanic and Atmospheric Administration (NOAA), in cooperation with the National Weather Service, sponsors weather radio broadcasts at selected locations across the United States. Known as *NOAA weather radio* (and transmitted at VHF–FM frequencies), this service provides continuous weather information and regional forecasts (as well as special weather advisories, including watches and warnings) for over 90 percent of the nation.

Summary

This chapter provides an overview of the earth's atmosphere. Our atmosphere is one rich in nitrogen and oxygen as well as smaller amounts of other gases, such as water vapor, carbon dioxide, and other greenhouse gases whose increasing levels may result in global warming. We examined the earth's early atmosphere and found it to be much different from the air we breathe today.

We investigated the various layers of the atmosphere: the troposphere (the lowest layer), where almost all weather events occur, and the stratosphere, where ozone protects us from a portion of the sun's harmful rays. In the stratosphere, ozone appears to be decreasing in concentration over parts of the Northern and Southern Hemispheres. Above the stratosphere lies the mesosphere, where the air temperature drops dramatically with height. Above the mesosphere lies the warmest part of the atmosphere, the thermosphere. At the top of the thermosphere is the exosphere, where collisions between gas molecules and atoms are so infrequent that fast-moving lighter molecules can actually escape the earth's gravitational pull and shoot off into space. The ionosphere represents that portion of the upper atmosphere where large numbers of ions and free electrons exist.

We looked briefly at the weather map and a satellite photo and observed that dispersed throughout the atmosphere are storms and clouds of all sizes and shapes. The movement, intensification, and weakening of these systems, as well as the dynamic nature of air itself, produce a variety of weather events that we described in terms of weather elements. The sum total of weather and its extremes over a long period of time is what we call climate. Although sudden changes in weather may occur in a moment, climatic change takes place gradually over many years. The study of the atmosphere and all of its related phenomena is called *meteorology,* a term whose origin dates back to the days of Aristotle. Finally, we discussed some of many ways weather and climate influence our lives.

Key Terms

The following terms are listed in the order they appear in the text. Define each. Doing so will aid you in reviewing the material covered in this chapter.

atmosphere	thermosphere
nitrogen	exosphere
oxygen	homosphere
water vapor	heterosphere
carbon dioxide	ionosphere
ozone	weather
aerosol	weather elements
pollutant	climate
outgassing	meteorology
density	middle latitudes
pressure	middle latitude cyclonic
air pressure	storm
lapse rate	hurricane
temperature inversion	thunderstorm
troposphere	tornado
radiosonde	wind
stratosphere	wind direction
tropopause	front
mesosphere	

Questions for Review

1. What is the primary source of energy for the earth's atmosphere?
2. List the four most abundant gases in today's atmosphere.
3. Of the four most abundant gases in our atmosphere, which one shows the greatest variation at the earth's surface?
4. What are some of the important roles that water plays in our atmosphere?
5. Briefly explain the production and natural destruction of carbon dioxide near the earth's surface. Give a reason for the increase of carbon dioxide over the past 100 years.
6. List the two most abundant greenhouse gases in the earth's atmosphere. What makes them greenhouse gases?
7. Explain how the atmosphere "protects" inhabitants at the earth's surface.
8. What are some of the aerosols in our atmosphere?
9. How has the composition of the earth's atmosphere changed over time? Briefly outline the evolution of the earth's atmosphere.
10. (a) Explain the concept of air pressure in terms of mass of air above some level.
    (b) Why does air pressure always decrease with increasing height above the surface?
11. What is standard atmospheric pressure at sea level in (a) inches of mercury, (b) millibars, and (c) hectopascals?
12. What is the average or standard lapse rate in the troposphere?
13. Briefly describe how the air temperature changes from the earth's surface to the lower thermosphere.
14. On the basis of temperature, list the layers of the atmosphere from the lowest layer to the highest.
15. What atmospheric layer contains all of our weather?
16. (a) In what atmospheric layer do we find the lowest average air temperature?
    (b) The highest average temperature?
    (c) The highest concentration of ozone?
17. How does the ionosphere affect AM radio transmission during the day versus during the night?
18. Even though the actual concentration of oxygen is close to 21 percent (by volume) in the upper stratosphere, explain why you would not be able to survive there.
19. Define *meteorology* and discuss the origin of this word.
20. When someone says that "the wind direction today is south," does this mean that the wind is blowing *toward the south* or *from the south*?
21. Describe some of the features observed on a surface weather map.
22. Explain how wind blows around low- and high-pressure areas in the Northern Hemisphere.
23. How does weather differ from climate?
24. Describe some of the ways weather and climate influence the lives of people.
25. How are fronts defined?
26. Rank the following storms in size from largest to smallest: hurricane, tornado, middle-latitude cyclonic storm, thunderstorm.
27. Weather in the middle latitudes tends to move in what general direction?

Questions for Thought

1. Which of the following statements relate more to weather and which relate more to climate?
   (a) The summers here are warm and humid.
   (b) Cumulus clouds presently cover the entire sky.
   (c) Our lowest temperature last winter was −29°C (−18°F).
   (d) The air temperature outside is 22°C (72°F).
   (e) December is our foggiest month.
   (f) The highest temperature ever recorded in Phoenixville, Pennsylvania, was 44°C (111°F) on July 10, 1936.
   (g) Snow is falling at the rate of 5 cm (2 in.) per hour.
   (h) The average temperature for the month of January in Chicago, Illinois, is −3°C (26°F).
2. Why do you think that winds are named from the direction they are blowing?
3. A standard pressure of 1013.25 millibars is also known as one atmosphere (1 ATM). (a) Look at Fig. 1.8 and determine at approximately what levels you would record a pressure of 0.5 ATM and 0.1 ATM. (b) The surface air pressure on the planet Mars is about 0.007 ATM. If you were standing on Mars, the surface air pressure would be equivalent to a pressure observed at approximately what elevation in the Earth's atmosphere?
4. If you were suddenly placed at an altitude of 100 km (62 mi) above the earth, would you expect your stomach to expand or contract? Explain.

Problems and Exercises

1. Keep track of the weather. On an outline map of North America, mark the daily position of fronts and pressure systems for a period of several weeks or more. (This information can be obtained from newspapers, the TV news, the Internet, or from the Blue Skies CD-ROM.) Plot the general upper-level flow pattern on the map. Observe how the surface systems move. Relate this information to the material on wind, fronts, and cyclones covered in later chapters.
2. Compose a one-week journal, including daily newspaper weather maps and weather forecasts from the newspaper, the Internet, or from the Blue Skies CD-ROM. Provide a commentary for each day regarding the coincidence of actual and predicted weather.

3. Formulate a short-term climatology for your city for one month by recording maximum and minimum temperatures and precipitation amounts every day. You can get this information from television, newspapers, the Internet, your own measurements, or from the Blue Skies CD-ROM. Compare it to the actual climatology for that month. How can you explain any large differences between the two?

 ## Questions for Exploration

On the Blue Skies: College Edition CD-ROM go to the **Atmospheric Basics** section of the CD and click on **"Layers of the Atmosphere."**

1. Explore the "Standard Atmosphere" by piloting up through this "average" atmosphere.
   (a) Does the temperature decrease or increase with height near the surface?
   (b) What heating process do you feel is responsible for this pattern?
   (c) The tropopause is marked by the point, usually above 8 km above sea level, where temperature systematically stops dropping with height and becomes either isothermal or increasing with height. At what height does this happen?
2. Explore the vertical profile of temperature for your location. Note the time of the sounding as either 00Z (GMT) or 12Z. (Instructions for converting GMT to local time are given in Appendix F.)
   (a) Does the temperature decrease or increase with height near the surface?
   (b) At what height does the tropopause happen over your location?
   (c) If the height over you is different from that in the standard atmosphere what might explain the difference?

 Go to the Brooks/Cole Earth Sciences Resource Center (http://earthscience.brookscole.com) for critical thinking exercises, articles, and additional readings from InfoTrac College Edition, Brooks/Cole's online student library.

The aurora borealis, which forms as energetic particles from the sun interact with the earth's atmosphere. (Photo © Lindsey Martin)

Energy: Warming the Earth and the Atmosphere

CONTENTS

At high latitudes after darkness has fallen, a faint, white glow may appear in the sky. Lasting from a few minutes to a few hours, the light may move across the sky as a yellow green arc much wider than a rainbow; or, it may faintly decorate the sky with flickering draperies of blue, green, and purple light that constantly change in form and location, as if blown by a gentle breeze.

For centuries curiosity and superstition have surrounded these eerie lights. Eskimo legend says they are the lights from demons' lanterns as they search the heavens for lost souls. Nordic sagas called them a reflection of fire that surrounds the seas of the north. Even today there are those who proclaim that the lights are reflected sunlight from polar ice fields. Actually, this light show in the Northern Hemisphere is the aurora borealis—the northern lights—which is caused by invisible energetic particles bombarding our upper atmosphere. Anyone who witnesses this, one of nature's spectacular color displays, will never forget it.

nergy is everywhere. It is the basis for life. It comes in various forms: It can warm a house, melt ice, and drive the atmosphere, producing our everyday weather events. When the sun's energy interacts with our upper atmosphere we see energy at work in yet another form, a shimmering display of light from the sky—the aurora. What, precisely, is this common, yet mysterious, quantity we call "energy?" What is its primary source? How does it warm our earth and provide the driving force for our atmosphere? And in what form does it reach our atmosphere to produce a dazzling display like the aurora?

To answer these questions, we must first begin with the concept of energy itself. Then we will examine energy in its various forms and how energy is transferred from one form to another in our atmosphere. Finally, we will look more closely at the sun's energy and its influence on our atmosphere.

Energy, Temperature, and Heat

By definition, **energy** is the ability or capacity to do work on some form of matter. (Matter is anything that has mass and occupies space.) Work is done on matter when matter is either pushed, pulled, or lifted over some distance. When we lift a brick, for example, we exert a force against the pull of gravity—we "do work" on the brick. The higher we lift the brick, the more work we do. So, by doing work on something, we give it "energy," which it can, in turn, use to do work on other things. The brick that we lifted, for instance, can now do work on your toe—by falling on it.

The total amount of energy stored in any object (internal energy) determines how much work that object is capable of doing. A lake behind a dam contains energy by virtue of its position. This is called *gravitational potential energy* or simply **potential energy** because it represents the potential to do work—a great deal of destructive work if the dam were to break. The potential energy (PE) of any object is given as

$$PE = mgh,$$

where m is the object's mass, g is the acceleration of gravity, and h is the object's height above the ground.

A volume of air aloft has more potential energy than the same size volume of air just above the surface. This fact is so because the air aloft has the potential to sink and warm through a greater depth of atmosphere. A substance also possesses potential energy if it can do work when a chemical change takes place. Thus, coal, natural gas, and food all contain chemical potential energy.

Any moving substance possesses energy of motion, or **kinetic energy.** The kinetic energy (KE) of an object is equal to half its mass multiplied by its velocity squared; thus

$$KE = \tfrac{1}{2} mv^2.$$

Consequently, the faster something moves, the greater its kinetic energy; hence, a strong wind possesses more kinetic energy than a light breeze. Since kinetic energy also depends on the object's mass, a volume of water and an equal volume of air may be moving at the same speed, but, because the water has greater mass, it has more kinetic energy. The atoms and molecules that comprise all matter have kinetic energy due to their motion. This form of kinetic energy is often referred to as *heat energy.* Probably the most important form of energy in terms of weather and climate is the energy we receive from the sun—*radiant energy.*

Energy, therefore, takes on many forms, and it can change from one form into another. But the total amount of energy in the universe remains constant. *Energy cannot be created nor can it be destroyed.* It merely changes from one form to another in any ordinary physical or chemical process. In other words, the energy lost during one process must equal the energy gained during another. This is what we mean when we say that energy is conserved. This statement is known as the *law of conservation of energy,* and is also called the *first law of thermodynamics.*

We know that air is a mixture of countless billions of atoms and molecules. If they could be seen, they would appear to be moving about in all directions, freely darting, twisting, spinning, and colliding with one another like an angry swarm of bees. Close to the earth's surface, each individual molecule will travel only about a thousand times its diameter before colliding with another molecule. Moreover, we would see that all the atoms and molecules are not moving at the same speed, as some are moving faster than others. The temperature of the air (or any substance) is a measure of its average kinetic energy. Simply stated, **temperature** *is a measure of the average speed of the atoms and molecules,* where higher temperatures correspond to faster average speeds.

Suppose we examine a volume of surface air about the size of a large flexible balloon. If we warm the air inside, the molecules would move faster, but they also would move slightly farther apart—the air becomes less dense. Conversely, if we cool the air, the molecules would slow down, crowd closer together, and the air would become more dense. This molecular behavior is why, in many places throughout the book, we refer to surface air as either *warm, less-dense air* or as *cold, more-dense air.*

The atmosphere and oceans contain *internal energy,* which is the total energy (potential and kinetic) stored in their molecules. As we have just seen, the temperature of air and water is determined only by the *average* kinetic energy (average speed) of *all* their molecules. Since temperature only indicates how "hot" or "cold" something is relative to some set standard value, it does not always tell us how much internal energy that something possesses. For example, two identical mugs, each half-filled with water and each with the same temperature, contain the same internal energy. If the water from one mug is poured into the other, the total internal energy of the filled mug has doubled because its mass has doubled. Its temperature, however, has not changed, since the average speed of all of the molecules is still the same (see Fig. 2.1).

Now, imagine that you are sipping a hot cup of tea on a small raft in the middle of a lake. The tea has a much higher temperature than the lake, yet the lake contains more internal energy because it is composed of many more molecules. If the

Figure 2.1
Temperature is a measure of the average speed of the molecules. The beverage in each mug has the same temperature because the average speed of the molecules in both mugs is the same. The mug on the left, however, contains more internal energy because it contains more molecules.

cup of tea is allowed to float on top of the water, the tea would cool rapidly. The energy that would be transferred from the hot tea to the cool water (because of their temperature difference) is called *heat.*

In essence, **heat** *is energy in the process of being transferred from one object to another because of the temperature difference between them.* After heat is transferred, it is stored as internal energy. How is this energy transfer process accomplished? In the atmosphere, heat is transferred by *conduction, convection,* and *radiation.* We will examine these mechanisms of energy transfer after we look at temperature scales and at the important concepts of *specific heat* and *latent heat.*

Temperature Scales   Suppose we take a small volume of air and allow it to cool. As the air slowly cools, its atoms and molecules would move slower and slower until the air reaches a temperature of −273°C (−459°F), which is the lowest temperature possible. At this temperature, called **absolute zero,** the atoms and molecules would possess a minimum amount of energy and theoretically no thermal motion. At absolute zero, we can begin a temperature scale called the *absolute* or **Kelvin scale** after Lord Kelvin (1824–1907), a famous British scientist who first introduced it. Since the Kelvin scale begins at absolute zero, it contains no negative numbers and is, therefore, quite convenient for scientific calculations.

Two other temperature scales commonly used today are the Fahrenheit and Celsius (formerly centigrade). The **Fahrenheit scale** was developed in the early 1700s by the physicist G. Daniel Fahrenheit, who assigned the number 32 to the temperature at which water freezes, and the number 212 to the temperature at which water boils. The zero point was simply the lowest temperature that he obtained with a mixture of ice, water, and salt. Between the freezing and boiling points are 180 equal divisions, each of which is called a degree. A thermometer calibrated with this scale is referred to as a Fahrenheit thermometer, for it measures an object's temperature in degrees Fahrenheit (°F).

The **Celsius scale** was introduced later in the eighteenth century. The number 0 (zero) on this scale is assigned to the temperature at which pure water freezes, and the number 100 to the temperature at which pure water boils at sea level. The space between freezing and boiling is divided into 100 equal degrees. Therefore, each Celsius degree is 180/100 or 1.8 times larger than a Fahrenheit degree. Put another way, an increase in temperature of 1°C equals an increase of 1.8°F. A formula for converting °C to °F is

$$°C = \tfrac{5}{9}\,(°F - 32).$$

On the Kelvin scale, degrees Kelvin are called *Kelvins* (abbreviated K). Each degree on the Kelvin scale is exactly the same size as a degree Celsius, and a temperature of 0 K is equal to −273°C. Converting from °C to K can be made by simply adding 273 to the Celsius temperature, as

$$K = °C + 273.$$

Figure 2.2 compares the Kelvin, Celsius, and Fahrenheit scales. Converting a temperature from one scale to another can be done by simply reading the corresponding temperature from the adjacent scale. Thus, 303 on the Kelvin scale is the equivalent of 30°C and 86°F.*

---

*A more complete table of conversions is given in Appendix A.

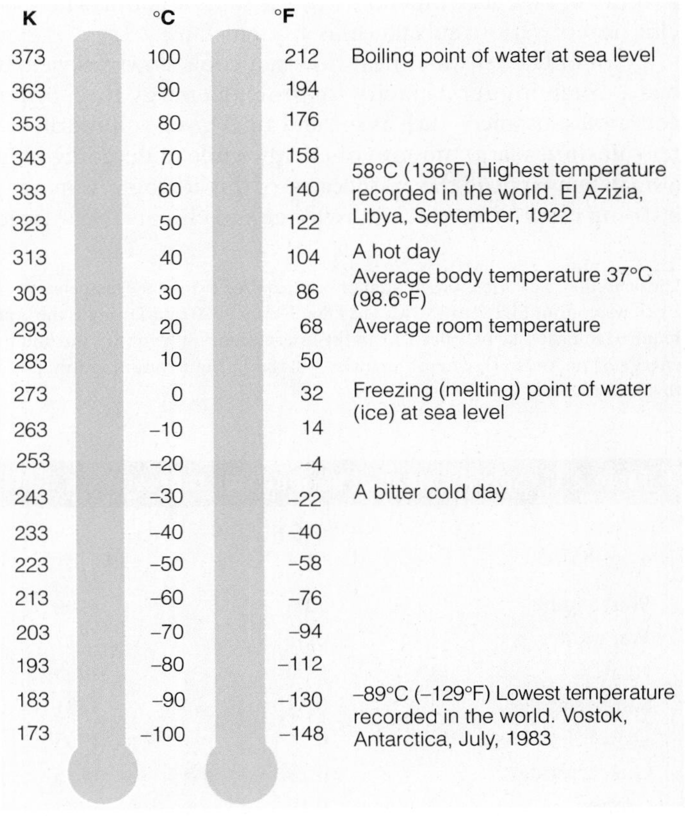

K	°C	°F	
373	100	212	Boiling point of water at sea level
363	90	194	
353	80	176	
343	70	158	58°C (136°F) Highest temperature
333	60	140	recorded in the world. El Azizia,
323	50	122	Libya, September, 1922
313	40	104	A hot day
303	30	86	Average body temperature 37°C (98.6°F)
293	20	68	Average room temperature
283	10	50	
273	0	32	Freezing (melting) point of water (ice) at sea level
263	−10	14	
253	−20	−4	
243	−30	−22	A bitter cold day
233	−40	−40	
223	−50	−58	
213	−60	−76	
203	−70	−94	
193	−80	−112	
183	−90	−130	−89°C (−129°F) Lowest temperature
173	−100	−148	recorded in the world. Vostok, Antarctica, July, 1983

Figure 2.2
Comparison of the Kelvin, Celsius, and Fahrenheit scales.

In most of the world, temperature readings are taken in °C. In the United States, however, temperatures above the surface are taken in °C, while temperatures at the surface are typically read in °F. Currently, then, temperatures on upper-level maps are plotted in °C, while, on surface weather maps, they are in °F. Since both scales are in use, temperature readings in this book will, in most cases, be given in °C followed by their equivalent in °F.

Specific Heat A watched pot never boils, or so it seems. The reason for this is that water requires a relatively large amount of heat energy to bring about a small temperature change. The **heat capacity** of a substance is the ratio of the amount of heat energy absorbed by that substance to its corresponding temperature rise. The heat capacity of a substance per unit mass is called **specific heat**. In other words, specific heat is the amount of heat needed to raise the temperature of one gram (g) of a substance one degree Celsius.

If we heat 1 g of liquid water on a stove, it would take about 1 calorie* (cal) to raise its temperature by 1°C. So water has a specific heat of 1. If, however, we put the same amount (that is, same mass) of compact dry soil on the flame, we would see that it would take about one-fifth the heat (about 0.2 cal) to raise its temperature by 1°C. The specific heat of water is therefore 5 times greater than that of soil. In other words, water must absorb 5 times as much heat as the same quantity of soil in order to raise its temperature by the same amount. The specific heat of various substances is given in Table 2.1.

Not only does water heat slowly, it cools slowly as well. It has a much higher capacity for storing energy than other common substances, such as soil and air. A given volume of water can store a large amount of energy while undergoing only a small temperature change. Because of this attribute, water has a strong modifying effect on weather and climate. Near large

---

*By definition, a calorie is the amount of heat required to raise the temperature of 1 g of water from 14.5°C to 15.5°C. The kilocalorie is 1000 calories and is the heat required to raise 1 kg of water 1°C. In the International System (SI), the unit of energy is the joule (J), where 1 calorie = 4.186 J. (For pronunciation: joule rhymes with pool.)

Table 2.1	Specific Heat of Various Substances	
SUBSTANCE	SPECIFIC HEAT (Cal/g × °C)	J/kg × °C
Water (pure)	1.00	4186
Wet mud	0.60	2512
Ice (0°C)	0.50	2093
Sandy clay	0.33	1381
Dry air (sea level)	0.24	1005
Quartz sand	0.19	795
Granite	0.19	794

bodies of water, for example, winters usually remain warmer and summers cooler than nearby inland regions—a fact well known to people who live adjacent to oceans or large lakes.

Latent Heat—The Hidden Warmth We know from Chapter 1 that water vapor is an invisible gas that becomes visible when it changes into larger liquid or solid (ice) particles. This process of transformation is known as a *change of state* or, simply, a *phase change*. The heat energy required to change a substance, such as water, from one state to another is called **latent heat**. But why is this heat referred to as "latent"? To answer this question, we will begin with something familiar to most of us—the cooling produced by evaporating water.

Suppose we microscopically examine a small drop of pure water. At the drop's surface, molecules are constantly escaping (evaporating). Because the more energetic, faster-moving molecules escape most easily, the average motion of all the molecules left behind decreases as each additional molecule evaporates. Since temperature is a measure of average molecular motion, the slower motion suggests a lower water temperature. *Evaporation is, therefore, a cooling process.* Stated another way, evaporation is a cooling process because the energy needed to evaporate the water—that is, to change its phase from a liquid to a gas—may come from the water or other sources, including the air.

In the everyday world, we experience evaporational cooling as we step out of a shower or swimming pool into a dry area. Because some of the energy used to evaporate the water comes from our skin, we may experience a rapid drop in skin temperature, even to the point where goose bumps form. In fact, on a hot, dry, windy day in Tucson, Arizona, cooling may be so rapid that we begin to shiver even though the air temperature is hovering around 38°C (100°F).

The energy lost by liquid water during evaporation can be thought of as carried away by, and "locked up" within, the water vapor molecule. The energy is thus in a "stored" or "hidden" condition and is, therefore, called *latent heat*. It is latent (hidden) in that the temperature of the substance changing from liquid to vapor is still the same. However, the heat energy will reappear as **sensible heat** (the heat we can feel, "sense," and measure with a thermometer) when the vapor condenses back into liquid water. Therefore, *condensation (the opposite of evaporation) is a warming process.*

The heat energy released when water vapor condenses to form liquid droplets is called *latent heat of condensation.* Conversely, the heat energy used to change liquid into vapor at the same temperature is called *latent heat of evaporation* (vaporization). Nearly 600 cal (2500 J) are required to evaporate a single gram of water at room temperature. With many hundreds of grams of water evaporating from the body, it is no wonder that after a shower we feel cold before drying off.

In a way, latent heat is responsible for keeping a cold drink with ice colder than one without ice. As ice melts, its temperature does not change. The reason for this fact is that the heat added to

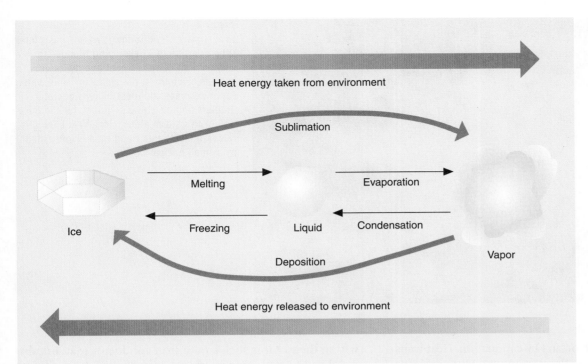

Figure 2.3
Heat energy absorbed and
released.

the ice only breaks down the rigid crystal pattern, changing the ice to a liquid without changing its temperature. The energy used in this process is called *latent heat of fusion* (melting). Roughly 80 cal (335 J) are required to melt a single gram of ice. Consequently, heat added to a cold drink with ice primarily melts the ice, while heat added to a cold drink without ice warms the beverage. If a gram of water at 0°C changes back into ice at 0°C, this same amount of heat (80 cal) would be released as sensible heat to the environment. Therefore, when ice melts, heat is taken in; when water freezes, heat is liberated.

The heat energy required to change ice into vapor (a process called *sublimation*) is referred to as *latent heat of sublimation*. For a single gram of ice to transform completely into vapor at 0°C requires nearly 680 cal—80 cal for the latent heat of fusion plus 600 cal for the latent heat of evaporation. If this same vapor transformed back into ice (a process called *deposition*), approximately 680 cal (2850 J) would be released.

Figure 2.3 summarizes the concepts examined so far. When the change of state is from left to right, heat is absorbed by the substance and taken away from the environment. The processes of melting, evaporation, and sublimation all cool the environment. When the change of state is from right to left, heat energy is given up by the substance and added to the environment. The process of freezing, condensation, and deposition all warm their surroundings.

Latent heat is an important source of atmospheric energy. Once vapor molecules become separated from the earth's surface, they are swept away by the wind, like dust before a broom. Rising to high altitudes where the air is cold, the vapor changes into liquid and ice cloud particles. During these processes, a tremendous amount of heat energy is released into the environment. This heat provides energy for storms, such as hurricanes, middle latitude cyclones, and thunderstorms (see Fig. 2.4).

Water vapor evaporated from warm, tropical water can be carried into polar regions, where it condenses and gives up its heat energy. Thus, as we will see, evaporation–transportation–condensation is an extremely important mechanism for the relocation of heat energy (as well as water) in the atmosphere. (Before going on to the next section, you may wish to read the Focus section on p. 33, which summarizes some of the concepts considered thus far.)

Heat Transfer in the Atmosphere

Conduction   The transfer of heat from molecule to molecule within a substance is called **conduction.** Hold one end of a metal straight pin between your fingers and place a flaming candle under the other end (see Fig. 2.5). Because of the energy they absorb from the flame, the molecules in the pin vibrate faster. The faster-vibrating molecules cause adjoining molecules to vibrate faster. These, in turn, pass vibrational energy on to their neighboring molecules, and so on, until the molecules at the finger-held end of the pin begin to vibrate rapidly. These fast-moving molecules eventually cause the molecules of your finger to vibrate more quickly. Heat is now being transferred from the pin to your finger, and both the pin and your finger feel hot. If enough heat is transferred, you will drop the pin. The transmission of heat from one end of the pin to the other, and

Figure 2.4
Every time a cloud forms, it warms the atmosphere. Inside this developing thunderstorm a vast amount of stored heat energy (latent heat) is given up to the air, as invisible water vapor becomes countless billions of water droplets and ice crystals. In fact, for the duration of this storm alone, more heat energy is released inside this cloud than is unleashed by a small nuclear bomb.

from the pin to your finger, occurs by conduction. Heat transferred in this fashion always flows from *warmer to colder* regions. Generally, the greater the temperature difference, the more rapid the heat transfer.

When materials can easily pass energy from one molecule to another, they are considered to be good conductors of heat. How well they conduct heat depends upon how their molecules are structurally bonded together. Table 2.2 shows that solids, such as metals, are good heat conductors. It is often difficult, therefore, to judge the temperature of metal objects. For example, if you grab a metal pipe at room temperature, it will seem to be much colder than it actually is because the metal conducts heat away from the hand quite rapidly. Conversely, *air is an extremely poor conductor of heat,* which is why most insulating materials have a large number of air spaces trapped within them. Air is such a poor heat conductor that, in calm weather, the hot ground only warms a shallow layer of air a few centimeters thick by conduction. Yet, air can carry this energy rapidly from one region to another. How then does this phenomenon happen?

Convection The transfer of heat by the mass movement of a fluid (such as water and air) is called **convection.** This type of heat transfer takes place in liquids and gases be-

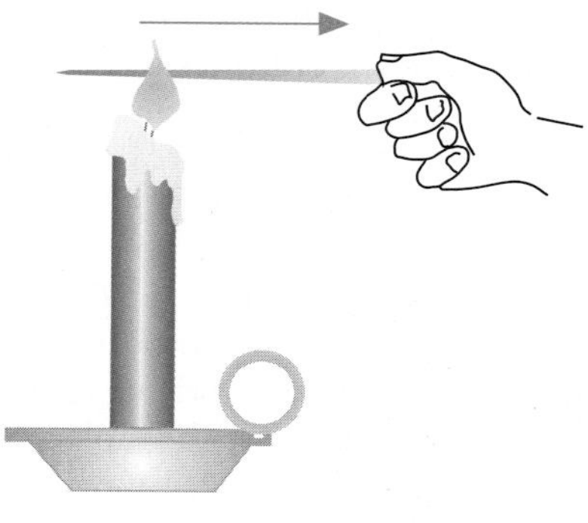

Figure 2.5
The transfer of heat from the hot end of the metal pin to the cool end by molecular contact is called *conduction.*

Table 2.2 Heat Conductivity* of Various Substances

SUBSTANCE	HEAT CONDUCTIVITY (Watts† per meter per °C)
Still air	0.023 (at 20°C)
Wood	0.08
Dry soil	0.25
Water	0.60 (at 20°C)
Snow	0.63
Wet soil	2.1
Ice	2.1
Sandstone	2.6
Granite	2.7
Iron	80
Silver	427

*Heat (thermal) conductivity describes a substance's ability to conduct heat as a consequence of molecular motion.

†A watt (W) is a unit of power where one watt equals one joule (J) per second (J/s). One joule equals 0.24 calories.

Focus on A SPECIAL TOPIC

The Fate of a Sunbeam

Consider sunlight in the form of radiant energy striking a large lake. (See Fig. 1.) Part of the incoming energy heats the water, causing greater molecular motion and, hence, an increase in the water's kinetic energy. This greater kinetic energy allows more water molecules to evaporate from the surface. As each molecule escapes, work is done to break it away from the remaining water molecules. This energy becomes the latent heat energy that is carried with the water vapor.

Above the lake, a large bubble* of warm, moist air rises and expands. In order for this expansion to take place, the gas molecules inside the bubble must use some of their kinetic energy to do work against the bubble's sides. This results in a slower molecular speed and a lower temperature. Well above the surface, the water vapor in the rising, cooling bubble of moist air condenses into clouds. The condensation of water vapor releases latent heat energy into the atmosphere, warming the air. The tiny suspended cloud droplets possess potential energy, which becomes kinetic energy

Figure 1
Solar energy striking a large body of water goes through many transformations.

when these droplets grow into raindrops that fall earthward.

When the drops reach the surface, their kinetic energy erodes the land. As rain-swollen streams flow into a lake behind a dam, there is a buildup of potential energy, which can be transformed into kinetic energy as water is harnessed to flow down a chute. If the moving water drives a generator, kinetic energy is converted into

electrical energy, which is sent to cities. There, it heats, cools, and lights the buildings in which people work and live. Meanwhile, some of the water in the lake behind the dam evaporates and is free to repeat the cycle. Hence, the energy from the sunlight on a lake can undergo many transformations and help provide the moving force for many natural and human-made processes.

---

*A bubble of rising (or sinking) air about the size of a large balloon is often called *a parcel of air.*

---

cause they can move freely and it is possible to set up currents within them.

Convection happens naturally in the atmosphere. On a warm, sunny day, certain areas of the earth's surface absorb more heat from the sun than others; as a result, the air near the earth's surface is heated somewhat unevenly. Air molecules adjacent to these hot surfaces bounce against them, thereby gaining some extra energy by conduction. The heated air expands and becomes less dense than the surrounding cooler air. The expanded warm air is buoyed upward and rises. In this manner, large bubbles of warm air rise and transfer heat energy upward. Cooler, heavier air flows toward the surface to replace

the rising air. This cooler air becomes heated in turn, rises, and the cycle is repeated. In meteorology, this vertical exchange of heat is called *convection*, and the rising air bubbles are known as **thermals** (see Fig. 2.6).

The rising air expands and gradually spreads outward. It then slowly begins to sink. Near the surface, it moves back into the heated region, replacing the rising air. In this way, a *convective circulation*, or thermal "cell," is produced in the atmosphere. In a convective circulation the warm, rising air cools. In our atmosphere, *any air that rises will expand and cool,* and *any air that sinks is compressed and warms.* This important concept is detailed in the Focus section on p. 34.

Focus on A SPECIAL TOPIC

Rising Air Cools and Sinking Air Warms

To understand why rising air cools and sinking air warms we need to examine some air. Suppose we place air in an imaginary thin, elastic wrap about the size of a large balloon (see Fig. 2). This invisible balloonlike "blob" is called a *parcel*. The air parcel can expand and contract freely, but neither external air nor heat is able to mix with the air inside. By the same token, as the parcel moves, it does not break apart, but remains as a single unit.

At the earth's surface, the parcel has the same temperature and pressure as the air surrounding it. Suppose we lift the parcel. Recall from Chapter 1 that air pressure always decreases as we move up into the atmosphere. Consequently, as the parcel rises, it enters a region where the surrounding air pressure is lower. To equalize the pressure, the parcel molecules inside push the parcel walls outward, expanding it. Because there is no other energy source, the air molecules inside use some of their own energy to expand the parcel. This energy loss shows up as slower molecular speeds, which represent a lower parcel temperature. Hence, *any air that rises always expands and cools.*

If the parcel is lowered to the earth, it returns to a region where the air pressure is higher. The higher outside pressure squeezes (compresses) the parcel back to its original (smaller) shape. Because air molecules have a faster rebound velocity after striking the sides of a collapsing parcel, the average speed of the molecules inside goes up. (A Ping-Pong ball moves faster after striking a paddle that is moving toward it.) This increase in molecular speed represents a warmer parcel temperature. Therefore, *any air that sinks (subsides), warms by compression.*

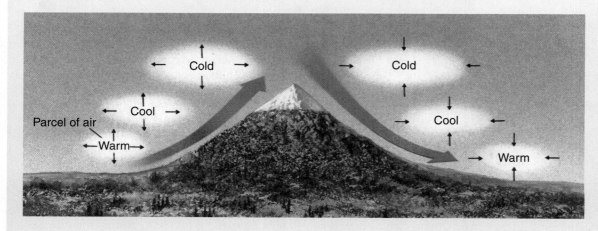

Figure 2
Rising air expands and cools; sinking air is compressed and warms.

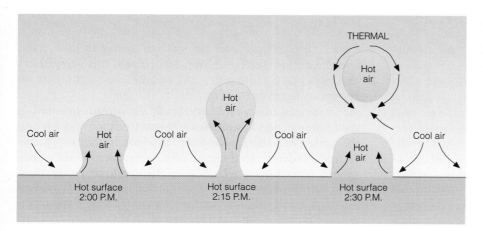

Figure 2.6
The development of a thermal. A thermal is a rising bubble of air that carries heat energy upward by *convection.*

Weather Watch

Although we can't see air, there are signs that tell us where the air is rising. One example: On a calm day, you can watch a hawk circle and climb high above level ground while its wings remain motionless. A rising thermal carries the hawk upward as it scans the terrain for prey. Another example: If the water vapor of a rising thermal condenses into liquid cloud droplets, the thermal becomes visible to us as a puffy cumulus cloud. Flying in a light aircraft beneath these clouds usually produces a bumpy ride, as passengers are jostled around by the rising and sinking air associated with convection.

Although the entire process of heated air rising, spreading out, sinking, and finally flowing back toward its original location is known as a convective circulation, meteorologists usually restrict the term *convection* to the process of the rising and sinking part of the circulation.

The horizontally moving part of the circulation (called *wind*) carries properties of the air in that particular area with it. The transfer of these properties by horizontally moving air is called **advection.** For example, wind blowing across a body of water will "pick up" water vapor from the evaporating surface and transport it elsewhere in the atmosphere. If the air cools, the water vapor may condense into cloud droplets and release latent heat. In a sense, then, heat is advected (carried) by the water vapor as it is swept along with the wind. Earlier we saw that this is an important way to redistribute heat energy in the atmosphere.

Brief Review   Before moving on to the next section, here is a summary of some of the important concepts and facts we have covered:

- The temperature of a substance is a measure of the average kinetic energy (average speed) of its atoms and molecules.
- Evaporation (the transformation of liquid into vapor) is a cooling process that can cool the air, whereas condensation (the transformation of vapor into liquid) is a warming process that can warm the air.
- Heat is energy in the process of being transferred from one object to another because of the temperature difference between them.
- In conduction, which is the transfer of heat by molecule-to-molecule contact, heat always flows from warmer to colder regions.
- Air is a poor conductor of heat.
- Convection is an important mechanism of heat transfer, as it represents the vertical movement of warmer air upward and cooler air downward.

There is yet another mechanism for the transfer of energy—radiation, or *radiant energy,* which is what we receive from the sun. In this method, energy may be transferred from one object to another without the space between them necessarily being heated.

Radiation

On a summer day, you may have noticed how warm and flushed your face feels as you stand facing the sun. Sunlight travels through the surrounding air with little effect upon the air itself. Your face, however, absorbs this energy and converts it to thermal energy. Thus, sunlight warms your face without actually warming the air. The energy transferred from the sun to your face is called **radiant energy,** or **radiation.** It travels in the form of waves that release energy when they are absorbed by an object. Because these waves have magnetic and electrical properties, we call them **electromagnetic waves.** Electromagnetic waves do not need molecules to propagate them. In a vacuum, they travel at a constant speed of nearly 300,000 km (186,000 mi) per second—the speed of light.

Figure 2.7 shows some of the different wavelengths of radiation. Notice that the **wavelength** (which is usually expressed by the Greek letter lambda, λ) is the distance measured along a wave from one crest to another. Also notice that some of the waves have exceedingly short lengths. For example, radiation that we can see (visible light) has an average wavelength of less than one-millionth of a meter—a distance nearly one-hundredth the diameter of a human hair. To measure these short lengths, we introduce a new unit of measurement called a **micrometer** (represented by the symbol μm), which is equal to one-millionth of a meter (m); thus

$$1 \text{ micrometer } (\mu m) = 0.000001 \text{ m} = 10^{-6} \text{ m}.$$

In Fig. 2.7, we can see that the average wavelength of visible light is about 0.0000005 m, which is the same as 0.5 μm. To give you a common object for comparison, the average height of a letter on this page is about 2000 μm, or 2 millimeters (2 mm), whereas the thickness of this page is about 100 μm.

We can also see in Fig. 2.7 that the longer waves carry less energy than do the shorter waves. When comparing the energy carried by various waves, it is useful to give electromagnetic radiation characteristics of particles in order to explain some of the waves' behavior. We can actually think of radiation as streams of particles or **photons** that are discrete packets of energy.*

An ultraviolet photon carries more energy than a photon of visible light. In fact, certain ultraviolet photons have enough energy to produce sunburns and penetrate skin tissue, sometimes causing skin cancer. As we discussed in Chapter 1, it is ozone in the stratosphere that protects us from the vast majority of these harmful rays.

---

*Packets of photons make up waves, and groups of waves make up a beam of radiation.

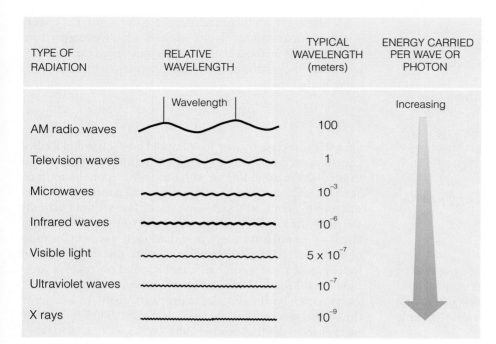

TYPE OF RADIATION	RELATIVE WAVELENGTH	TYPICAL WAVELENGTH (meters)	ENERGY CARRIED PER WAVE OR PHOTON
	Wavelength		Increasing
AM radio waves		100	
Television waves		1	
Microwaves		10^{-3}	
Infrared waves		10^{-6}	
Visible light		5×10^{-7}	
Ultraviolet waves		10^{-7}	
X rays		10^{-9}	

Figure 2.7
Radiation characterized according to wavelength. As the wavelength decreases, the energy carried per wave increases.

Radiation and Temperature   *All things (whose temperature is above absolute zero), no matter how big or small, emit radiation.* This book, your body, flowers, trees, air, the earth, the stars are all radiating a wide range of electromagnetic waves. The energy originates from rapidly vibrating electrons, billions of which exist in every object.

The wavelengths that each object emits depend primarily on the object's temperature. The higher the temperature, the faster the electrons vibrate, and the shorter are the wavelengths of the emitted radiation. This can be visualized by attaching one end of a rope to a post and holding the other end. If the rope is shaken rapidly (high temperature), numerous short waves travel along the rope; if the rope is shaken slowly (lower temperature), longer waves appear on the rope. Although objects at a temperature of about 500°C radiate waves with many lengths, some of them are short enough to stimulate the sensation of vision. We actually see these objects glow red. Objects cooler than this radiate at wavelengths that are too long for us to see. The page of this book, for example, is radiating electromagnetic waves. But because its temperature is only around 20°C (68°F), the waves emitted are much too long to stimulate vision. We are able to see the page, however, because light waves from other sources (such as light bulbs or the sun) are being *reflected* (bounced) off the paper. If this book were carried into a completely dark room, it would continue to radiate, but the pages would appear black because there are no visible light waves in the room to reflect off the pages.

Objects that have a very high temperature emit energy at a greater rate or intensity than objects at a lower temperature. Thus, *as the temperature of an object increases, more total radia-tion is emitted each second.* This can be expressed mathematically as

$$E = \sigma T^4 \text{ (Stefan-Boltzmann law)},$$

where E is the maximum rate of radiation emitted by each square meter of surface area of the object, σ (the Greek letter sigma) is the Stefan-Boltzmann constant,* and T is the object's surface temperature in degrees Kelvin. This relationship, called the **Stefan-Boltzmann law** after Josef Stefan (1835–1893) and Ludwig Boltzmann (1844–1906), who derived it, states that all objects with temperatures above absolute zero (0 K or –273°C) emit radiation at a rate proportional to the fourth power of their absolute temperature. Consequently, a small increase in temperature results in a large increase in the amount of radiation emitted because doubling the absolute temperature of an object increases the maximum energy output by a factor of 16, which is 2^4.

Radiation of the Sun and Earth   Most of the sun's energy is emitted from its surface, where the temperature is nearly 6000 K (10,500°F). The earth, on the other hand, has an average surface temperature of 288 K (15°C, 59°F). The sun, therefore, radiates a great deal more energy than does the earth (see Fig. 2.8). At what wavelengths do the sun and the earth radiate most of their energy? Fortunately, the sun and the earth both have characteristics (discussed in a later section) that enable us to

---

*The Stefan-Boltzmann constant σ in SI units is 5.67×10^{-8} W/m^{2}k^4. A watt (W) is a unit of power where one watt equals one joule (J) per second (J/s). One joule is equal to 0.24 cal. More conversions are given in Appendix A.

use the following relationship called **Wien's law** (or W*ien's displacement law*) after the German physicist Wilhelm Wien (pronounced Wēēn, 1864–1928), who discovered it:

$$\lambda_{max} = \frac{constant}{T} \text{ (Wien's law)},$$

where λ_{max} is the wavelength in micrometers at which maximum radiation emission occurs, T is the object's temperature in Kelvins, and the constant is 2897 μm K. To make the numbers easy to deal with, we will round off the constant to the number 3000.

For the sun, with a surface temperature of 6000 K, the equation becomes

$$\lambda_{max} = \frac{3000 \text{ μm K}}{6000 \text{ K}} = 0.5 \text{ μm}.$$

Thus, the sun emits a maximum amount of radiation at wavelengths near 0.5 μm. The cooler earth, with an average surface temperature of 288 K (rounded to 300 K), emits maximum radiation near wavelengths of 10 μm, since

$$\lambda_{max} = \frac{3000 \text{ μm K}}{300 \text{ K}} = 10 \text{ μm}.$$

Thus, the earth emits most of its radiation at longer wavelengths between about 5 and 25 μm, while the sun emits the majority of its radiation at wavelengths less than 2 μm. For this reason, the earth's radiation (*terrestrial radiation*) is often called **longwave radiation,** whereas the sun's energy (*solar radiation*) is referred to as **shortwave radiation.**

Wien's law demonstrates that, as the temperature of an object increases, the wavelength at which maximum emission occurs is shifted toward shorter values. For example, if the sun's surface temperature were to double to 12,000 K, its wavelength of maximum emission would be halved to about 0.25 μm. If, on the other hand, the sun's surface cooled to 3000 K, it would emit its maximum amount of radiation near 1.0 μm.

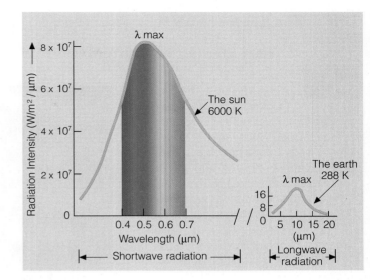

Figure 2.8
The hotter sun not only radiates more energy than that of the cooler earth (the area under the curve), but it also radiates the majority of its energy at much shorter wavelengths. (The area under the curves is equal to the total energy emitted, and the scales for the two curves differ by a factor of 100,000.)

Even though the sun radiates at a maximum rate at a particular wavelength, it nonetheless emits some radiation at almost all other wavelengths. If we look at the amount of radiation given off by the sun at each wavelength, we obtain the sun's *electromagnetic spectrum.* A portion of this spectrum is shown in Fig. 2.9.

Since our eyes are sensitive to radiation between 0.4 and 0.7 μm, these waves reach the eye and stimulate the sensation of color. This portion of the spectrum is referred to as the **visible region,** and the light that reaches our eye is called *visible light.* The sun emits nearly 44 percent of its radiation in this zone, with the peak

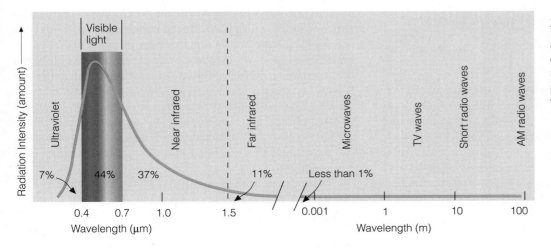

Figure 2.9
The sun's electromagnetic spectrum and some of the descriptive names of each region. The numbers underneath the curve approximate the percent of energy the sun radiates in various regions.

Focus on AN ENVIRONMENTAL ISSUE

Wave Energy, Sun Burning, and UV Rays

Standing close to a fire makes us feel warmer than we do when we stand at a distance from it. Does this mean that, as we move away from a hot object, the waves carry less energy and are, therefore, weaker? Not really. The intensity of radiation decreases as we move away from a hot object because radiating energy spreads outward in all directions. Figure 3 illustrates that, as the distance from a radiating object increases, a given amount of energy is distributed over a larger area, so that the energy received per unit of area and per unit of time decreases. In fact, at twice the distance from the source, the radiation is spread over four times the area.

Another interesting fact about radiation that we learned earlier in this chapter is that shorter waves carry much more energy than do longer waves. Hence, a photon of ultraviolet light carries more energy than a photon of visible light. In fact, ultraviolet (UV) wavelengths in the range of 0.20 and 0.29 μm (known as *UV–C radiation*) are harmful to living things, as

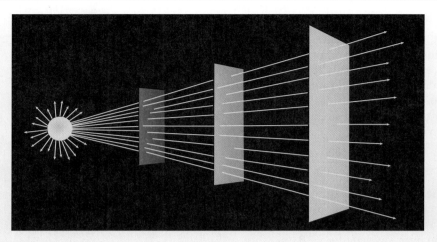

Figure 3
The intensity, or amount, of radiant energy transported by electromagnetic waves decreases as we move away from a radiating object because the same amount of energy is spread over a larger area.

certain waves can cause chromosome mutations, kill single-celled organisms, and damage the cornea of the eye. Fortunately, virtually all the ultraviolet radiation at wavelengths in the UV–C range is absorbed by ozone in the stratosphere.

Ultraviolet wavelengths between about 0.29 and 0.32 μm (known as

UV–B radiation) reach the earth in small amounts. Photons in this wavelength range have enough energy to produce sunburns and penetrate skin tissues, sometimes causing skin cancer. About 90 percent of all skin cancers are linked to sun exposure and UV–B radiation. Oddly enough, these same wavelengths activate provitamin

---

Weather Watch

The ultraviolet rays that sunburn humans the quickest fall in the UV-B range of 0.306 μm.

---

of energy output found at the wavelength corresponding to the color blue-green. The color violet is the shortest wavelength of visible light. Wavelengths shorter than violet (0.4 μm) are **ultraviolet (UV).** X-rays and gamma rays with exceedingly short wavelengths also fall into this category. The sun emits only about 7 percent of its total energy at ultraviolet wavelengths.

The longest wavelengths of visible light correspond to the color red. Wavelengths longer than red (0.7 μm) are **infrared (IR).** These waves cannot be seen by humans. Nearly 37 percent of the sun's energy is radiated between 0.7 μm and 1.5 μm, with only 12 percent radiated at wavelengths longer than 1.5 μm.

Whereas the hot sun emits only a part of its energy in the infrared portion of the spectrum, the relatively cool earth emits almost all of its energy at infrared wavelengths. Although we cannot see infrared radiation, there are instruments called *infrared sensors* that can. Weather satellites that orbit the globe use these sensors to observe radiation emitted by the earth, the clouds, and the atmosphere. Since objects of different temperatures radiate their maximum energy at different wavelengths, infrared photographs can distinguish among objects of different temperatures. Clouds always radiate infrared energy; thus, cloud pictures using infrared sensors can be taken during both day and night.

In summary, both the sun and earth emit radiation. The *hot sun* (6000 K) radiates nearly 88 percent of its energy at wavelengths less than 1.5 μm, with maximum emission in the *visible region* near 0.5 μm. The *cooler earth* (288 K) radiates nearly all its energy between 5 and 25 μm with a peak intensity in the *infrared*

D in the skin and convert it into vitamin D, which is essential to health.

Longer ultraviolet waves with lengths of about 0.32 to 0.40 μm (called *UV–A radiation*) are less energetic, but can still tan the skin. Although UV–B is mainly responsible for burning the skin, UV–A can cause skin redness. It can also interfere with the skin's immune system and cause long-term skin damage that shows up years later as accelerated aging and skin wrinkling. Moreover, recent studies indicate that longer UV–A exposures needed to create a tan pose about the same cancer risk as a UV–B tanning dose.

Upon striking the human body, ultraviolet radiation is absorbed beneath the outer layer of skin. To protect the skin from these harmful rays, the body's defense mechanism kicks in. Certain cells (when exposed to UV radiation) produce a dark pigment *(melanin)* that begins to absorb some of the UV radiation. (It is the production of melanin that produces a tan.) Consequently, a body that produces little melanin—one with pale skin—

has little natural protection from UV–B.

Additional protection can come from a sunscreen. Unlike the old lotions that simply moisturized the skin before it baked in the sun, sunscreens today block UV rays from ever reaching the skin. Some contain chemicals (such as zinc oxide) that reflect UV radiation. (These are the white pastes seen on the noses of lifeguards.) Others consist of a mixture of chemicals (such as benzophenone and paraaminobenzoic acid, PABA) that actually absorb ultraviolet radiation, usually UV–B, although new products with UV–A-absorbing qualities are now on the market. The *Sun Protection Factor* (SPF) number on every container of sunscreen dictates how effective the product is in protecting from UV–B—the higher the number, the better the protection.

Protecting oneself from excessive exposure to the sun's energetic UV rays is certainly wise. Estimates are that, in a single year, over 30,000 Americans will be diagnosed with malignant melanoma, the most

deadly form of skin cancer. And as the protective ozone shield diminishes, there is an ever-increasing risk of problems associated with UV–B. Using a good sunscreen and proper clothing can certainly help. The best way to protect yourself from too much sun, however, is to limit your time in direct sunlight, especially between the hours of 11 A.M. and 3 P.M. when the sun is highest in the sky and its rays are most direct.

Presently, the National Weather Service makes a daily prediction of UV radiation levels for selected cities throughout the United States. The forecast, known as the *Experimental Ultraviolet Index,* gives the UV level at its peak, around noon standard time or 1 P.M. daylight savings time. The 15-point index corresponds to five exposure categories set by the Environmental Protection Agency (EPA). An index value of between 0 and 2 is considered "minimal," whereas a value of 10 or greater is deemed "very high."

region near 10 μm (Fig. 2.8). The sun's surface is nearly 20 times hotter than the earth's surface. From the Stefan-Boltzmann relationship, this fact means that a unit area on the sun emits nearly 160,000 (20^4) times more energy during a given time period than the same size area on the earth. And since the sun has such a huge surface area from which to radiate, the total energy emitted by the sun each minute amounts to a staggering 6 billion, billion, billion calories! (Additional information on radiation intensity and its effect on humans is given in the Focus section beginning on p. 38.)

Balancing Act—Absorption, Emission, and Equilibrium

If the earth and all things on it are continually radiating energy, why doesn't everything get progressively colder? The answer is that all objects not only radiate energy, they absorb it as well. If

an object radiates more energy than it absorbs, it gets colder; if it absorbs more energy than it emits, it gets warmer. On a sunny day, the earth's surface warms by absorbing more energy from the sun and the atmosphere than it radiates, while at night the earth cools by radiating more energy than it absorbs from its surroundings. When an object emits and absorbs energy at equal rates, its temperature remains constant.

The rate at which something radiates and absorbs energy depends strongly on its surface characteristics, such as color, texture, and moisture, as well as temperature. For example, a black object in direct sunlight is a good absorber of visible radiation. It converts energy from the sun into internal energy, and its temperature ordinarily increases. You need only walk barefoot on a black asphalt road on a summer afternoon to experience this. At night, the blacktop road will cool quickly by emitting infrared radiation and, by early morning, it may be cooler than surrounding surfaces.

Any object that is a perfect absorber (that is, absorbs all the radiation that strikes it) and a perfect emitter (emits the maximum radiation possible at its given temperature) is called a **blackbody.** Blackbodies do not have to be colored black, they simply must absorb and emit all possible radiation. Since the earth's surface and the sun absorb and radiate with nearly 100 percent efficiency for their respective temperatures, they both behave as blackbodies. This is the reason we were able to use Wien's law and the Stefan-Boltzmann law to determine the characteristics of radiation emitted from the sun and the earth.

When we look at the earth from space, we see that half of it is in sunlight, the other half is in darkness. The outpouring of solar energy constantly bathes the earth with radiation, while the earth, in turn, constantly emits infrared radiation. If we assume that there is no other method of transferring heat, then, when the rate of absorption of solar radiation equals the rate of emission of infrared earth radiation, a state of *radiative equilibrium* is achieved. The average temperature at which this occurs is called the **radiative equilibrium temperature.** At this temperature, the earth (behaving as a blackbody) is absorbing solar radiation and emitting infrared radiation at equal rates, and its average temperature does not change. Because the earth is about 150 million km (93 million mi) from the sun, the earth's *radiative equilibrium temperature* is about 255 K (−18°C, 0°F). But this temperature is *much* lower than the earth's observed average surface temperature of 288 K (15°C, 59°F). Why is there such a large difference?

The answer lies in the fact that *the earth's atmosphere absorbs and emits infrared radiation.* Unlike the earth, the atmosphere does *not* behave like a blackbody, as it absorbs some wavelengths of radiation and is transparent to others. Objects that selectively absorb and emit radiation, such as gases in our atmosphere, are known as **selective absorbers.** Let's examine this concept more closely.

Selective Absorbers and the Atmospheric Greenhouse Effect

Just as some people are selective eaters of certain foods, most substances in our environment are selective absorbers; that is, they absorb only certain wavelengths of radiation. Glass is a good example of a selective absorber in that it absorbs some of the infrared and ultraviolet radiation it receives, but not the visible radiation that is transmitted through the glass. As a result, it is difficult to get a sunburn through the windshield of your car, although you can see through it.

Objects that selectively absorb radiation also selectively emit radiation at the same wavelength. This phenomenon is called **Kirchhoff's law.** This law states that *good absorbers are good emitters at a particular wavelength, and poor absorbers are poor emitters at the same wavelength.**

Snow is a good absorber as well as a good emitter of infrared energy (white snow actually behaves as a blackbody in the infrared wavelengths). The bark of a tree absorbs sunlight and

Figure 2.10
The melting of snow outward from the trees causes small depressions to form. The melting is caused mainly by the snow's absorption of the infrared energy being emitted from the warmer tree and its branches. The trees are warmer because they are better absorbers of sunlight than is the snow.

emits infrared energy, which the snow around it absorbs. During the absorption process, the infrared radiation is converted into internal energy, and the snow melts outward away from the tree trunk, producing a small depression that encircles the tree (see Fig. 2.10).

Figure 2.11 shows some of the most important selectively absorbing gases in our atmosphere. The shaded area represents the percent of radiation absorbed by each gas at various wavelengths. Notice that both water vapor (H_2O) and carbon dioxide (CO_2) are strong absorbers of infrared radiation and poor absorbers of visible solar radiation. Other, less important, selective absorbers include nitrous oxide (N_2O), methane (CH_4), and ozone (O_3), which is most abundant in the stratosphere. As these gases absorb infrared radiation emitted from the earth's surface, they gain kinetic energy (energy of motion). The gas molecules share this energy by colliding with neighboring air molecules, such as oxygen and nitrogen (both of which are poor absorbers of infrared energy). These collisions increase the average kinetic energy of the air, which results in an increase in air temperature. Thus, most of the infrared energy emitted from the earth's surface keeps the lower atmosphere warm.

Besides being selective absorbers, water vapor and CO_2 selectively emit radiation at infrared wavelengths.† This radiation travels away from these gases in all directions. A portion of this energy is radiated toward the earth's surface and absorbed, thus heating the ground. The earth, in turn, radiates in-

---

*Strictly speaking, this law only applies to gases.

†Nitrous oxide, methane, and ozone also emit infrared radiation, but their concentration in the atmosphere is much smaller than water vapor and carbon dioxide (see Table 1.1, p. 3.)

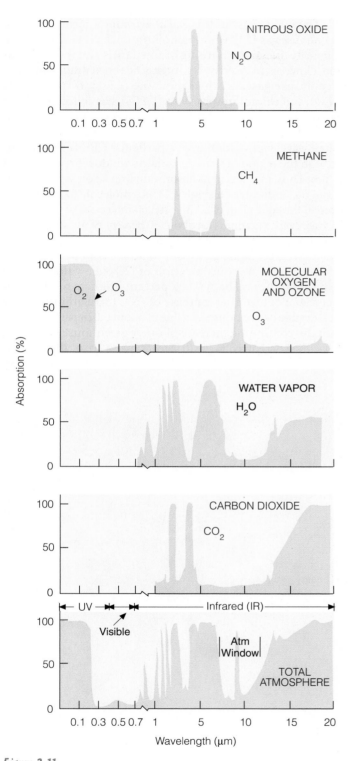

Figure 2.11
Absorption of radiation by gases in the atmosphere. The shaded area represents the percent of radiation absorbed. The strongest absorbers of infrared radiation are water vapor and carbon dioxide.

frared energy upward, where it is absorbed and warms the lower atmosphere. In this way, water vapor and CO_2 absorb and radiate infrared energy and act as an insulating layer around the earth, keeping part of the earth's infrared radiation from escaping rapidly into space. Consequently, the earth's surface and the lower atmosphere are much warmer than they would be if these selectively absorbing gases were not present. In fact, as we saw earlier, the earth's mean radiative equilibrium temperature without CO_2 and water vapor would be around −18°C (0°F), or about 33°C (59°F) lower than at present.

The absorption characteristics of water vapor, CO_2, and other gases such as methane and nitrous oxide (Fig. 2.11) were, at one time, thought to be similar to the glass of a florist's greenhouse. In a greenhouse, the glass allows visible radiation to come in, but inhibits to some degree the passage of outgoing infrared radiation. For this reason, the absorption of infrared radiation from the earth by water vapor and CO_2 is popularly called the **greenhouse effect.** However, studies have shown that the warm air inside a greenhouse is probably caused more by the air's inability to circulate and mix with the cooler outside air, rather than by the entrapment of infrared energy. Because of these findings, some scientists insist that the greenhouse effect should be called the *atmosphere effect.* To accommodate everyone, we will usually use the term *atmospheric greenhouse effect* when describing the role that water vapor, CO_2, and other greenhouse gases* play in keeping the earth's mean surface temperature higher than it otherwise would be.

Look again at Fig. 2.11 and observe that, in the bottom diagram, there is a region between about 8 and 11 µm where neither water vapor nor CO_2 readily absorb infrared radiation. Because these wavelengths of emitted energy pass upward through the atmosphere and out into space, the wavelength range (between 8 and 11 µm) is known as the **atmospheric window.** Clouds can enhance the atmospheric greenhouse effect. Tiny liquid cloud droplets are selective absorbers in that they are good absorbers of infrared radiation but poor absorbers of visible solar radiation. Clouds even absorb the wavelengths between 8 and 11 µm, which are otherwise "passed up" by water vapor and CO_2. Thus, they have the effect of enhancing the atmospheric greenhouse effect by closing the atmospheric window.

Clouds—especially low, thick ones—are excellent emitters of infrared radiation. Their tops radiate infrared energy upward and their bases radiate energy back to the earth's surface where it is absorbed and, in a sense, re-radiated back to the clouds. This process keeps calm, cloudy nights warmer than calm, clear ones. If the clouds remain into the next day, they prevent much of the sunlight from reaching the ground by reflecting it back to space. Since the ground does not heat up as much as it would in full sunshine, cloudy, calm days are normally

---

*The term "greenhouse gases" derives from the standard use of "greenhouse effect." Greenhouse gases include, among others, water vapor, carbon dioxide, methane, nitrous oxide, and ozone.

cooler than clear, calm days. Hence, the presence of clouds tends to keep nighttime temperatures higher and daytime temperatures lower.

In summary, the atmospheric greenhouse effect occurs because water vapor, CO_2, and other greenhouse gases are selective absorbers. They allow most of the sun's visible radiation to reach the surface, but they absorb a good portion of the earth's outgoing infrared radiation, preventing it from escaping into space (see Fig. 2.12). It is the atmospheric greenhouse effect, then, that keeps the temperature of our planet at a level where life can survive. The greenhouse effect is not just a "good thing"; it is essential to life on earth.

Enhancement of the Greenhouse Effect   In spite of the inaccuracies that have plagued temperature measurements, studies suggest that for the past 100 years or so, the earth's surface air temperature has undergone a warming of about 0.6°C (1°F). Today, there are scientific computer models, called *general circulation models* (GCMs) that mathematically simulate the physical processes of the atmosphere and oceans. These models (also referred to as *climate models*) predict that, if such a warming should continue unabated, we would be irrevocably committed to the negative effects of climate change, such as a rise in sea level.

The main cause of this *global warming* appears to be the greenhouse gas CO_2, whose concentration has been increasing primarily due to the burning of fossil fuels and to deforestation. However, in recent years, increasing concentration of other greenhouse gases, such as methane (CH_4), nitrous oxide (N_2O), and chlorofluorocarbons (CFCs), has collectively been shown to have an effect almost equal to that of CO_2. Look at Fig. 2.11 and notice that both CH_4 and N_2O absorb strongly at infrared wavelengths. Moreover, a particular CFC (CFC-12) absorbs in the region of the atmospheric window between 8 and 11 μm. Thus, in terms of its absorption impact on infrared radiation, the addition of a single CFC-12 molecule to the atmosphere is the equivalent of adding 10,000 molecules of CO_2. Overall, water vapor accounts for about 60 percent of the atmospheric greenhouse effect, CO_2 accounts for about 26 percent, and the remaining greenhouse gases contribute about 14 percent.

Presently, the concentration of CO_2 in a volume of air near the surface is about 0.037 percent. Climate models predict that a continuing increase of CO_2 to an amount more than double its preindustrial value of about 0.028 percent, along with the continuing increase of other greenhouse gases, will cause the current average surface temperature of the earth to rise between 1.4° C and 5.8°C (2.5°F and 10.5°F) by the end of

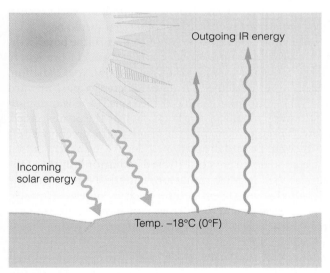

(a) Without greenhouse effect

(b) With greenhouse effect

Figure 2.12
Sunlight warms the earth's surface only during the day, whereas the surface constantly emits infrared radiation upward during the day and at night. (a) Near the surface *without* water vapor, CO_2, and other greenhouse gases, the earth's surface would constantly emit infrared radiation (IR) energy; incoming energy from the sun would be equal to outgoing IR energy from the earth's surface. Since the earth would receive no IR energy from its lower atmosphere (no atmospheric greenhouse effect), the earth's average surface temperature would be a frigid −18°C (0°F). (b) With greenhouse gases, the earth's surface receives energy from the sun and infrared energy from its atmosphere. Incoming energy still equals outgoing energy, but the added IR energy from the greenhouse gases raises the earth's average surface temperature about 33°C, to a comfortable 15°C (59°F).

Weather Watch

What an absorber! First detected in the earth's atmosphere in 1999, a greenhouse gas (trifluoromethyl sulfur pentafluoride, SF_5CF_3) pound for pound absorbs about 18,000 times more infrared radiation than CO_2 does. This trace gas, which may form in high-voltage electrical equipment, is increasing in the atmosphere by about 6 percent per year, but it is present in very tiny amounts—about 0.00000012 ppm.

this century. If the rise is 3°C (5°F), it will be five times faster than the warming that happened during the twentieth century. How can increasing such a small quantity of CO_2 and adding miniscule amounts of other greenhouse gases bring about such a large temperature increase?

Mathematical climate models predict that rising ocean temperatures will cause an increase in evaporation rates. The added *water vapor*—the primary greenhouse gas—will enhance the atmospheric greenhouse effect and double the temperature rise in what is known as a *positive feedback*. But there are other feedbacks to consider.*

The two potentially largest and least understood feedbacks in the climate system are the clouds and the oceans. Clouds can change area, depth, and radiation properties simultaneously with climatic changes. The net effect of all these changes is not totally clear at this time. Oceans, on the other hand, cover 70 percent of the planet. The response of ocean circulations, ocean temperatures, and sea ice to global warming will determine the global pattern and speed of climate change. Unfortunately, it is not now known how quickly each of these feedbacks will respond.

Satellite data from the *Earth Radiation Budget Experiment* (ERBE) suggest that clouds overall appear to *cool* the earth's climate, as they reflect and radiate away more energy than they retain. (The earth would be warmer if clouds were not present.) So an increase in global cloudiness (if it were to occur) might offset some of the global warming brought on by an enhanced atmospheric greenhouse effect. Therefore, if clouds were to act on the climate system in this manner, they would provide a *negative feedback* on climate change.†

Uncertainties unquestionably exist about the impact that increasing levels of CO_2 and other trace gases will have on enhancing the atmospheric greenhouse effect. Nonetheless, many

scientific studies suggest that increasing the concentration of these gases in our atmosphere will lead to global-scale climatic change by the end of this century. Such change could adversely affect water resources and agricultural productivity. (We will examine this topic further in Chapter 19, when we cover climatic change in more detail.)

Brief Review   In the last several sections, we have explored examples of some of the ways radiation is absorbed and emitted by various objects. Before reading the next several sections, let's review a few important facts and principles:

- *All* objects with a temperature above absolute zero emit radiation.
- The higher an object's temperature, the greater the amount of radiation emitted per unit surface area and the shorter the wavelength of maximum emission.
- The earth absorbs solar radiation only during the daylight hours; however, it emits infrared radiation continuously, both during the day and at night.
- The earth's surface behaves as a blackbody, making it a much better absorber and emitter of radiation than the atmosphere.
- Water vapor and carbon dioxide are important atmospheric greenhouse gases that selectively absorb and emit infrared radiation, thereby keeping the earth's average surface temperature warmer than it otherwise would be.
- Cloudy, calm nights are often warmer than clear, calm nights because clouds strongly emit infrared radiation.
- It is *not* the greenhouse effect itself that is of concern, but the *enhancement* of it due to increasing levels of greenhouse gases.

With these concepts in mind, we will first examine how the air near the ground warms, then we will consider how the earth and its atmosphere maintain a yearly energy balance. (But before reading on, you may wish to read the Focus section on p. 44 that describes, in more detail, some of the concepts presented so far.)

Warming the Air from Below   On a clear day, solar energy passes through the lower atmosphere with little effect upon the air. Ultimately it reaches the surface, warming it (see Fig. 2.13). Air molecules in contact with the heated surface bounce against it, gain energy by *conduction,* then shoot upward like freshly popped kernels of corn, carrying their energy with them. Because the air near the ground is very dense, these molecules only travel a short distance (about 10^{-7} m) before they collide with other molecules. During the collision, these more rapidly moving molecules share their energy with less energetic molecules, raising the average temperature of the air. But air is such a poor heat conductor that this process is only important within a few centimeters of the ground.

---

*A feedback is a process whereby an initial change in a process will tend to either reinforce the process (positive feedback) or weaken the process (negative feedback). The *water vapor-greenhouse effect* feedback is a positive feedback because the initial increase in temperature is reinforced by the addition of more water vapor, which absorbs more of the earth's infrared energy, thus strengthening the greenhouse effect and enhancing the warming.

†Overall, current climate models tend to show that changes in clouds could provide either a net negative or a net positive feedback on climate change.

Radiative Equilibrium and Forcing—The Ins and Outs

We know that all objects emit radiation, and that the hotter the object, the more radiant energy it emits. Earlier, we learned that this relationship between temperature and radiation is called the Stefan-Boltzmann law, which is written as

$$E = \sigma T^4$$

where E is the energy being emitted by each square meter of surface area of the object, T is the object's temperature in Kelvins, and σ is the Stephan-Boltzmann constant. The constant σ is 5.67×10^{-8} with units of Watts per square meter per Kelvin to the fourth power, or W/m^2K^4. We can obtain the units for E by plugging into the equation the units for σ and T; thus

$$E = \sigma T^4$$

$$E = \left(\frac{W}{m^2K^4}\right)(K^4)$$

$$E = \left(\frac{W}{m^2}\right).$$

So the units of energy E (called the *flux radiance* or *emittance*) are Watts per square meter.

In a previous section, we learned that the earth's radiative equilibrium temperature is about $-18°C$ ($0°F$). How much energy would the earth be emitting at this temperature? Remember that we have to convert °C to Kelvins, otherwise at a temperature of $-18°C$ the earth would be emitting negative amounts of energy, which is meaningless; consequently

$$K = °C + 273$$

$$K = -18 + 273$$

$$K = 255 \ K.$$

If we plug this temperature (255 K) into the Stefan-Boltzmann equation we obtain

$$E = \sigma T^4$$

$$E = (5.67 \times 10^{-8} \left(\frac{W}{m^2K^4}\right)(255 \ K)^4$$

$$E = 240 \left(\frac{W}{m^2}\right).$$

Thus the earth, in radiative equilibrium and behaving as a blackbody, would be emitting 240 watts of energy over each square meter of surface area.

Over the earth as a whole, outgoing infrared energy equals incoming solar energy (see Fig. 4). Consequently, without an atmospheric greenhouse effect, the earth's surface would (on average) emit 240 W/m^2 upward and, at the same time, receive 240 W/m^2 from the sun. But due to a greenhouse effect this equilibrium of 240 W/m^2 is only achieved at the *top* of the atmosphere. Moreover, as greenhouse gases slowly increase in concentration they alter this balance by gradually absorbing more and more of the earth's infrared radiation, thereby preventing this energy from escaping into space. So without any changes in the climate system, outgoing energy would gradually drop below a value of 240 W/m^2.

Climate models predict that, as long as everything else remains the same, a sudden doubling of the current levels of atmospheric CO_2 would result in a net radiation reduction (imbalance) of 4 watts per square meter at the top of the atmosphere. To restore this imbalance, the earth's surface and lower atmosphere must warm by about 1.2 Celsius degrees so that more infrared energy is directed upward.* Therefore, as levels of CO_2 and other greenhouse gases increase, they alter the amount of infrared energy lost to space and, in effect, *force* the atmosphere to respond by increasing the surface air temperature.

Any change in average net radiation that occurs at the top of the atmosphere (actually the top of the tro-

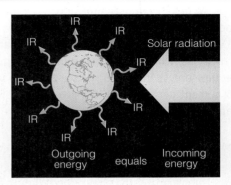

Figure 4
In radiative equilibrium, over the earth as a whole, incoming solar energy equals outgoing infrared (IR) energy.

posphere) which is due to some change in the climate system (such as increasing levels of CO_2) is called *radiative forcing*. Therefore, greenhouse gases (which are increasing in concentration) are referred to as *radiative forcing agents.†*

As levels of greenhouse gases increase, they alter the infrared radiation leaving the atmosphere. This process enhances the atmospheric greenhouse effect, which causes the surface air temperature to rise. As the surface air warms, more evaporation occurs from the oceans, and the water vapor content of the atmosphere increases. The added water vapor enhances the temperature rise, producing a positive feedback on the climate system. Most climate models show that doubling the concentration of CO_2 and allowing the atmospheric water vapor content to rise, will result in an increase in average surface air temperature of more than 2.5°C (4.5°F)—a much larger rise in temperature than that produced by CO_2 alone.

---

*Remember that a small increase in temperature results in a great deal more energy emitted, as $E \sim T^4$.

---

†Additional examples of radiative forcing agents include changes in solar output and land surface modifications such as extensive deforestation.

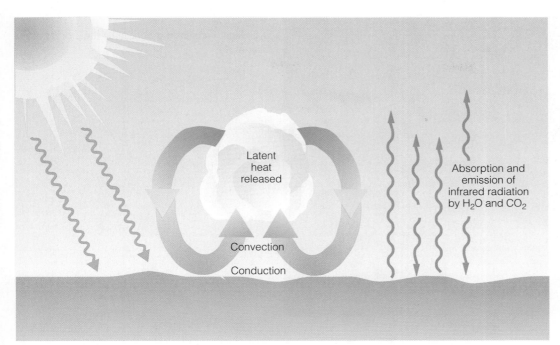

Figure 2.13
Air in the lower atmosphere is heated from below. Sunlight warms the ground, and the air above is warmed by conduction, convection, and radiation. Further warming occurs during condensation as latent heat is given up to the air inside the cloud.

As the surface air warms, it actually becomes less dense than the air directly above it. The warmer air rises and the cooler air sinks, setting up thermals, or *free convection cells* that transfer heat upward and distribute it through a deeper layer of air. The rising air expands and cools, and, if sufficiently moist, the water vapor condenses into cloud droplets, releasing latent heat that warms the air. Meanwhile, the earth constantly emits infrared energy. Some of this energy is absorbed by greenhouse gases (such as water vapor and carbon dioxide) that emit infrared energy upward and downward, back to the surface. Since the concentration of water vapor decreases rapidly above the earth, most of the absorption occurs in a layer near the surface. Hence, the lower atmosphere is mainly heated from below.

Incoming Solar Energy

As the sun's radiant energy travels through space, essentially nothing interferes with it until it reaches the atmosphere. At the top of the atmosphere, solar energy received on a surface perpendicular to the sun's rays appears to remain fairly constant at nearly two calories on each square centimeter each minute or 1367 W/m^2—a value called the **solar constant.**[*]

---

[*]By definition, the solar constant (which, in actuality, is *not* "constant") is the rate at which radiant energy from the sun is received on a surface at the outer edge of the atmosphere perpendicular to the sun's rays when the earth is at an average distance from the sun. Satellite measurements from the *Earth Radiation Budget Satellite* suggest the solar constant varies slightly as the sun's radiant output varies. The average is about 1.96 cal/cm^2/min, or between 1365 W/m^2 and 1372 W/m^2 in the SI system of measurement.

Scattered and Reflected Light   When solar radiation enters the atmosphere, a number of interactions take place. For example, some of the energy is absorbed by gases, such as ozone, in the upper atmosphere. Moreover, when sunlight strikes very small objects, such as air molecules and dust particles, the light itself is deflected in all directions—forward, sideways, and backwards. The distribution of light in this manner is called **scattering.** (Scattered light is also called *diffuse light.*) Because air molecules are much smaller than the wavelengths of visible light, they are more effective scatterers of the shorter (blue) wavelengths than the longer (red) wavelengths. Hence, when we look away from the direct beam of sunlight, blue light strikes our eyes from all directions, turning the daytime sky blue. At midday, all the wavelengths of visible light from the sun strike our eyes, and the sun is perceived as white. At sunrise and sunset, when the white beam of sunlight must pass through a thick portion of the atmosphere, scattering by air molecules removes the blue light, leaving the longer wavelengths of red, orange, and yellow to pass on through, creating the image of a ruddy or yellowish sun (see Fig. 2.14).

Sunlight can be **reflected** from objects. Generally, reflection differs from scattering in that during the process of reflection more light is sent *backwards*. **Albedo** is the percent of radiation returning from a given surface compared to the amount of radiation initially striking that surface. Albedo, then, represents the *reflectivity* of the surface. In Table 2.3, notice that thick clouds have a higher albedo than thin clouds. On the average, the albedo of clouds is near 60 percent. When solar energy strikes a surface covered with snow, up to 95 percent of the sunlight may be reflected. Most of this energy is in the visible and

Figure 2.14
A brilliant red sunset produced by the process of scattering.

ultraviolet wavelengths. Consequently, reflected radiation, coupled with direct sunlight, can produce severe sunburns on the exposed skin of unwary snow skiers, and unprotected eyes can suffer the agony of snow blindness.

Water surfaces, on the other hand, reflect only a small amount of solar energy. For an entire day, a smooth water surface will have an average albedo of about 10 percent. Water has the highest albedo (and can therefore reflect sunlight best) when the sun is low on the horizon and the water is a little choppy. This may explain why people who wear brimmed hats

SURFACE	ALBEDO (PERCENT)
Fresh snow	75 to 95
Clouds (thick)	60 to 90
Clouds (thin)	30 to 50
Venus	78
Ice	30 to 40
Sand	15 to 45
Earth and atmosphere	30
Mars	17
Grassy field	10 to 30
Dry, plowed field	5 to 20
Water	10*
Forest	3 to 10
Moon	7

Table 2.3 Typical Albedo of Various Surfaces

*Daily average.

while fishing from a boat in choppy water on a sunny day can still get sunburned during midmorning or midafternoon. Averaged for an entire year, the earth and its atmosphere (including its clouds) will redirect about 30 percent of the sun's incoming radiation back to space, which gives the earth and its atmosphere a combined albedo of 30 percent (see Fig. 2.15).

The Earth's Annual Energy Balance   Although the average temperature at any one place may vary considerably from year to year, the earth's overall average equilibrium temperature changes only slightly from one year to the next. This fact indicates that, each year, the earth and its atmosphere combined must send off into space just as much energy as they receive from the sun. The same type of energy balance must exist between the earth's surface and the atmosphere. That is, each year, the earth's surface must return to the atmosphere the same amount of energy that it absorbs. If this did not occur, the earth's average surface temperature would change. How do the earth and its atmosphere maintain this yearly energy balance?

Suppose 100 units of solar energy reach the top of the earth's atmosphere. We can see in Fig. 2.15 that, on the average, clouds, the earth, and the atmosphere reflect and scatter 30 units back to space, and that the atmosphere and clouds together absorb 19 units, which leaves 51 units of direct and indirect solar radiation to be absorbed at the earth's surface.

Figure 2.16 shows approximately what happens to the solar radiation that is absorbed by the surface and the atmosphere. Out of 51 units reaching the surface, a large amount (23 units) is used to evaporate water, and about 7 units are lost through conduction and convection, which leaves 21 units to be radiated away as infrared energy. Look closely at Fig. 2.16 and notice that the earth's surface actually radiates upward a whopping 117 units. It does so because, although it receives solar radiation only during the day, it constantly emits infrared energy both during the day and at night. Additionally, the atmosphere above only allows a small fraction of this energy (6 units) to pass through into space. The majority of it (111 units) is absorbed mainly by the greenhouse gases water vapor and CO_2, and by clouds. Much of this energy (96 units) is radiated back to earth, producing the atmospheric greenhouse effect. Hence, the earth's surface receives nearly twice as much longwave infrared energy from its atmosphere as it does shortwave radiation from the sun. In all these exchanges, notice that the energy lost at the earth's surface (147 units) is exactly balanced by the energy gained there (147 units).

A similar balance exists between the earth's surface and its atmosphere. Again in Fig. 2.16 observe that the energy gained by the atmosphere (160 units) balances the energy lost. More-

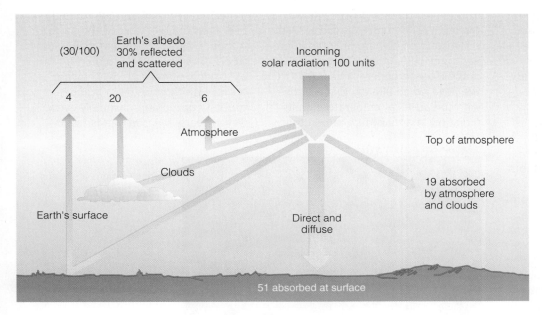

Figure 2.15
On the average, of all the solar energy that reaches the earth's atmosphere annually, about 30 percent ($^{30}/_{100}$) is reflected and scattered back to space, giving the earth and its atmosphere an albedo of 30 percent. Of the remaining solar energy, about 19 percent is absorbed by the atmosphere and clouds, and 51 percent is absorbed at the surface.

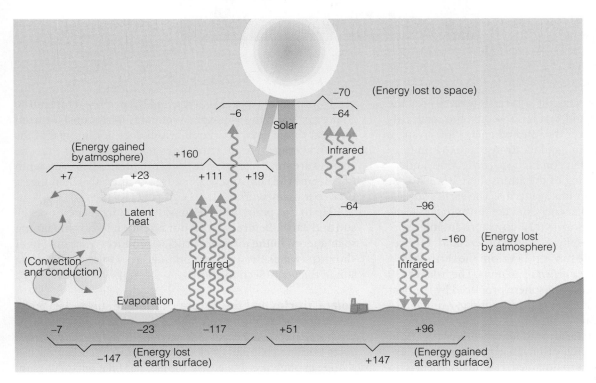

Figure 2.16
The earth-atmosphere energy balance. Numbers represent approximations based on surface observations and satellite data. While the actual value of each process may vary by several percent, it is the relative size of the numbers that is important.

Focus on A SPECIAL TOPIC

Characteristics of the Sun

The sun is our nearest star. It is some 150 million km (93 million mi) from earth. The next star, Alpha Centauri, is more than 250,000 times further away. Even though the earth only receives about one two-billionths of the sun's total energy output, it is this energy that allows life to flourish. Sunlight determines the rate of photosynthesis in plants and strongly regulates the amount of evaporation from the oceans. It warms this planet and drives the atmosphere into the dynamic patterns we experience as everyday wind and weather. Without the sun's radiant energy, the earth would gradually cool, in time becoming encased in a layer of ice! Evidence of life on the cold, dark, and barren surface would be found only in fossils. Fortunately, the sun has been shining for billions of years, and it is likely to shine for at least several billion more.

The sun is a giant celestial furnace. Its core is extremely hot, with a temperature estimated to be near 15 million degrees Celsius. In the core,

hydrogen nuclei (protons) collide at such fantastically high speeds that they fuse together to form helium nuclei. This thermonuclear process generates an enormous amount of energy, which gradually works its way to the sun's outer luminous surface—the *photosphere* ("sphere of light"). Temperatures here are much cooler than in the interior, generally near 6000°C. We have noted already that a body with this surface temperature emits radiation at a maximum rate in the

visible region of the spectrum. The sun is, therefore, a shining example of such an object.

Dark blemishes on the photosphere called *sunspots* are huge, cooler regions that typically average more than five times the diameter of the earth. Although sunspots are not well understood, they are known to be regions of strong magnetic fields. They are cyclic, with the maximum number of spots occurring approximately every eleven years. Measurements from

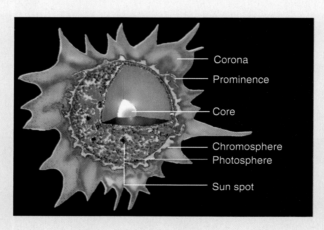

Figure 5
Various regions of the sun.

Corona
Prominence
Core
Chromosphere
Photosphere
Sun spot

---

over, averaged for an entire year, the solar energy received at the earth's surface (51 units) and that absorbed by the earth's atmosphere (19 units) balances the infrared energy lost to space by the earth's surface (6 units) and its atmosphere (64 units).

We can see the effect that conduction, convection, and latent heat play in the warming of the atmosphere if we look at the energy balance only in radiative terms. The earth's surface receives 147 units of radiant energy from the sun and its own atmosphere, while it radiates away 117 units, producing a *surplus* of 30 units. The atmosphere, on the other hand, receives 130 units (19 units from the sun and 111 from the earth), while it loses 160 units, producing a *deficit* of 30 units. The balance (30 units) is the warming of the atmosphere produced by the heat transfer processes of conduction and convection (7 units) and by the release of latent heat (23 units).

And so, the earth and the atmosphere absorb energy from the sun, as well as from each other. In all of the energy exchanges, a delicate balance is maintained. Essentially, there is no

yearly gain or loss of total energy, and the average temperature of the earth and the atmosphere remains fairly constant from one year to the next. This equilibrium does not imply that the earth's average temperature does not change, but that the changes are small from year to year (usually less than one-tenth of a degree Celsius) and become significant only when measured over many years.

Up to this point we have considered radiant energy of the sun and earth. Before we turn our attention to how incoming solar energy, in the form of particles, produces a dazzling light show known as the aurora, you may wish to read about the sun in the Focus section above.

Solar Particles and the Aurora   From the sun and its tenuous atmosphere comes a continuous discharge of particles. This discharge happens because, at extremely high temperatures, gases become stripped of electrons by violent collisions and acquire enough speed to escape the gravitational pull of the sun.

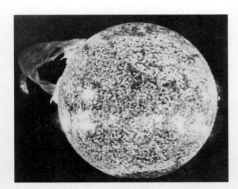

Figure 6
A spectacular solar flare spanning more than half a million kilometers across the solar surface.

satellites reveal that during a sunspot maximum, more radiation may actually leave the photosphere. The reason for this lies in the fact that the bright areas around sunspots (known as *faculae*) radiate more energy as sunspot activity increases.

Above the photosphere are the *chromosphere* and the *corona* (see Fig. 5). The chromosphere ("color sphere") acts as a boundary between the relatively cool (6000°C) photosphere and the much hotter (2,000,000°C) corona, the outermost envelope of the solar atmosphere. During a solar eclipse, the corona is visible. It appears as a pale, milky cloud encircling the sun. Although much hotter than the photosphere, the corona radiates much less energy because its density is extremely low. This very thin solar atmosphere extends into space for many millions of kilometers.*

Violent solar activity occasionally occurs in the regions of sunspots. The most dramatic of these events are *prominences* and *flares*. Prominences are huge cloudlike jets of gas that of-

---

*During a solar eclipse or at any other time, you should not look at the sun's corona either with sunglasses or through exposed negatives. Take this warning seriously. Viewing just a small area of the sun directly permits large amounts of UV radiation to enter the eye, causing serious and permanent damage to the retina. View the sun by projecting its image onto a sheet of paper, using a telescope or pinhole camera.

ten shoot up into the corona in the form of an arch. Solar flares are tremendous, but brief, eruptions (see Fig. 6). They emit large quantities of high-energy ultraviolet radiation, as well as energized charged particles, mainly protons and electrons, which stream outward away from the sun at extremely high speeds.

An intense solar flare can disturb the earth's magnetic field, producing a so-called *magnetic storm*. Because these storms can intensify the electrical properties of the upper atmosphere, they are often responsible for interruptions in radio and satellite communications. One such storm knocked out electricity throughout the province of Quebec, Canada, during March, 1989. And in May, 1998, after a period of intense solar activity, a communications satellite failed, causing 45 million pagers to suddenly go dead.

As these charged particles (ions and electrons) travel through space, they are known as *plasma*, or **solar wind.** When the solar wind moves close enough to the earth, it interacts with the earth's magnetic field.

The magnetic field that surrounds the earth is much like the field around an ordinary bar magnet (see Fig. 2.17). Both have north and south magnetic poles, and both have invisible lines of force (field lines) that link the poles. On the earth, these field lines form closed loops as they enter near the magnetic north pole and leave near the magnetic south pole. Most scientists believe that an electric current coupled with fluid motions deep in the earth's hot molten core is responsible for its magnetic field. This field protects the earth, to some degree, from the onslaught of the solar wind.

Observe in Fig. 2.18 that, when the solar wind encounters the earth's magnetic field, it severely deforms it into a teardrop-shaped cavity known as the *magnetosphere*. On the side facing the sun, the pressure of the solar wind compresses the field lines.

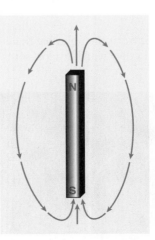
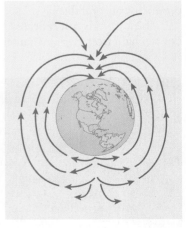

Bar magnet   Earth

Figure 2.17
Magnetic field about a bar magnet and about the earth.

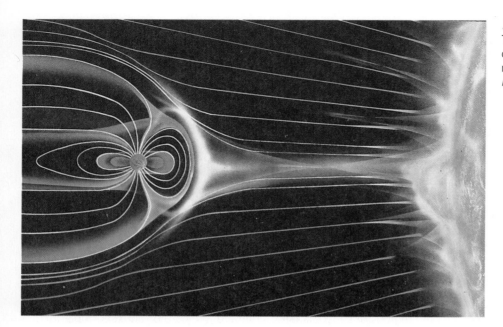

Figure 2.18
The stream of charged particles from the sun—called the *solar wind*—distorts the earth's magnetic field into a teardrop shape known as the *magnetosphere*.

On the opposite side, the magnetosphere stretches out into a long tail—the *magnetotail*—which reaches far beyond the moon's orbit. In a way, the magnetosphere acts as an obstacle to the solar wind by causing some of its particles to flow around the earth.

Inside the earth's magnetosphere are ionized gases. Some of these gases are solar wind particles, while others are ions from the earth's upper atmosphere that have moved upward along electric field lines into the magnetosphere.

Normally, the solar wind approaches the earth at an average speed of 400 km/sec. However, during periods of high solar activity (many sunspots and flares), the solar wind is more dense, travels much faster, and carries more energy. When these energized solar particles reach the earth, they cause a variety of effects, such as changing the shape of the magnetosphere and producing auroral displays.

The aurora is not reflected light from the polar ice fields, nor is it light from demons' lanterns as they search for lost souls.

The *aurora* is produced by the solar wind disturbing the magnetosphere. The disturbance involves high-energy particles within the magnetosphere being ejected into the earth's upper atmosphere, where they excite atoms and molecules. The excited atmospheric gases emit visible radiation, which causes the sky to glow like a neon light. Let's examine this process more closely.

A high-energy particle from the magnetosphere will, upon colliding with an air molecule (or atom), transfer some of its energy to the molecule. The molecule then becomes excited (see Fig. 2.19). Just as excited football fans leap up when their favorite team scores the winning touchdown, electrons in an excited molecule jump into a higher energy level as they orbit its center. As the fans sit down after all the excitement is over, so electrons quickly return to their lower level. When molecules de-excite, they release the energy originally received from the energetic particle, either all at once (one big jump), or in steps (several smaller jumps). This emitted energy is given up as radiation. If its wavelength is in the visible range, we see it as vis-

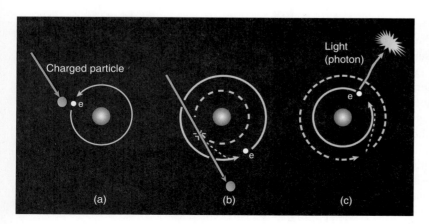

Figure 2.19
When an excited atom, ion, or molecule de-excites, it can emit visible light. The electron in its normal orbit (a) becomes excited by a charged particle and (b) jumps into a higher energy level. When the electron returns to its normal orbit, it (c) emits a photon of light.

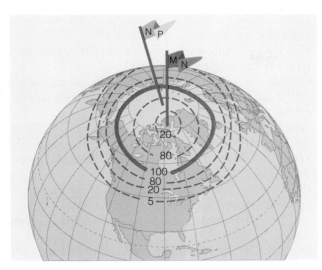

Figure 2.20
The aurora belt (solid red line) represents the region where you would most likely observe the aurora on a clear night. (The numbers represent the average number of nights per year on which you might see an aurora if the sky were clear.) The flag MN denotes the magnetic north pole, whereas the flag NP denotes the geographic north pole.

ible light. In the Northern Hemisphere, we call this light show the **aurora borealis,** or *northern lights;* its counterpart in the Southern Hemisphere is the **aurora australis,** or *southern lights.*

Since each atmospheric gas has its own set of energy levels, each gas has its own characteristic color. For example, the de-excitation of atomic oxygen can emit green or red light. Molecular nitrogen gives off red and violet light. The shades of these colors can be spectacular as they brighten and fade, sometimes in the form of waving draperies, sometimes as unmoving, yet flickering, arcs and soft coronas. On a clear, quiet night the aurora is an eerie yet beautiful spectacle. (See the chapter-opening photograph on p. 26.)

The aurora is most frequently seen in polar latitudes. Energetic particles trapped in the magnetosphere move along the earth's magnetic field lines. Because these lines emerge from the earth near the magnetic poles, it is here that the particles interact with atmospheric gases to produce an aurora. Notice in Fig. 2.20 that the zone of most frequent auroral sightings (aurora belt) is not at the magnetic pole (marked by the flag MN), but equatorward of it, where the field lines emerge from the earth's surface. At lower latitudes, where the field lines are oriented almost horizontal to the earth's surface, the chances of seeing an aurora diminish rapidly.

On rare occasions, however, the aurora is seen in the southern United States. Such sightings happen only when the sun is very active—as giant flares hurl electrons and protons earthward at a fantastic rate. These particles move so fast that some of them penetrate unusually deep into the earth's magnetic field before they are trapped by it. In a process not fully understood, particles from the magnetosphere are accelerated toward the earth along electrical field lines that parallel the magnetic field lines. The acceleration of these particles gives them sufficient energy so that when they enter the upper atmosphere they are capable of producing an auroral display much farther south than usual.

How high above the earth is the aurora? The exact height appears to vary. The base of an aurora is rarely lower than 80 km, and it averages about 105 km. Since the light of an aurora gradually fades, it is difficult to define an exact upper limit. Most auroras, however, are observed below 200 km.

In summary, energy for the aurora comes from the solar wind, which disturbs the earth's magnetosphere. This disturbance causes energetic particles to enter the upper atmosphere, where they collide with atoms and molecules. The atmospheric gases become excited and emit energy in the form of visible light.

But there is other light coming from the atmosphere—a faint glow at night much weaker than the aurora. This feeble luminescence, called **airglow,** is detected at all latitudes and shows no correlation with solar wind activity. Apparently, this light comes from ionized oxygen and nitrogen and other gases that have been excited by solar radiation.

Summary

In this chapter, we have seen how the concepts of heat and temperature differ and how heat is transferred in our environment. We learned that latent heat is an important source of atmospheric heat energy. We also learned that conduction, the transfer of heat by molecular collisions, is most effective in solids. Because air is a poor heat conductor, conduction in the atmosphere is only important in the shallow layer of air in contact with the earth's surface. A more important process of atmospheric heat transfer is convection, which involves the mass movement of air (or any fluid) with its energy from one region to another. Another significant heat transfer process is radiation—the transfer of energy by means of electromagnetic waves.

The hot sun emits most of its radiation as shortwave radiation. A portion of this energy heats the earth, and the earth, in turn, warms the air above. The cool earth emits most of its radiation as longwave infrared radiation. Selective absorbers in the atmosphere, such as water vapor and carbon dioxide, absorb some of the earth's infrared radiation and radiate a portion of it back to the surface, where it warms the surface, producing the atmospheric greenhouse effect. Because clouds are both good absorbers and good emitters of infrared radiation, they keep calm, cloudy nights warmer than calm, clear nights. The average equilibrium temperature of the earth and the atmosphere remains fairly constant from one year to the next because the amount of energy they absorb each year is equal to the amount of energy they lose.

Finally, we examined how the sun's energy in the form of solar wind particles interacts with our atmosphere to produce auroral displays.

Key Terms

The following terms are listed in the order they appear in the text. Define each. Doing so will aid you in reviewing the material covered in this chapter.

energy	Stefan-Boltzmann law
potential energy	Wien's law
kinetic energy	longwave radiation
temperature	shortwave radiation
heat	visible region
absolute zero	ultraviolet (UV) radiation
Kelvin scale	infrared (IR) radiation
Fahrenheit scale	blackbody
Celsius scale	radiative equilibrium
heat capacity	temperature
specific heat	selective absorbers
latent heat	Kirchhoff's law
sensible heat	greenhouse effect
conduction	atmospheric window
convection	solar constant
thermals	scattering
advection	reflected (light)
radiant energy (radiation)	albedo
electromagnetic waves	solar wind
wavelength	aurora borealis
micrometer	aurora australis
photons	airglow

Questions for Review

1. How does the average speed of air molecules relate to the air temperature?
2. Distinguish between temperature and heat.
3. (a) How does the Kelvin temperature scale differ from the Celsius scale? (b) Why is the Kelvin scale often used in scientific calculations? (c) Based on your experience, would a temperature of 250K be considered warm or cold? Explain.
4. Explain how heat is transferred by: (a) conduction; (b) convection; (c) radiation.
5. How is latent heat an important source of atmospheric energy?
6. In the atmosphere, how does advection differ from convection?

7. How does the temperature of an object influence the radiation that it emits?
8. How does the amount of radiation emitted by the earth differ from that emitted by the sun?
9. How do the wavelengths of most of the radiation emitted by the sun differ from those emitted by the surface of the earth?
10. Which photon carries the most energy—infrared, visible, or ultraviolet?
11. When a body reaches a radiative equilibrium temperature, what is taking place?
12. If the earth's surface continually radiates energy, why doesn't it become colder and colder?
13. Why are carbon dioxide and water vapor called selective absorbers?
14. Explain how the earth's atmospheric greenhouse effect works.
15. What gases appear to be responsible for the enhancement of the earth's greenhouse effect?
16. Why do some climate models predict that the earth's average surface temperature might increase by more than 2.5°C toward the end of this century?
17. What processes contribute to the earth's albedo being 30%?
18. Explain how the atmosphere near the earth's surface is warmed from below.
19. If a blackbody is a theoretical object, why can both the sun and earth be treated as blackbodies?
20. What is the solar wind?
21. Explain how the aurora is produced.

Questions for Thought

1. Explain why the bridge in the diagram is the first to become icy.

2. Explain why the first snowfall of the winter usually "sticks" better to tree branches than to bare ground.
3. At night, why do materials that are poor heat conductors cool to temperatures less than the surrounding air?
4. Explain how ice can form on puddles (in shaded areas) when the temperature above and below the puddle is slightly above freezing.

5. In northern latitudes, the oceans are warmer in summer than they are in winter. In which season do the oceans lose heat most rapidly to the atmosphere by conduction? Explain.

6. How is heat transferred away from the surface of the moon? (Hint: The moon has no atmosphere.)

7. Why is ultraviolet radiation more successful in dislodging electrons from air atoms and molecules than is visible radiation?

8. Why must you stand closer to a small fire to experience the same warmth you get when standing further away from a large fire?

9. If water vapor were no longer present in the atmosphere, how would the earth's energy budget be affected?

10. Which will show the greatest increase in temperature when illuminated with direct sunlight: a plowed field or a blanket of snow? Explain.

11. Why does the surface temperature often increase on a clear, calm night as a low cloud moves overhead?

12. Which would have the greatest effect on the earth's greenhouse effect: Removing all of the CO_2 from the atmosphere or removing all of the water vapor? Explain why you chose your answer.

13. Explain why an increase in cloud cover surrounding the earth would increase the earth's albedo, yet not necessarily lead to a lower earth surface temperature.

14. Could a liquid thermometer register a temperature of −273°C when the air temperature is actually 1000°C? Where would this happen in the atmosphere, and why?

15. Why is it that auroral displays above Colorado can be forecast several days in advance?

16. Why does the aurora usually occur more frequently above Maine than above Washington State?

Problems and Exercises

1. Suppose that 500 g of water vapor condense to make a cloud about the size of an average room. If we assume that the latent heat of condensation is 600 cal/g, how much heat would be released to the air? If the total mass of air be-

fore condensation is 100 kg, how much warmer would the air be after condensation? Assume that the air is not undergoing any pressure changes. (Hint: Use the specific heat of air in Table 2.1, p. 30.)

2. Suppose planet A is exactly twice the size (in surface area) of planet B. If both planets have the same exact surface temperature (1500 K), which planet would be emitting the most radiation? Determine the wavelength of maximum energy emission of both planets, using Wien's law.

3. Suppose, in question 2, the temperature of planet B doubles. (a) What would be its wavelength of maximum energy emission? (b) In what region of the electromagnetic spectrum would this wavelength be found? (c) If the temperature of planet A remained the same, determine which planet (A or B) would now be emitting the most radiation (use the Stefan-Boltzmann relationship). Explain your answer.

4. Suppose your surface body temperature averages 90°F. How much radiant energy in W/m² would be emitted from your body? (Hint: look at the Focus section on p. 44 and remember to convert °F to Kelvins.)

Questions for Exploration

1. The Aurora (http://www.exploratorium.edu/learning_studio/auroras/selfguide1.html): Compare the appearance of auroras as viewed from earth and as viewed from space.

2. Ultraviolet Radiation Index (http://www1.tor.ec.gc.ca/uvindex/index_e.cfm?xvz): On what information do you think the UV index is based? What are some of the activities that you engage in that might put you at risk for extended exposure to ultraviolet radiation?

 Go to the Brooks/Cole Earth Sciences Resource Center (http://earthscience.brookscole.com) for critical thinking exercises, articles, and additional readings from InfoTrac College Edition, Brooks/Cole's online student library.

Shorter days and longer nights (created by a tilted earth revolving about the sun) promote cooler weather and the brilliant colors of autumn in New England. (Photo: Larry Ulrich, Tony Stone Images)

Seasonal and Daily Temperatures

CONTENTS

The sun doesn't rise or fall: it doesn't move, it just sits there, and we rotate in front of it. Dawn means that we are rotating around into sight of it, while dusk means we have turned another 180 degrees and are being carried into the shadow zone. The sun never "goes away from the sky." It's still there sharing the same sky with us; it's simply that there is a chunk of opaque earth between us and the sun which prevents our seeing it. Everyone knows that, but I really see it now. No longer do I drive down a highway and wish the blinding sun would set; instead I wish we could speed up our rotation a bit and swing around into the shadows more quickly.

Michael Collins, *Carrying the Fire*

As you sit quietly reading this book, you are part of a moving experience. The earth is speeding around the sun at thousands of kilometers per hour while, at the same time, it is spinning on its axis. When we look down upon the North Pole, we see that the direction of spin is counterclockwise, meaning that we are moving toward the east at hundreds of kilometers per hour. We normally don't think of it in that way, but, of course, this is what causes the sun, moon, and stars to rise in the east and set in the west. It is these motions coupled with the fact that the earth is tilted on its axis that causes our seasons. Therefore, we will begin this chapter by examining how the earth's motions and the sun's energy work together to produce temperature variations on a seasonal basis. Later, we will examine temperature variations on a daily basis.

Why the Earth Has Seasons

The earth revolves completely around the sun in an elliptical path (not quite a circle) in slightly longer than 365 days (one year). As the earth revolves around the sun, it spins on its own axis, completing one spin in 24 hours (one day). The average distance from the earth to the sun is 150 million km (93 million mi). Because the earth's orbit is an ellipse instead of a circle, the actual distance from the earth to the sun varies during the year. The earth comes closer to the sun in January (147 million km) than it does in July (152 million km)* (see Fig. 3.1). From this we might conclude that our warmest weather should occur in January and our coldest weather in July. But, in the Northern Hemisphere, we normally experience cold weather in January when we are closer to the sun and warm weather in July when we are farther away. If nearness to the sun were the primary cause of the seasons then, indeed, January would be warmer than July. However, nearness to the sun is only a small part of the story.

---

*The time around January 3rd, when the earth is closest to the sun, is called *perihelion* (from the Greek *peri*, meaning "near" and *helios*, meaning "sun"). The time when the earth is farthest from the sun (around July 4th) is called *aphelion* (from the Greek *ap*, "away from").

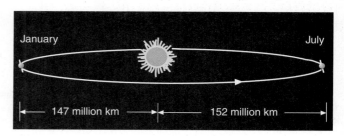

Figure 3.1
The elliptical path (highly exaggerated) of the earth about the sun brings the earth slightly closer to the sun in January than in July.

Our seasons are regulated by the amount of solar energy received at the earth's surface. This amount is determined primarily by the angle at which sunlight strikes the surface, and by how long the sun shines on any latitude (daylight hours). Let's look more closely at these factors.

Solar energy that strikes the earth's surface perpendicularly (directly) is much more intense than solar energy that strikes the same surface at an angle. Think of shining a flashlight straight at a wall—you get a small, circular spot of light (see Fig. 3.2). Now, tip the flashlight and notice how the spot of light spreads over a larger area. The same principle holds for sunlight. Sunlight striking the earth at an angle spreads out and must heat a larger region than sunlight impinging directly on the earth. Everything else being equal, an area experiencing more direct solar rays will receive more heat than the same size area being struck by sunlight at an angle. In addition, the more the sun's rays are slanted from the perpendicular, the more atmosphere they must penetrate. And the more atmosphere they penetrate, the more they can be scattered and absorbed (attenuated). As a consequence, when the sun is high in the sky, it can heat the ground to a much higher temperature than when it is low on the horizon.

The second important factor determining how warm the earth's surface becomes is the length of time the sun shines each day. Longer daylight hours, of course, mean that more energy is available from sunlight. In a given location, more solar energy

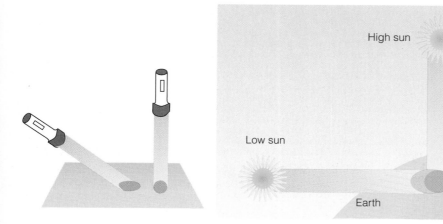

Figure 3.2
Sunlight that strikes a surface at an angle is spread over a larger area than sunlight that strikes the surface directly. Oblique sun rays deliver less energy (are less intense) to a surface than direct sun rays.

Focus on **A SPECIAL TOPIC**

Is December 21 Really the First Day of Winter?

On December 21 (or 22, depending on the year) after nearly a month of cold weather, and perhaps a snowstorm or two, someone on the radio or TV has the audacity to proclaim that "today is the first official day of winter." If during the last several weeks it was not winter, then what season was it?

Actually December 21 marks the *astronomical* first day of winter in the Northern Hemisphere (NH), just as June 21 marks the *astronomical* first day of summer (NH). The earth is tilted on its axis by 23½° as it revolves around the sun. This fact causes the sun (as we view it from earth) to move in the sky from a point

where it is directly above 23½° South latitude on December 21, to a point where it is directly above 23½° North latitude on June 21. The astronomical first day of spring (NH) occurs around March 20 as the sun crosses the equator moving northward and, likewise, the astronomical first day of autumn (NH) occurs around September 22 as the sun crosses the equator moving southward.

In the middle latitudes, summer is defined as the warmest season and winter the coldest season. If the year is divided into four seasons with each season consisting of three months, then the meteorological definition of summer over much of the Northern

Hemisphere would be the three warmest months of June, July, and August. Winter would be the three coldest months of December, January, and February. Autumn would be September, October, and November—the transition between summer and winter. And spring would be March, April, and May—the transition between winter and summer.

So, the next time you hear someone remark on December 21 that "winter officially begins today," remember that this is the astronomical definition of the first day of winter. According to the meteorological definition, winter has been around for several weeks.

reaches the earth's surface on a clear, long day than on a day that is clear but much shorter. Hence, more surface heating takes place.

From a casual observation, we know that summer days have more daylight hours than winter days. Also, the noontime summer sun is higher in the sky than is the noontime winter sun. Both of these events occur because our spinning planet is inclined on its axis (tilted) as it revolves around the sun. As Fig. 3.3 illustrates, the angle of tilt is 23½° from the perpendicular drawn to the plane of the earth's orbit. The earth's axis points to the same direction in space all year long; thus, the Northern Hemisphere is tilted toward the sun in summer (June), and away from the sun in winter (December). (If you have ever wondered what the "official" first day of a season really is, you may wish to read the Focus section above.)

Seasons in the Northern Hemisphere   Let's first discuss the *warm summer* season. Note in Fig. 3.3 that, on June 21, the northern half of the world is directed toward the sun. At noon on this day, solar rays beat down upon the Northern Hemisphere more directly than during any other time of year. The sun is at its highest position in the noonday sky, directly above 23½° north (N) latitude (Tropic of Cancer). If you were standing at this latitude on June 21, the sun at noon would be directly overhead. This day, called the **summer solstice,** is the astronomical first day of summer in the Northern Hemisphere.*

Study Fig. 3.3 closely and notice that, as the earth spins on its axis, the side facing the sun is in sunshine and the other side is in darkness. Thus, half of the globe is always illuminated. If the earth's axis were not tilted, the noonday sun would always be directly overhead at the equator, and there would be 12 hours of daylight and 12 hours of darkness at each latitude every day of the year. However, the earth is tilted. Since the Northern Hemisphere faces toward the sun on June 21, each latitude in the Northern Hemisphere will have more than 12 hours of daylight. The farther north we go, the longer are the daylight hours. When we reach the Arctic Circle (66½°N), daylight lasts for 24 hours. Notice in Fig. 3.3 how the region above 66½°N never gets into the "shadow" zone as the earth spins. At the North Pole, the sun actually rises above the horizon on March 20 and has six months until it sets on September 22. No wonder this region is called the "Land of the Midnight Sun"! (See Fig. 3.4.)

Do longer days near polar latitudes mean that the highest daytime summer temperatures are experienced there? Not really. Nearly everyone knows that New York City (41°N) "enjoys" much hotter summer weather than Barrow, Alaska (71°N). The days in Barrow are much longer, so why isn't Barrow warmer? To figure this out, we must examine the *incoming solar radiation* (called *insolation*) on June 21. Figure 3.5 shows two curves: The upper curve represents the amount of insolation at the top of the earth's atmosphere on June 21, while the bottom curve represents the amount of radiation that eventually reaches the earth's surface on the same day.

The upper curve increases from the equator to the pole. This increase indicates that, during the entire day of June 21, more so-

*As we will see later in this chapter, the seasons are reversed in the Southern Hemisphere. Hence, in the Southern Hemisphere, this same day is the winter solstice, or the astronomical first day of winter.

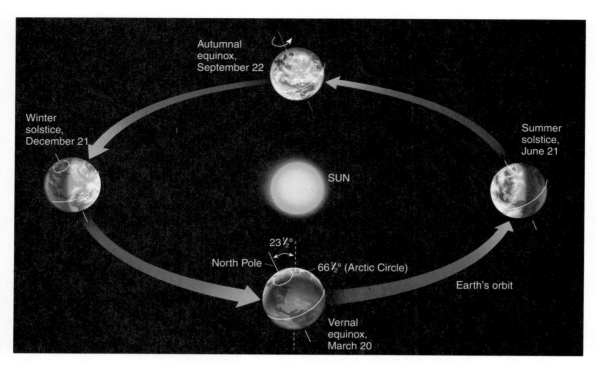

Figure 3.3
As the earth revolves about the sun, it is tilted on its axis by an angle of 23½°. The earth's axis always points to the same area in space (as viewed from a distant star). Thus, in June, when the Northern Hemisphere is tipped toward the sun, more direct sunlight and long hours of daylight cause warmer weather than in December, when the Northern Hemisphere is tipped away from the sun. (Diagram, of course, is not to scale.)

lar radiation reaches the top of the earth's atmosphere above the poles than above the equator. True, the sun shines on these polar latitudes at a relatively large angle, but it does so for 24 hours, causing the maximum to occur there. The lower curve shows that the amount of solar radiation eventually reaching the earth's

surface on June 21 is maximum near 30°N. From there, the amount of insolation reaching the ground decreases as we move poleward.

The reason the two curves are different is that once sunlight enters the atmosphere, fine dust and air molecules scatter it,

Figure 3.4
Land of the Midnight Sun. A series of exposures of the sun taken before, during, and after midnight in northern Alaska during July.

clouds reflect it, and some of it is absorbed by atmospheric gases. What remains reaches the surface. Generally, the greater the thickness of atmosphere that sunlight must penetrate, the greater are the chances that it will be either scattered, reflected, or absorbed by the atmosphere. During the summer in far northern latitudes, the sun is never very high above the horizon,

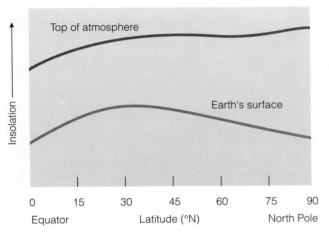

Figure 3.5
The relative amount of radiant energy received at the top of the earth's atmosphere and at the earth's surface on June 21—the summer solstice.

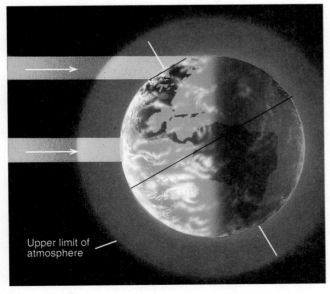

Figure 3.6
During the Northern Hemisphere summer, sunlight that reaches the earth's surface in far northern latitudes has passed through a thicker layer of absorbing, scattering, and reflecting atmosphere than sunlight that reaches the earth's surface farther south. Sunlight is lost through both the thickness of the pure atmosphere and by impurities in the atmosphere. As the sun's rays become more oblique, these effects become more pronounced.

so its radiant energy must pass through a thick portion of atmosphere before it reaches the earth's surface (see Fig. 3.6). And because of the increased cloud cover during the arctic summer, much of the sunlight is reflected before it reaches the ground.

Solar energy that eventually reaches the surface in the far north does not heat the surface effectively. A portion of the sun's energy is reflected by ice and snow, while some of it melts frozen soil. The amount actually absorbed is spread over a large area. So, even though northern cities, such as Barrow, experience 24 hours of continuous sunlight on June 21, they are not warmer than cities farther south. Overall, they receive less radiation at the surface, and what radiation they do receive does not effectively heat the surface.

In our discussion of Fig. 3.5, we saw that, on June 21, solar energy incident on the earth's surface is maximum near latitude 30°N. On this day, the sun is shining directly above latitude 23½°N. Why, then, isn't the most sunlight received here? A quick look at a world map shows that the major deserts of the world are centered near 30°N. Cloudless skies and drier air predominate near this latitude. At latitude 23½°N, the climate is more moist and cloudy, causing more sunlight to be scattered and reflected before reaching the surface. In addition, day length is longer at 30°N than at 23½°N on June 21. For these reasons, more radiation falls on 30°N latitude than at the Tropic of Cancer (23½°N).

Each day past June 21, the noon sun is slightly lower in the sky. Summer days in the Northern Hemisphere begin to shorten. June eventually gives way to September, and fall begins.

Look at Fig. 3.3 (p. 58) again and notice that, by September 22, the earth will have moved so that the sun is directly above the equator. Except at the poles, the days and nights throughout the world are of equal length. This day is called the **autumnal** (fall) **equinox,** and it marks the astronomical beginning of fall in the Northern Hemisphere. At the North Pole, the sun appears on the horizon for 24 hours, due to the bending of light by the atmosphere. The following day (or at least within several days), the sun disappears from view, not to rise again for a long, cold six months. Throughout the northern half of the world on each successive day, there are fewer hours of daylight, and the noon sun is slightly lower in the sky. Less direct sunlight and

Weather Watch

On an equinox, is the time between sunrise and sunset exactly 12 hours? The answer depends on how we define "sunrise" and "sunset." For example, sunrise may be defined as the time when the sun's upper edge becomes visible, and sunset when the sun's upper edge disappears. This definition of sunrise and sunset causes the actual date when day and night are of equal length (as, for example, reported in the newspaper) to occur several days before the vernal equinox and several days after the autumnal equinox.

Focus on AN OBSERVATION

Does the First Frost Cause the Leaves to Change Color in Autumn?

Contrary to what many people believe, it is not the first frost that causes the leaves of deciduous trees to change color. The yellow and orange colors are actually in the leaves during the summer, but we do not see them because the green pigments—known as *chlorophylls*—are far more dominant.

Chlorophylls absorb and use the energy of red and violet wavelengths of sunlight to manufacture the simple sugars and starches that trees use as food. Most of the green wavelengths are not absorbed; instead, they are reflected. This, of course, causes the leaf to appear green.

The leaves remain green as long as the tree is able to replenish the chlorophylls it uses up. About several weeks before the first frost, however, a chemical change begins in the leaf, as shorter days and cooler nights cause leaf activity to diminish. As the chlorophylls decrease, the green slowly disappears. Other pigments, such as the yellow and orange carotenoid, which were hidden by the green of the leaf, now begin to show through. Additionally, the cooler weather stimulates the manufacture of other pigments, such

Figure 1
The pageantry of fall colors along a country road in Vermont.

as the anthocyanins, which turn the leaves red or purple. The combination of these pigments can produce a fiery display of autumn color (see Fig. 1).

The weather most suitable for an impressive display of fall colors is warm, sunny days followed by clear, cool nights, with temperatures dropping below 7°C (45°F), but remaining above freezing.

---

shorter hours of daylight spell cooler weather for the Northern Hemisphere. Reduced radiation, lower air temperatures, and cooling breezes stimulate the beautiful pageantry of fall colors. (Does the first frost cause the beautiful colors? If you would like to know, read the Focus section above.)

In some years around the middle of autumn, there is an unseasonably warm spell, especially in the eastern two-thirds of the United States. This warm period, referred to as **Indian summer,**[*] may last from several days up to a week or more. It usually occurs when a large high-pressure area stalls near the south-

east coast. The clockwise flow of air around this system moves warm air from the Gulf of Mexico into the central or eastern half of the nation. The warm, gentle breezes and smoke from a variety of sources respectively make for mild, hazy days. The warm weather ends abruptly when an outbreak of polar air reminds us that winter is not far away.

On December 21 (three months after the autumnal equinox), the Northern Hemisphere is tilted as far away from the sun as it will be all year (see Fig. 3.3, p. 58). Nights are long and days are short. Notice in Table 3.1 that daylight decreases from 12 hours at the equator to 0 (zero) at latitudes above $66\frac{1}{2}°$N. This is the shortest day of the year, called the **winter solstice,** the astronomical beginning of winter in the northern world. On this day, the sun shines directly above latitude $23\frac{1}{2}°$S (Tropic of Capricorn). In the northern half of the world, the sun

---

[*]The origin of the term is uncertain, as it dates back to the eighteenth century. It may have originally referred to the good weather that allowed the Indians time to harvest their crops. Normally, a period of cool autumn weather must precede the warm weather period to be called Indian summer.

is at its lowest position in the noon sky. Its rays pass through a thick section of atmosphere and spread over a large area on the surface. Notice in Fig. 3.7 that on the average in the Northern Hemisphere, little (if any) solar energy reaches the earth's surface at high latitudes. With shorter days and less intense sunlight, we find ourselves bundled up for the cold winter.

With so little incident sunlight, the earth's surface cools quickly. A blanket of clean snow covering the ground aids in the cooling. The snow reflects much of the sunlight that reaches the surface and continually radiates away infrared energy during the long nights. In northern Canada and Alaska, the arctic air rapidly becomes extremely cold as it lies poised, ready to do battle with the milder air to the south. Periodically, this cold arctic air pushes down into the northern United States, producing a rapid drop in temperature called a *cold wave*, which occasionally reaches far into the south during the winter.

On each winter day after December 21, the sun climbs a bit higher in the midday sky. The periods of daylight grow longer until days and nights are of equal length, and we have another equinox.

The date of March 20, which marks the astronomical arrival of spring, is called the **vernal (spring) equinox.** At this equinox, the noonday sun is shining directly on the equator, while, at the North Pole, the sun (after hiding for six months) peeks above the horizon. Longer days and more direct solar radiation spell warmer weather for the northern world.

Three months after the vernal equinox, it is June again. The Northern Hemisphere is tilted toward the sun, which shines high in the noonday sky. The days have grown longer and warmer, and another summer season has begun.

At this point it is interesting to note that although sunlight is most intense in the Northern Hemisphere on June 21, the warmest weather in middle latitudes normally occurs weeks later, usually in July or August. This situation (called the *lag in seasonal temperature*) arises because although incoming energy from the sun is greatest in June, it still exceeds outgoing energy from the earth for a period of at least several weeks. When incoming solar energy and outgoing earth energy are in balance, the highest average temperature is attained. When outgoing energy exceeds incoming energy, the average temperature drops. Because outgoing earth energy exceeds incoming solar energy well past the winter solstice (December 21), we normally find our coldest weather occurring in January or February. As we will see later in this chapter, there is a similar lag in daily temperature between the time of most intense sunlight and the time of highest air temperature for the day.

Up to now, we have seen that the seasons are controlled by solar energy striking our tilted planet, as it makes its annual voyage around the sun. This tilt of the earth causes a seasonal variation in both the length of daylight and the intensity of sunlight that reaches the surface. Because of these facts, high latitudes tend to lose more energy to space each year than they receive from the sun, while low latitudes tend to gain more energy during the course of a year than they lose. From Fig. 3.8 we

Weather Watch

The Land of Total Darkness. Does darkness (constant night) really occur at the Arctic Circle ($66\frac{1}{2}°$N) on the winter solstice? The answer is no. Due to the bending and scattering of sunlight by the atmosphere, the sky is not totally dark at the Arctic Circle on December 21. In fact, on this date, total darkness only happens north of about 82° latitude. Even at the North Pole, total darkness does not occur from September 22 through March 20, but rather from about November 5 through February 5.

Table 3.1 Length of Time from Sunrise to Sunset for Various Latitudes on Different Dates

| LATITUDE | NORTHERN HEMISPHERE (READ DOWN) | | | |
	MARCH 20	JUNE 21	SEPT. 22	DEC. 21
0°	12 hr	12.0 hr	12 hr	12.0 hr
10°	12 hr	12.6 hr	12 hr	11.4 hr
20°	12 hr	13.2 hr	12 hr	10.8 hr
30°	12 hr	13.9 hr	12 hr	10.1 hr
40°	12 hr	14.9 hr	12 hr	9.1 hr
50°	12 hr	16.3 hr	12 hr	7.7 hr
60°	12 hr	18.4 hr	12 hr	5.6 hr
70°	12 hr	2 months	12 hr	0 hr
80°	12 hr	4 months	12 hr	0 hr
90°	12 hr	6 months	12 hr	0 hr
LATITUDE	SEPT. 22	DEC. 21	MARCH 20	JUNE 21
	SOUTHERN HEMISPHERE (READ UP)			

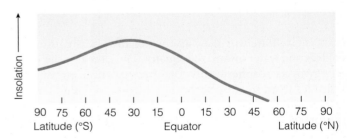

Figure 3.7
The relative amount of solar energy received at the earth's surface for various latitudes on December 21—the winter solstice.

can see that only at middle latitudes near 37° does the amount of energy received each year balance the amount lost. From this situation, we might conclude that polar regions are growing colder each year, while tropical regions are becoming warmer. But this does not happen. To compensate for these gains and losses of energy, winds in the atmosphere and currents in the

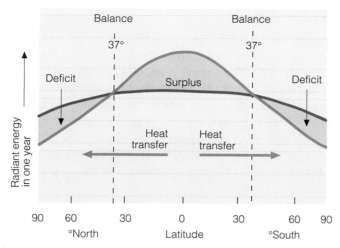

Figure 3.8
The average annual incoming solar radiation (red line) absorbed by the earth and the atmosphere along with the average annual infrared radiation (blue line) emitted by the earth and the atmosphere.

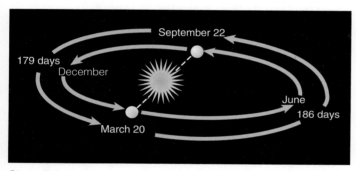

Figure 3.9
Because the earth travels more slowly when it is farther from the sun, it takes the earth a little more than 7 days longer to travel from March 20 to September 22 than from September 22 to March 20.

oceans circulate warm air and water toward the poles, and cold air and water toward the equator. Thus, the transfer of heat energy by atmospheric and oceanic circulations prevents low latitudes from steadily becoming warmer and high latitudes from steadily growing colder. These circulations are extremely important to weather and climate, and will be treated more completely in Chapter 11.

Seasons in the Southern Hemisphere   On June 21, the southern hemisphere is adjusting to an entirely different season. Because this part of the world is now tilted away from the sun, nights are long, days are short, and solar rays come in at an angle. All of these factors keep air temperatures fairly low. The June solstice marks the astronomical beginning of winter in the Southern Hemisphere. In this part of the world, summer will not "officially" begin until the sun is over the Tropic of Capricorn (23½°S)—remember that this occurs on December 21. So, when it is winter and June in the Southern Hemisphere, it is

summer and June in the Northern Hemisphere. If you are tired of the hot June weather in your Northern Hemisphere city, travel to the winter half of the world and enjoy the cooler weather. The tilt of the earth as it revolves around the sun makes all this possible.

We know the earth comes nearer to the sun in January than in July. Even though this difference in distance amounts to only about 3 percent, the energy that strikes the top of the earth's atmosphere is almost 7 percent greater on January 3 than on July 4. These statistics might lead us to believe that summer should be warmer in the Southern Hemisphere than in the Northern Hemisphere, which, however, is not the case. A close examination of the Southern Hemisphere reveals that nearly 81 percent of the surface is water compared to 61 percent in the Northern Hemisphere. The added solar energy due to the closeness of the sun is absorbed by large bodies of water, becoming well mixed and circulated within them. This process keeps the average summer (January) temperatures in the Southern Hemisphere cooler than summer (July) temperatures in the Northern Hemisphere. Because of water's large heat capacity, it also tends to keep winters in the Southern Hemisphere warmer than we might expect.*

Another difference between the seasons of the two hemispheres concerns their length. Because the earth describes an ellipse as it journeys around the sun, the total number of days from the vernal (March 20) to the autumnal (September 22) equinox is about 7 days longer than from the autumnal to vernal equinox (see Fig. 3.9). This means that spring and summer in the Northern Hemisphere not only last about a week longer than northern fall and winter, but also about a week longer than spring and summer in the Southern Hemisphere. Hence, the shorter spring and summer of the Southern Hemisphere somewhat offset the extra insolation received due to a closer proximity to the sun.

Up to now, we have considered the seasons on a global scale. We will now shift to more local considerations. (Before going on to the next section you may wish to read the Focus section on p. 63; which relates to seasonal changes and their impact on how we feel.)

Local Seasonal Variations

Figure 3.10 shows how the sun's position changes in the middle latitudes of the Northern Hemisphere during the course of one year. Note that, during the winter, the sun rises in the southeast and sets in the southwest. During the summer, it rises in the northeast, reaches a much higher position in the sky at noon, and sets in the northwest. Clearly, objects facing south will receive more sunlight during a year than those facing north. This fact becomes strikingly apparent in hilly or mountainous country.

Hills that face south receive more sunshine and, hence, become warmer than the partially shielded north-facing hills.

---

*For a comparison of January and July temperatures, see Figs. 3.21 and 3.22, p. 71.

Focus on **A SPECIAL TOPIC**

The Changing Seasons and How We Feel—It Could Be SAD

Can a seasonal change affect how we feel? For example, when winter sets in, do you feel lethargic, down, or depressed? Do you have similar feelings when the heat of summer arrives? These psychological feelings may relate to the changing seasons—what scientists call *Seasonal Affective Disorder*, or *SAD*.

Studies suggest that SAD may relate to two main seasonal factors: a decrease in the amount of sunlight that accompanies the winter months and an increase in the temperature that occurs in summer. These changing seasonal events may affect one's eating patterns, sleeping patterns, and overall mental health. For example, as winter approaches and sunlight hours diminish, some people report feelings of listlessness, lack of motivation, antisocial behaviors, sadness, and even suicidal tendencies. People who report symptoms of winter SAD also tend to need extra sleep and crave large amounts of carbohydrates.

To alleviate these symptoms, doctors have experimented with light therapy. In one study, patients with extreme winter SAD were subjected to one or more hours of extremely bright fluorescent light. In 80 percent of those treated, symptoms were relieved in 3 to 7 days. In another study, people with winter SAD were subjected to 30-minute exposures of bright light in the early morning in an attempt to trick the mind into believing the sun was rising earlier than it was. Nearly 60 percent of those receiving morning light therapy reported marked improvement in their SAD symptoms.

People who suffer from summer SAD report loss of energy, social withdrawal, oversleeping, sadness, and depression. Many of those reported that their environment (namely, increasing temperature and elevated relative humidity) seems to adversely influence their psychological well-being more than anything else.

The exact cause of winter and summer SAD is being investigated. The cause of winter SAD may be influenced by biological activity in the brain. Some scientists feel that light

either triggers, or at least brings into balance, certain neurotransmitters (chemical messengers involved in nerve cell communication), such as serotonin and dopamine. For winter SAD patients, reduction in sunlight may cause some form of imbalance in neurotransmitter activity and hence the onset of psychological discomfort. Recent studies tend to suggest that artificial morning bright light may change the brain's pattern of secreting melatonin, a hormone that regulates sleep and other daily biochemical rhythms. More and more studies are indicating that light therapy helps some people with winter SAD. So during the dark days of winter, when the blahs are abundant, a trip to a sunny tropical island may be exactly what the doctor orders.

Higher temperatures usually mean greater rates of evaporation and slightly drier soil conditions. Thus, south-facing hillsides are usually warmer and drier as compared to north-facing slopes at the same elevation. In many areas of the far west, only sparse vegetation grows on south-facing slopes, while, on the same hill, dense vegetation grows on the cool, moist hills that face north (see Fig. 3.11).

In northern latitudes, hillsides that face south usually have a longer growing season. Winemakers in western New York State do not plant grapes on the north side of hills. Grapes from vines grown on the warmer south side make better wine. Moreover, because air temperatures normally decrease with increasing height, trees found on the cooler north-facing side of mountains are often those that usually grow at higher elevations, while the warmer south-facing side of the mountain often supports trees usually found at lower elevations.

In the mountains, snow usually lingers on the ground for a longer time on north slopes than on the warmer south slopes. For this reason, ski runs are built facing north wherever possible.

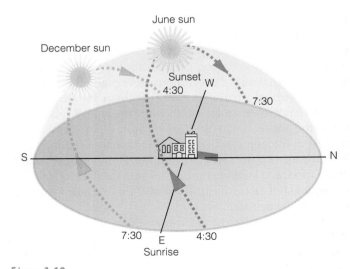

Figure 3.10
The changing position of the sun, as observed in middle latitudes in the Northern Hemisphere.

Figure 3.11
In areas where small temperature changes can cause major changes in soil moisture, sparse vegetation on the south-facing slopes will often contrast with lush vegetation on the north-facing slopes.

Also, homes and cabins built on the north side of a hill usually have a steep pitched roof, as well as a reinforced deck to withstand the added weight of snow from successive winter storms.

The seasonal change in the sun's position during the year can have an effect on the vegetation around the home. In winter, a large two-story home can shade its own north side, keeping it much cooler than its south side. Trees that require warm, sunny weather should be planted on the south side, where sunlight reflected from the house can even add to the warmth.

The design of a home can be important in reducing heating and cooling costs. Large windows should face south, allowing sunshine to penetrate the home in winter. To block out excess sunlight during the summer, a small eave or overhang should be built. A kitchen with windows facing east will let in enough warm morning sunlight to help heat this area. Because the west side warms rapidly in the afternoon, rooms having small windows (such as garages) should be placed here to act as a thermal buffer. Deciduous trees planted on the west or south side of a home provide shade in the summer. In winter, they drop their leaves, allowing the winter sunshine to warm the house. If you like the bedroom slightly cooler than the rest of the home, face it toward the north. Let nature help with the heating and air conditioning. Proper house design, orientation, and landscaping can help cut the demand for electricity, as well as for natural gas and fossil fuels, which are rapidly being depleted.

From our reading of the last several sections, it should be apparent that, when solar heating a home, proper roof angle is important in capturing much of the winter sun's energy. (The information needed to determine the angle at which sunlight will strike a roof is given in the Focus section on p. 65.)

Daily Temperature Variations

In a way, each sunny day is like a tiny season as the air goes through a daily cycle of warming and cooling. The air warms during the morning hours, as the sun gradually rises higher in the sky, spreading a blanket of heat energy over the ground. The sun reaches its highest point around noon, after which it begins its slow journey toward the western horizon. It is around noon when the earth's surface receives the most intense solar rays. However, somewhat surprisingly, noontime is usually not the warmest part of the day. Rather, the air continues to be

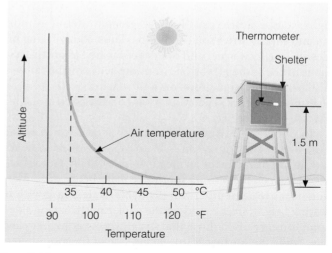

Figure 3.12
On a sunny, calm day, the air near the surface can be substantially warmer than the air a meter or so above the surface.

Focus on AN ENVIRONMENTAL ISSUE

Solar Heating and the Noonday Sun

The amount of solar energy that falls on a typical American home each summer day is many times the energy needed to heat the inside for a year. Thus, some people are turning to the sun as a clean, safe, and virtually inexhaustible source of energy. If solar collectors are used to heat a home, they should be placed on south-facing roofs to take maximum advantage of the energy provided. The roof itself should be constructed as nearly perpendicular to winter sun rays as possible. To determine the proper roof angle at any latitude, we need to know how high the sun will be above the southern horizon at noon.

The noon angle of the sun can be calculated in the following manner:

1. Determine the number of degrees between your latitude and the latitude where the sun is currently directly overhead.

2. Subtract the number you calculated in step 1 from 90°. This will give you the sun's elevation above the southern horizon at noon at your latitude.

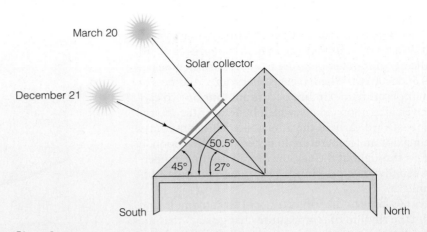

Figure 2
The roof of a solar-heated home constructed in Denver, Colorado, at an angle of 45° absorbs the sun's energy in midwinter at nearly right angles.

For example, suppose you live in Denver, Colorado (latitude 39½°N), and the date is December 21. The difference between your latitude and where the sun is currently overhead is 63° (39½°N to 23½°S), so the sun is 27° (90° − 63°) above the southern horizon at noon. On March 20 in Denver, the angle of the sun is 50½° (90° − 39½°). To determine a reasonable roof angle, we must consider the average altitude of the midwinter sun (about 39° for Denver), building costs, and snow loads. Figure 2 illustrates that a roof constructed in Denver, Colorado, at an angle of 45° will be nearly perpendicular to much of the winter sun's energy. Hence, the roofs of solar-heated homes in middle latitudes are generally built at an angle between 45° and 50°.

---

heated, often reaching a maximum temperature later in the afternoon. To find out why this *lag in temperature* occurs, we need to examine a shallow layer of air in contact with the ground.

Daytime Warming   As the sun rises in the morning, sunlight warms the ground, and the ground warms the air in contact with it by conduction. However, air is such a poor heat conductor that this process only takes place within a few centimeters of the ground. As the sun rises higher in the sky, the air in contact with the ground becomes even warmer, and there exists a thermal boundary separating the hot surface air from the slightly cooler air above. Given their random motion, some air molecules will cross this boundary: The "hot" molecules below bring greater kinetic energy to the cooler air; the "cool" molecules above bring a deficit of energy to the hot, surface air. However, on a windless day, this form of heat exchange is slow, and a substantial temperature difference usually exists just above the ground (see

Fig. 3.12). This explains why joggers on a clear, windless, summer afternoon may experience air temperatures of over 50°C (122°F) at their feet and only 32°C (90°F) at their waist.

Near the surface, convection begins, and rising air bubbles (thermals) help to redistribute heat. In calm weather, these thermals are small and do not effectively mix the air near the surface. Thus, large vertical temperature gradients are able to exist. On windy days, however, turbulent eddies are able to mix hot surface air with the cooler air above. This form of mechanical stirring, sometimes called *forced convection*, helps the thermals to transfer heat away from the surface more efficiently. Therefore, on sunny, windy days the molecules near the surface are more quickly carried away than on sunny, calm days. Figure 3.13 shows a typical vertical profile of air temperature on windy days and on calm days in summer.

We can now see why the warmest part of the day is usually in the afternoon. Around noon, the sun's rays are most intense.

However, even though incoming solar radiation decreases in intensity after noon, it still exceeds outgoing heat energy from the surface for a time. This yields an energy surplus for two to four hours after noon and substantially contributes to a lag between the time of maximum solar heating and the time of maximum air temperature several meters above the surface (see Fig. 3.14).

The exact time of the highest temperature reading varies somewhat. Where the summer sky remains cloud-free all afternoon, the maximum temperature may occur sometime between 3:00 and 5:00 P.M. Where there is afternoon cloudiness or haze, the temperature maximum occurs an hour or two earlier. In Denver, afternoon clouds, which build over the mountains, drift eastward early in the afternoon. This sometimes causes the maximum temperature to occur as early as noon. If clouds persist throughout the day, the overall daytime temperatures are usually lower, as clouds reflect a great deal of incoming sunlight.

Adjacent to large bodies of water, cool air moving inland may modify the rhythm of temperature change such that the warmest part of the day occurs at noon or before. In winter, atmospheric storms circulating warm air northward can even cause the highest temperature to occur at night.

Just how warm the air becomes depends on such factors as the type of soil, its moisture content, and vegetation cover. When the soil is a poor heat conductor (as loosely packed sand is), heat energy does not readily transfer into the ground. This fact allows the surface layer to reach a higher temperature, availing more energy to warm the air above. On the other hand, if the soil is moist or covered with vegetation, much of the available energy evaporates water, leaving less to heat the air. As you might expect, the highest summer tempera-

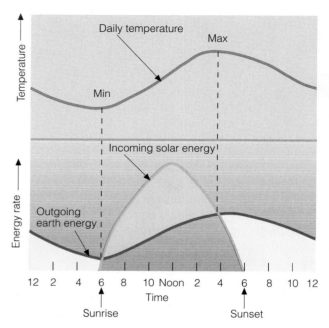

Figure 3.14
The daily variation in air temperature is controlled by incoming energy (primarily from the sun) and outgoing energy from the earth's surface. Where incoming energy exceeds outgoing energy (orange shade), the air temperature rises. Where outgoing energy exceeds incoming energy (blue shade), the air temperature falls.

tures usually occur over desert regions, where clear skies coupled with low humidities and meager vegetation permit the surface and the air above to warm up rapidly.

Where the air is humid, haze and cloudiness lower the maximum temperature by preventing some of the sun's rays from reaching the ground. In humid Atlanta, Georgia, the average maximum temperature for July is 30.5°C (87°F). In contrast, Phoenix, Arizona—in the desert southwest at the same latitude as Atlanta—experiences an average July maximum of 40.5°C (105°F).

Nighttime Cooling   As the sun lowers, its energy is spread over a larger area, which reduces the heat available to warm the ground. Observe in Fig. 3.14 that sometime in late afternoon or early evening, the earth's surface and air above begin to lose more energy than they receive; hence, they start to cool.

Both the ground and air above cool by radiating infrared energy, a process called **radiational cooling.** The ground, being a much better radiator than air, is able to cool more quickly. Consequently, shortly after sunset, the earth's surface is slightly cooler than the air directly above it. The surface air transfers some energy to the ground by conduction, which the ground, in turn, quickly radiates away.

As the night progresses, the ground and the air in contact with it continue to cool more rapidly than the air a few meters higher. The warmer upper air does transfer *some* heat down-

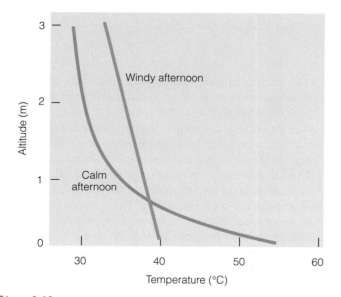

Figure 3.13
Vertical temperature profiles above an asphalt surface for a windy and a calm summer afternoon.

ward, a process that is slow due to the air's poor thermal conductivity. Therefore, by late night or early morning, the coldest air is found next to the ground, with slightly warmer air above (see Fig. 3.15).

This measured increase in air temperature just above the ground is known as a **radiation inversion** because it forms mainly through radiational cooling of the surface. Because radiation inversions occur on most clear, calm nights, they are also called **nocturnal inversions.**

Radiation Inversions   A strong radiation inversion occurs when the air near the ground is much colder than the air higher up. Ideal conditions for a strong inversion and, hence, very low nighttime temperatures exist when the air is calm, the night is long, and the air is fairly dry and cloud-free. Let's examine these ingredients one by one.

A windless night is essential for a strong radiation inversion because a stiff breeze tends to mix the colder air at the surface with the warmer air above. This mixing, along with the cooling of the warmer air as it comes in contact with the cold ground, causes a vertical temperature profile that is almost isothermal (constant temperature) in a layer several meters thick. In the absence of wind, the cooler, more dense surface air does not readily mix with the warmer, less dense air above, and the inversion is more strongly developed, as illustrated in Fig. 3.16.

A long night also contributes to a strong inversion. Generally, the longer the night, the longer the time of radiational cooling and the better are the chances that the air near the ground will be much colder than the air above. Consequently, winter nights provide the best conditions for a strong radiation inversion, other factors being equal.

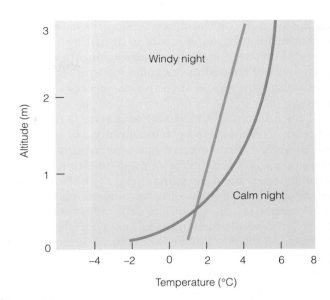

Figure 3.16
Vertical temperature profiles just above the ground on a windy night and on a calm night. Notice that the radiation inversion develops better on the calm night.

Finally, radiation inversions are more likely with a clear sky and dry air. Under these conditions, the ground is able to radiate its energy to outer space and thereby cool rapidly. However, with cloudy weather and moist air, much of the outgoing infrared energy is absorbed and radiated to the surface, retarding the rate of cooling. Also, on moist nights, condensation in the form of fog or dew will release latent heat, which warms the air. So, radiation inversions may occur on any night. But, during long winter nights, when the air is still, cloud-free, and relatively dry, these inversions can become strong and deep.

On winter nights in middle latitudes, it is common to experience below-freezing temperatures near the ground and air 5°C (9°F) warmer at your waist. In middle latitudes, the top of the inversion—the region where the air temperature stops increasing with height—is usually not more than 100 m (330 ft) above the ground. In dry, polar regions, where winter nights are measured in months, the top of the inversion is often 1000 m (about 3300 ft) above the surface. It may, however, extend to as high as 3000 m (about 10,000 ft).

It should now be apparent that how cold the night air becomes depends primarily on the length of the night, the moisture content of the air, cloudiness, and the wind. Even though wind may initially bring cold air into a region, the coldest nights usually occur when the air is clear and relatively calm.

There are, however, other factors that determine how cold the night air becomes. For example, a surface that is wet or covered with vegetation can add water vapor to the air, retarding nighttime cooling. Likewise, if the soil is a good heat conductor, heat ascending toward the surface during the night adds

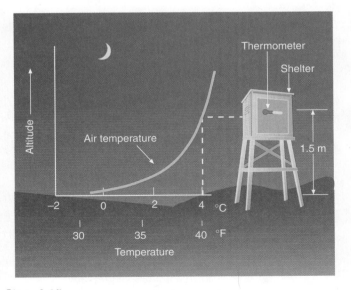

Figure 3.15
On a clear, calm night, the air near the surface can be much colder than the air above. The increase in air temperature with increasing height above the surface is called a radiation temperature inversion.

warmth to the air, which restricts cooling. On the other hand, snow covering the ground acts as an insulating blanket that prevents heat stored in the soil from reaching the air. Snow, a good emitter of infrared energy, radiates away energy rapidly at night, which helps keep the air temperature above a snow surface quite low.

Look back at Fig. 3.14, p. 66, and observe that the lowest temperature on any given day is usually observed around sunrise. However, the cooling of the ground and surface air may even continue beyond sunrise for a half hour or so, as outgoing energy can exceed incoming energy. This situation happens because light from the early morning sun passes through a thick section of atmosphere and strikes the ground at a low angle. Consequently, the sun's energy does not effectively heat the surface. Surface heating may be reduced further when the ground is moist and available energy is used for evaporation. (Any duck hunter lying flat in a marsh knows the sudden cooling that occurs as evaporation chills the air just after sunrise.) Hence, the lowest temperature may occur shortly after the sun has risen.

Cold, heavy surface air slowly drains downhill during the night and eventually settles in low-lying basins and valleys. Valley bottoms are thus colder than the surrounding hillsides (see Fig. 3.17). In middle latitudes, these warmer hillsides, called **thermal belts,** are less likely to experience freezing temperatures than the valley below. This encourages farmers to plant on hillsides those trees unable to survive the valley's low temperature.

On the valley floor, the cold, dense air is unable to rise. Smoke and other pollutants trapped in this heavy air restrict visibility. Therefore, valley bottoms are not only colder, but are also more frequently polluted than nearby hillsides. Even when the land is only gently sloped, cold air settles into lower-lying areas, such as river basins and floodplains. Because the flat floodplains are agriculturally rich areas, cold air drainage often forces farmers to seek protection for their crops.

Protecting Crops from the Cold On cold nights, many plants may be damaged by low temperatures. To protect small plants or shrubs, cover them with straw, cloth, or plastic sheeting. This prevents ground heat from being radiated away to the colder surroundings. If you are a household gardener concerned about outside flowers and plants during cold weather, simply wrap them in plastic or cover each with a paper cup.

Fruit trees are particularly vulnerable to cold weather in the spring when they are blossoming. The protection of such trees presents a serious problem to the farmer. Since the lowest temperatures on a clear, still night occur near the surface, the lower branches of a tree are the most susceptible to damage. Therefore, increasing the air temperature close to the ground may prevent damage. One way this increase can be achieved is to use **orchard heaters,** which warm the air around them by setting up convection currents close to the ground. Moreover, heat energy radiated from oil or gas-fired orchard heaters is intercepted by the buds of the trees, which raises their temperature.

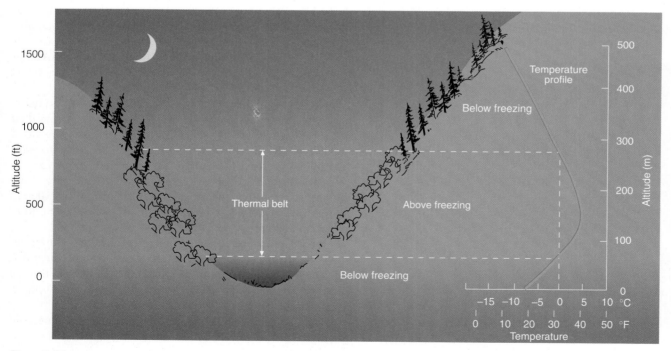

Figure 3.17
On cold, clear nights, the settling of cold air into valleys makes them colder than surrounding hillsides. The region along the side of the hill where the air temperature is above freezing is known as a *thermal belt*.

Figure 3.18
Orchard heaters circulate the air by setting up convection currents.

Figure 3.19
Wind machines mix cooler surface air with warmer air above.

Early forms of these heaters were called *smudge pots* because they produced large amounts of dense black smoke that caused severe pollution. People tolerated this condition only because they believed that the smoke acted like a blanket, trapping some of the earth's heat. Studies have shown this concept to be not as significant as previously thought. Orchard heaters are now designed to produce as little smoke as possible (see Fig. 3.18).

Another way to protect trees is to mix the cold air at the ground with the warmer air above, thus raising the temperature

of the air next to the ground. Such mixing can be accomplished by using **wind machines** (see Fig. 3.19), which are power-driven fans that resemble airplane propellers. One significant benefit of wind machines is that they can be thermostatically controlled to turn off and on at prescribed temperatures. Farmers without their own wind machines can rent air mixers in the form of helicopters. Although helicopters are effective in mixing the air, they are expensive to operate.

If sufficient water is available, trees can be protected by irrigation. On potentially cold nights, farmers might flood the orchard. Because water has a high heat capacity, it cools more slowly than dry soil. Consequently, the surface does not become as cold as it would if it were dry. Furthermore, wet soil has a higher thermal conductivity than dry soil. Hence, in wet soil, heat is conducted upward from subsurface soil more rapidly, which helps to keep the surface warmer.

So far, we have discussed protecting trees against the cold air near the ground during a radiation inversion. Farmers often face another nighttime cooling problem. For instance, when subfreezing air blows into a region, the coldest air is not found at the surface; the air actually becomes colder with height. This condition is known as a **freeze**.* A single freeze in California or Florida can cause several million dollars damage to citrus crops. As a case in point, several freezes during the spring of 2001 caused millions of dollars in damage to California's north coast vineyards, which resulted in higher wine prices.

Protecting an orchard from the damaging cold air blown by the wind can be a problem. Wind machines will not help because they would only mix cold air at the surface with the colder air above. Orchard heaters and irrigation are of little value as they would only protect the branches just above the ground. However, there is one form of protection that does work: An orchard's sprinkling system may be turned on so that it emits a fine spray of water. In the cold air, the water freezes around the branches and buds, coating them with a thin veneer of ice (see Fig. 3.20). As long as the spraying continues, the latent heat—given off as the water changes into ice—keeps the ice temperature at 0°C (32°F). The ice acts as a protective coating against the subfreezing air by keeping the buds (or fruit) at a temperature higher than their damaging point. Care must be taken since too much ice can cause the branches to break. The fruit may be saved from the cold air, while the tree itself may be damaged by too much protection. Sprinklers work well when the air is fairly humid. They do not work well when the air is dry, as a good deal of the water may be lost through evaporation.

---

*A freeze occurs over a widespread area when the surface air temperature remains below freezing for a long enough time to damage certain agricultural crops. The terms *frost* and *freeze* are often used interchangeably by various segments of society. However, to the grower of perennial crops (such as apples and citrus) who have to protect the crop against damaging low temperatures, it makes no difference if visible "frost" is present or not. The concern is whether or not the plant tissue has been exposed to temperatures equal to or below 32°F. The actual freezing point of the plant, however, can vary because perennial plants can develop hardiness in the fall that usually lasts through the winter, then wears off gradually in the spring.

Figure 3.20
A coating of ice protects these almond trees from damaging low temperatures, as an early spring freeze drops air temperatures well below freezing.

Presently under research are tests using genetically altered microorganisms to inhibit frost on plants. For example, laboratory tests using a particular bacterium (*Pseudomonas syringae*), known as *frost ban*, have shown promise in protecting plants from frost damage at temperatures as low as −5°C (23°F).

Brief Review Up to this point we have examined temperature variations on a seasonal and daily basis. Before going on, here is a review of some of the important concepts and facts we have covered:

■ The seasons are caused by the earth being tilted on its axis as it revolves around the sun. The tilt causes annual variations in the amount of sunlight that strikes the surface as well as variations in the length of time the sun shines at each latitude.

■ During the day, the earth's surface and air above will continue to warm as long as incoming energy (mainly sunlight) exceeds outgoing energy from the surface.

■ At night, the earth's surface cools, mainly by giving up more infrared radiation than it receives—a process called radiational cooling.

■ The coldest nights of winter normally occur when the air is calm, fairly dry (low water-vapor content), and cloud free.

■ The highest temperatures during the day and the lowest temperatures at night are normally observed at the earth's surface.

■ Radiation inversions exist usually at night when the air near the ground is colder than the air above.

The Controls of Temperature

The main factors that cause variations in temperature from one place to another are called the **controls of temperature.** Earlier we saw that the greatest factor in determining temperature is the amount of solar radiation that reaches the surface. This, of course, is determined by the length of daylight hours and the intensity of incoming solar radiation. Both of these factors are a function of latitude, hence, latitude is considered an important control of temperature. The main controls are listed as follows:

1. latitude
2. land and water distribution
3. ocean currents
4. elevation

We can obtain a better picture of these controls by examining Figs. 3.21 and 3.22, which show the average monthly temperatures throughout the world for January and July. The lines on the map are **isotherms**—lines connecting places that have the same temperature. Because air temperature normally decreases with height, cities at very high elevations are much colder than their sea level counterparts. Consequently, the isotherms in Figs. 3.21 and 3.22 are corrected to read at the same horizontal level (sea level) by adding to each station above sea level an amount of temperature that would correspond to an average temperature change with height.*

Figures 3.21 and 3.22 show the importance of latitude on temperature. Note that, on the average, temperatures decrease poleward from the tropics and subtropics in both January and July. However, because there is a greater variation in solar radiation between low and high latitudes in winter than in summer, the isotherms in January are closer together (a tighter gradient)† than they are in July. This fact means that if you travel from New Orleans to Detroit in January, you are more likely to experience greater temperature variations than if you make the same trip in July. Notice also in Figs. 3.21 and 3.22 that the isotherms do not run horizontally; rather, in many places they bend, especially where they approach an ocean-continent boundary.

On the January map, the temperatures are much lower in the middle of continents than they are at the same latitude near the oceans; on the July map, the reverse is true. The reason for these temperature variations can be attributed to the unequal heating and cooling properties of land and water. For one thing, solar energy reaching land is absorbed in a thin layer of soil; reaching water, it penetrates deeply. Because water is able to circulate, it distributes its heat through a much deeper layer.

---

*The amount of change is usually less than the standard temperature lapse rate of 6.5°C per 1000 m (3.6°F per 1000 ft). The reason is that the standard lapse rate is computed for altitudes above the earth's surface in the "free" atmosphere. In the less dense air at high elevations, the absorption of solar radiation by the ground causes an overall slightly higher temperature than that of the free atmosphere at the same level.
†Gradient represents the rate of change of some quantity (in this case, temperature) over a given distance.

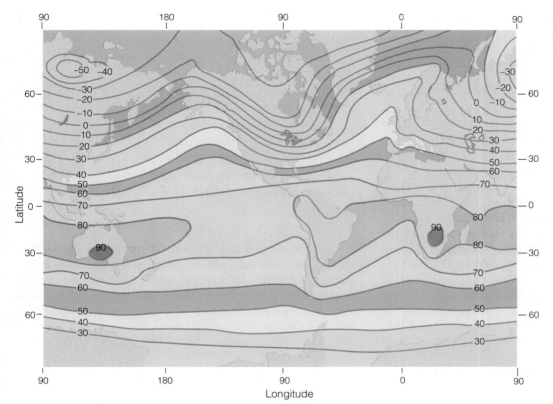

Figure 3.21
Average air temperature near sea level in January (°F).

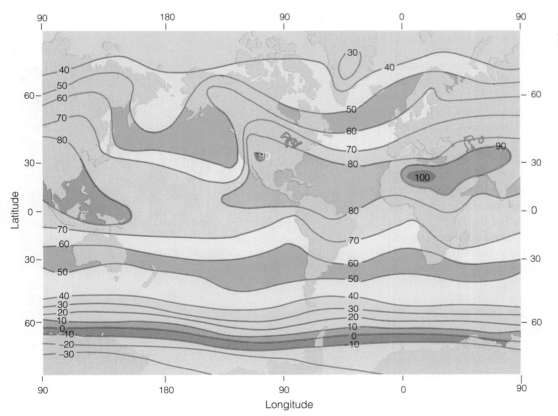

Figure 3.22
Average air temperature near sea level in July (°F).

Also, some of the solar energy striking the water is used to evaporate it rather than heat it.

Another important reason for the temperature contrasts is that water has a high *specific heat*. As we saw in Chapter 2, it takes a great deal more heat to raise the temperature of 1 gram of water 1°C than it does to raise the temperature of 1 gram of soil or rock by 1°C. Water not only heats more slowly than land, it cools more slowly as well, and so the oceans act like huge heat reservoirs. Thus, mid-ocean surface temperatures change relatively little from summer to winter compared to the much larger annual temperature changes over the middle of continents.

Along the margin of continents, ocean currents often influence air temperatures. For example, along the eastern margins, warm ocean currents transport warm water poleward, while, along the western margins, they transport cold water equatorward. As we will see in Chapter 11, some coastal areas also experience upwelling, which brings cold water from below to the surface.

Even large lakes can modify the temperature around them. In summer, the Great Lakes remain cooler than the land. As a result, refreshing breezes blow inland, bringing relief from the sometimes sweltering heat. As winter approaches, the water cools more slowly than the land. The first blast of cold air from Canada is modified as it crosses the lakes, and so the first freeze is delayed on the eastern shores of Lake Michigan.

Air Temperature Data

The careful recording and application of temperature data are tremendously important to us all. Without accurate information of this type, the work of farmers, power company engineers, weather analysts, and many others would be a great deal more difficult. In these next sections, we will study the ways temperature data are organized and used. We will also examine the significance of daily, monthly, and yearly temperature ranges and averages in terms of practical application to everyday living.

Daily, Monthly, and Yearly Temperatures   The greatest variation in daily temperature occurs right at the earth's surface. In fact, the difference between the daily maximum and minimum temperature—called the **daily** (or **diurnal**) **range of temperature**—is greatest next to the ground and becomes progressively smaller as we move away from the surface (see Fig. 3.23). This daily variation in temperature is also much larger on clear days than on cloudy ones.

The largest diurnal range of temperature occurs on high deserts, where the air is often cloud-free, and there is less CO_2 and water vapor above to radiate much infrared energy back to the surface. By day, clear summer skies allow the sun's energy to quickly warm the ground which, in turn, warms the air above to a temperature sometimes exceeding 35°C (95°F). At night, the ground cools rapidly by radiating infrared energy to space, and the minimum temperature in these regions occasionally dips below 5°C (41°F), thus giving a daily temperature range of 30°C (54°F).

Weather Watch

Talk about extreme temperature ranges. One of the greatest temperature ranges ever recorded in the Northern Hemisphere (56°C or 100°F) occurred at Browning, Montana, on January 23, 1916, when the air temperature plummeted from 7°C (44°F) to −49°C (−56°F) in less than 24 hours. This huge temperature range, however, would represent a rather typical day on the planet Mars. On Mars, the average high temperature reaches about −12°C (10°F) and the average low drops to −79°C (−110°F), producing a daily temperature range of 67°C (120°F).

A good example of a city with a large diurnal temperature range is Reno, Nevada, which is located on a plateau at an elevation of 1350 m (4400 ft) above sea level. Here, in the dry, thin summer air, the average daily maximum temperature for July is 33°C (92°F)—short-sleeve weather, indeed. But don't lose your shirt in Reno, for you will need it at night, as the average daily minimum temperature for July is 8°C (47°F). Reno has a daily range of 25°C (45°F)!

In humid regions, the diurnal temperature range is usually small. Here, haze and clouds lower the maximum temperature by preventing some of the sun's energy from reaching the surface. At night, the moist air keeps the minimum temperature high by absorbing the earth's infrared radiation and radiating a portion of it to the ground. An example of a humid city with

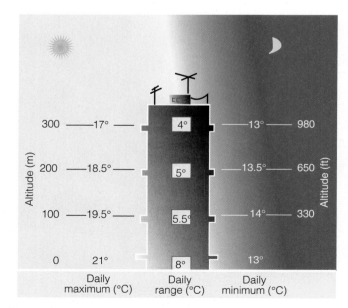

Figure 3.23
The daily range of temperature decreases as we climb away from the earth's surface. Hence, there is less day-to-night variation in air temperature near the top of a high-rise apartment complex than at the ground level.

Focus on A SPECIAL TOPIC

When It Comes to Temperature, What's Normal?

When the weathercaster reports that "the normal high temperature for today is 68°F" does this mean that the high temperature on this day is usually 68°F? Or does it mean that we should expect a high temperature near 68°F? Actually, we should expect neither one.

Remember that the word *normal*, or *norm,* refers to weather data averaged over a period of 30 years. For example, Fig. 3 shows the high temperature measured for 30 years in a southwestern city on March 15. The average (mean) high temperature for this period is 68°F; hence, the normal high temperature for this date is 68°F (dashed line). Notice, however, that only on one day during this 30-year period did the high temperature actually measure 68°F (large red dot). In fact, the most common high temperature (called the *mode*) was 60°F, and occurred on 4 days (blue dots).

So what would be considered a typical high temperature for this date? Actually, any high temperature that lies between about 47°F and 89°F (two standard deviations* on either side of 68°F) would be considered typical for this day. While a high temperature of 80°F may be quite warm and a high temperature of 47°F may be quite cool, they are both no more uncommon (unusual) than a high temperature of 68°F, which is the *normal* (average) high temperature for the 30-year period. This same type of reasoning applies to *normal rainfall,* as the actual amount of precipitation will likely be greater or less than the 30-year average.

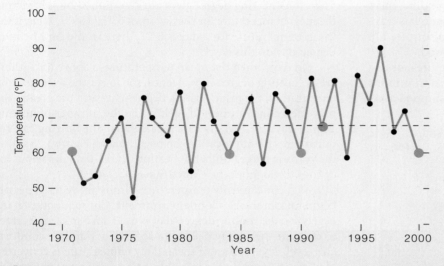

Figure 3
The high temperature measured (for 30 years) on March 15 in a city located in the southwestern United States. The dashed line represents the *normal* temperature for the 30-year period.

*A standard deviation is a statistical measure of the spread of the data. Two standard deviations for this set of data mean that 95 percent of the time the high temperature occurs between 47°F and 89°F.

---

a small summer diurnal temperature range is Charleston, South Carolina, where the average July maximum temperature is 32°C (90°F), the average minimum is 22°C (72°F), and the diurnal range is only 10°C (18°F).

Cities near large bodies of water typically have smaller diurnal temperature ranges than cities farther inland. This phenomenon is caused in part by the additional water vapor in the air and by the fact that water warms and cools much more slowly than land. Moreover, cities whose temperature readings are obtained at airports often have larger diurnal temperature ranges than those whose readings are obtained in downtown areas. The reason for this fact is that nighttime temperatures in cities tend to be warmer than those in outlying rural areas. This nighttime city warmth—called the *urban heat island*—is due to industrial and urban development, a topic that will be discussed more completely in Chapter 17.

The average of the highest and lowest temperature for a 24-hour period is known as the **mean (average) daily temperature.**

Most newspapers list the mean daily temperature along with the highest and lowest temperatures for the preceding day. The average of the mean daily temperatures for a particular date averaged for a 30-year period gives the average (or "*normal*") temperatures for that date. The average temperature for each month is the average of the daily mean temperatures for that month. (Additional information on the concept of "normal" temperature is given in the Focus section above.)

At any location, the difference between the average temperature of the warmest and coldest months is called the **annual range of temperature.** Usually the largest annual ranges occur over land, the smallest over water. Hence, inland cities have larger annual ranges than coastal cities. Near the equator (because daylight length varies little and the sun is always high in the noon sky), annual temperature ranges are small, usually less than 3°C (5°F). Quito, Ecuador—on the equator at an elevation of 2850 m (9350 ft)—experiences an annual range of less than 1°C. In middle and high latitudes, large seasonal variations in the amount of sunlight reaching the surface produce large temperature contrasts between winter and summer. Here, annual ranges are large, especially in the middle of a continent. Yakutsk, in northeastern Siberia near the Arctic Circle, has an extremely large annual temperature range of 62°C (112°F)!

The average temperature of any station for the entire year is the **mean (average) annual temperature,** which represents the average of the twelve monthly average temperatures.* When two cities have the same mean annual temperature, it might first seem that their temperatures throughout the year are quite similar. However, often this is not the case. For example, San Francisco, California, and Richmond, Virginia, are at the same latitude (37°N). Both have similar hours of daylight during the year; both have the same mean annual temperature—14°C (57°F). Here, the similarities end. The temperature differences between the two cities are apparent to anyone who has traveled to San Francisco during the summer with a suitcase full of clothes suitable for summer weather in Richmond.

Figure 3.24 summarizes the average temperatures for San Francisco and Richmond. Notice that the coldest month for both cities is January. Even though January in Richmond aver-

---

*The mean annual temperature may be obtained by taking the sum of the 12 monthly means and dividing that total by 12, or by obtaining the sum of the daily means and dividing that total by 365.

ages only 8°C (14°F) colder than January in San Francisco, people in Richmond awaken to an average January minimum temperature of −6°C (21°F), which is much colder than the lowest temperature ever recorded in San Francisco. Trees that thrive in San Francisco's weather would find it difficult surviving a winter in Richmond. So, even though San Francisco and Richmond have the same mean annual temperature, the behavior and range of their temperatures differ greatly.

The Use of Temperature Data   An application of daily temperature developed by heating engineers in estimating energy needs is the **heating degree-day.** The heating degree-day is based on the assumption that people will begin to use their furnaces when the mean daily temperature drops below 65°F. Therefore, heating degree-days are determined by subtracting the mean temperature for the day from 65°F (18°C). Thus, if the mean temperature for a day is 64°F, there would be 1 heating degree-day on this day.†

On days when the mean temperature is above 65°F, there are no heating degree-days. Hence, the lower the average daily temperature, the more heating degree-days and the greater the predicted consumption of fuel. When the number of heating degree-days for a whole year is calculated, the heating fuel requirements for any location can be estimated. Figure 3.25 shows the yearly average number of heating degree-days in various locations throughout the United States.

As the mean daily temperature climbs above 65°F, people begin to cool their indoor environment. Consequently, an index, called the **cooling degree-day,** is used during warm weather to estimate the energy needed to cool indoor air to a comfortable level. The forecast of mean daily temperature is converted to cooling degree-days by subtracting 65°F from the mean. The remaining value is the number of cooling degree-days for that day. For example, a day with a mean temperature of 70°F would correspond to 5 cooling degree-days (70 minus 65). High values indicate warm weather and high power production for cooling (see Fig. 3.26).

Knowledge of the number of cooling degree-days in an area allows a builder to plan the size and type of equipment that should be installed to provide adequate air conditioning. Also, the forecasting of cooling degree-days during the summer gives power companies a way of predicting the energy demand during peak energy periods. A composite of heating plus cooling degree-days would give a practical indication of the energy requirements over the year.

Farmers use an index called **growing degree-days** as a guide to planting and for determining the approximate dates when a crop will be ready for harvesting. There are a variety of methods of computing growing degree-days, but the most common one employs the mean daily temperature, since air temperature is the main factor that determines the physiological de-

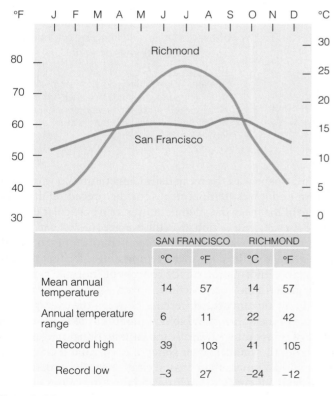

Figure 3.24
Temperature data for San Francisco, California (37°N), and Richmond, Virginia (37°N)—two cities with the same mean annual temperature.

	SAN FRANCISCO		RICHMOND	
	°C	°F	°C	°F
Mean annual temperature	14	57	14	57
Annual temperature range	6	11	22	42
Record high	39	103	41	105
Record low	−3	27	−24	−12

---

†In the United States, the National Weather Service and the Department of Agriculture use degrees Fahrenheit in their computations.

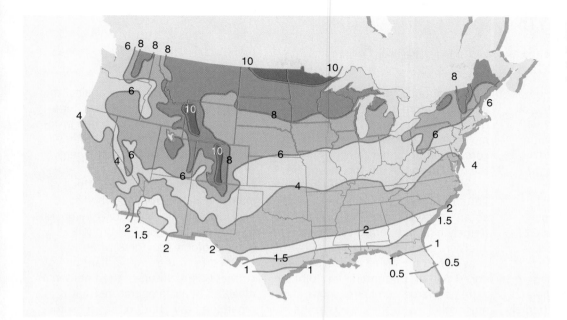

Figure 3.25
Mean annual total heating degree-days in thousands of °F, where the number 4 on the map represents 4000 (base 65°F).

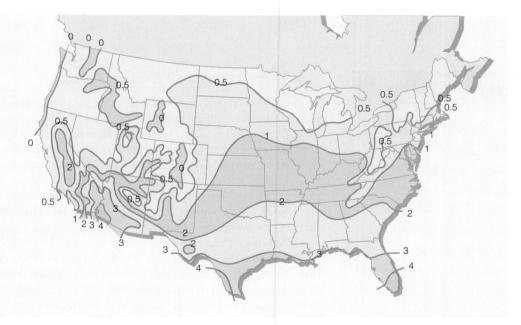

Figure 3.26
Mean annual total cooling degree-days in thousands of °F, where the number 1 on the map represents 1000 (base 65°F).

velopment of plants. Normally, a growing degree-day for a particular day is defined as a day on which the mean daily temperature is one degree above the *base temperature* (also known as *zero temperature*)—the minimum temperature required for growth of that crop. For sweet corn, the base temperature is 50°F and, for peas, it is 40°F.

On a summer day in Iowa, the mean temperature might be 80°F. From Table 3.2, we can see that, on this day, sweet corn would accumulate (80 − 50), or 30 growing degree-days. Theoretically, sweet corn can be harvested when it accumulates a total of 2200 growing degree-days. So, if sweet corn is planted in

early April and each day thereafter averages about 20 growing degree-days, the corn would be ready for harvest about 110 days later, or around the middle of July.*

At one time, corn varieties were rated in terms of "days to maturity." This rating system was unsuccessful because, in actual practice, corn took considerably longer in some areas than in

---

*As a point of interest, in the corn belt when the air temperature climbs above 86° F, the hot air puts added stress on the growth of the corn. Consequently, the corn grows more slowly. Because of this fact, any maximum temperature over 86°F is reduced to 86°F when computing the mean air temperature.

Focus on AN OBSERVATION

A Thousand Degrees and Freezing to Death

Is there somewhere in our atmosphere where the air temperature can be exceedingly high (say above 1000°C or 1800°F) yet a person might feel extremely cold? There is a region, but it's not at the earth's surface.

You may recall from Chapter 1, (Fig. 1.10, p. 15) that in the upper reaches of our atmosphere (in the middle and upper thermosphere), air temperatures may exceed 1000°C. However, a thermometer shielded from the sun in this region of the atmosphere would indicate an extremely low temperature. This apparent discrepancy lies in the meaning of air temperature and how we measure it.

In Chapter 2, we learned that the air temperature is directly related to the average speed at which the air molecules are moving—faster speeds correspond to higher temperatures. In the middle and upper thermosphere (at altitudes approaching 300 km, or 200 mi) air molecules are zipping about at speeds corresponding to extremely high temperatures. However, in order to transfer enough energy to heat something up by conduction (exposed skin or a thermometer bulb), an extremely large number of molecules must collide with the object. In the "thin" air of the upper atmosphere, air molecules are moving extraordinarily fast, but there are simply not

enough of them bouncing against the thermometer bulb for it to register a high temperature. In fact, when properly shielded from the sun, the thermometer bulb loses far more energy than it receives and indicates a temperature near absolute zero. This explains why an astronaut, when space walking, will not only survive temperatures exceeding 1000°C, but will also feel a profound coldness when shielded from the sun's radiant energy. At these high altitudes, the traditional meaning of air temperature (that is, regarding how "hot" or "cold" something feels) is no longer applicable.

Table 3.2 Estimated Growing Degree-Days for Certain Agricultural Crops to Reach Maturity		
CROP (VARIETY, LOCATION)	BASE TEMPERATURE (°F)	GROWING DEGREE-DAYS TO MATURITY
Beans (Snap/South Carolina)	50	1200–1300
Corn (Sweet/Indiana)	50	2200–2800
Cotton (Delta Smooth Leaf/Arkansas)	60	1900–2500
Peas (Early/Indiana)	40	1100–1200
Rice (Vegold/Arkansas)	60	1700–2100
Wheat (Indiana)	40	2100–2400

others. This discrepancy was the reason for defining "growing degree-days." Hence, in humid Iowa, where summer nighttime temperatures are high, growing degree-days accumulate much faster. Consequently, the corn matures in considerably fewer days than in the drier west, where summer nighttime temperatures are lower, and each day accumulates fewer growing degree-days. Although moisture and other conditions are not taken into account, growing degree-days nevertheless serve as a useful guide in forecasting approximate dates of crop maturity.

Air Temperature and Human Comfort

Probably everyone realizes that the same air temperature can feel differently on different occasions. For example, a temperature of 20°C (68°F) on a clear windless March afternoon in New York City can almost feel balmy after a long hard winter. Yet, this same temperature may feel uncomfortably cool on a summer afternoon in a stiff breeze. The human body's perception of temperature obviously changes with varying atmospheric conditions. The reason for these changes is related to how we exchange heat energy with our environment.

The body stabilizes its temperature primarily by converting food into heat (*metabolism*). To maintain a constant temperature, the heat produced and absorbed by the body must be equal to the heat it loses to its surroundings. There is, therefore, a constant exchange of heat—especially at the surface of the skin—between the body and the environment.

One way the body loses heat is by emitting infrared energy. But we not only emit radiant energy, we absorb it as well. Another way the body loses and gains heat is by conduction and convection, which transfer heat to and from the body by air motions. On a cold day, a thin layer of warm air molecules forms close to the skin, protecting it from the surrounding cooler air and from the rapid transfer of heat. Thus, in cold weather, when the air is calm, the temperature we perceive—called the **sensible temperature**—is often higher than a thermometer might indicate. (Could the opposite effect occur where the air temperature is very high and a person might feel exceptionally cold? If you are unsure, read the Focus section above.)

Once the wind starts to blow, the insulating layer of warm air is swept away, and heat is rapidly removed from the skin by the constant bombardment of cold air. When all other factors are the same, the faster the wind blows, the greater the heat loss, and the colder we feel. How cold the wind makes us feel is usually expressed as a **wind-chill index (WCI).**

The modern wind-chill index (see Tables 3.3 and 3.4) was formulated in 2001 by a joint action group of the National Weather Service and other agencies. The new index takes into account the wind speed at about 1.5 m (5 ft) above the ground instead of the 10 m (33 ft) where "official" readings are usually taken. In addition, it translates the ability of the air to take heat away from a person's face (the air's cooling power) into a wind-chill equivalent temperature.* For example, notice in Table 3.3 that an air temperature of 10°F with a wind speed of 10 mi/hr produces a wind-chill equivalent temperature of −4°F. Under

*The wind-chill equivalent temperature formulas are as follows: Wind chill (°F) = $35.74 + 0.6215T - 35.75\,(V^{0.16}) + 0.4275T\,(V^{0.16})$, where T is the air temperature in °F and V is the wind speed in mi/hr. Wind chill (°C) = $13.12 + 0.6215T - 11.37\,(V^{0.16}) + 0.3965T\,(V^{0.16})$, where T is the air temperature in °C, and V is the wind speed in km/hr.

Table 3.3   Wind-Chill Equivalent Temperature (°F). A 20-mi/hr Wind Combined with an Air Temperature of 20°F Produces a Wind-Chill Equivalent Temperature of 4°F.*

Wind Speed (mi/hr) \ Air Temperature (°F)	40	35	30	25	20	15	10	5	0	−5	−10	−15	−20	−25	−30	−35	−40
5	36	31	25	19	13	7	1	−5	−11	−16	−22	−28	−34	−40	−46	−52	−57
10	34	27	21	15	9	3	−4	−10	−16	−22	−28	−35	−41	−47	−53	−59	−66
15	32	25	19	13	6	0	−7	−13	−19	−26	−32	−39	−45	−51	−58	−64	−71
20	30	24	17	11	4	−2	−9	−15	−22	−29	−35	−42	−48	−55	−61	−68	−74
25	29	23	16	9	3	−4	−11	−17	−24	−31	−37	−44	−51	−58	−64	−71	−78
30	28	22	15	8	1	−5	−12	−19	−26	−33	−39	−46	−53	−60	−67	−73	−80
35	28	21	14	7	0	−7	−14	−21	−27	−34	−41	−48	−55	−62	−69	−76	−82
40	27	20	13	6	−1	−8	−15	−22	−29	−36	−43	−50	−57	−64	−71	−78	−84
45	26	19	12	5	−2	−9	−16	−23	−30	−37	−44	−51	−58	−65	−72	−79	−86
50	26	19	12	4	−3	−10	−17	−24	−31	−38	−45	−52	−60	−67	−74	−81	−88
55	25	18	11	4	−3	−11	−18	−25	−32	−39	−46	−54	−61	−68	−75	−82	−89
60	25	17	10	3	−4	−11	−19	−26	−33	−40	−48	−55	−62	−69	−76	−84	−91

Table 3.4   Wind-Chill Equivalent Temperature (°C).*

Wind Speed (km/hr) \ Air Temperature (°C)	10	5	0	−5	−10	−15	−20	−25	−30	−35	−40	−45	−50
10	8.6	2.7	−3.3	−9.3	−15.3	−21.1	−27.2	−33.2	−39.2	−45.1	−51.1	−57.1	−63.0
15	7.9	1.7	−4.4	−10.6	−16.7	−22.9	−29.1	−35.2	−41.4	−47.6	−51.6	−59.9	−66.1
20	7.4	1.1	−5.2	−11.6	−17.9	−24.2	−30.5	−36.8	−43.1	−49.4	−55.7	−62.0	−68.3
25	6.9	0.5	−5.9	−12.3	−18.8	−25.2	−31.6	−38.0	−44.5	−50.9	−57.3	−63.7	−70.2
30	6.6	0.1	−6.5	−13.0	−19.5	−26.0	−32.6	−39.1	−45.6	−52.1	−58.7	−65.2	−71.7
35	6.3	−0.4	−7.0	−13.6	−20.2	−26.8	−33.4	−40.0	−46.6	−53.2	−59.8	−66.4	−73.1
40	6.0	−0.7	−7.4	−14.1	−20.8	−27.4	−34.1	−40.8	−47.5	−54.2	−60.9	−67.6	−74.2
45	5.7	−1.0	−7.8	−14.5	−21.3	−28.0	−34.8	−41.5	−48.3	−55.1	−61.8	−68.6	−75.3
50	5.5	−1.3	−8.1	−15.0	−21.8	−28.6	−35.4	−42.2	−49.0	−55.8	−62.7	−69.5	−76.3
55	5.3	−1.6	−8.5	−15.3	−22.2	−29.1	−36.0	−42.8	−49.7	−56.6	−63.4	−70.3	−77.2
60	5.1	−1.8	−8.8	−15.7	−22.6	−29.5	−36.5	−43.4	−50.3	−57.2	−64.2	−71.1	−78.0

*Dark blue shaded areas represent conditions where frostbite occurs in 30 minutes or less.

these conditions, the skin of a person's exposed face would lose as much heat in one minute in air with a temperature of 10°F and a wind speed of 10 mi/hr as it would in calm air with a temperature of −4°F. Of course, how cold we feel actually depends on a number of factors, including the fit and type of clothing we wear, and the amount of sunshine striking the body, and the actual amount of exposed skin. High winds, in below-freezing air, can remove heat from exposed skin so quickly that the skin may actually freeze and discolor. The freezing of skin, called *frostbite*, usually occurs on the body extremities first because they are the greatest distance from the source of body heat.

In cold weather, wet skin can be a factor in how cold we feel. A cold rainy day (drizzly, or even foggy) often feels colder than a "dry" one because water on exposed skin conducts heat away from the body better than air does. In fact, in cold, wet, and windy weather a person may actually lose body heat faster than the body can produce it. This may even occur in relatively mild weather with air temperatures as high as 10°C (50°F). The rapid loss of body heat may lower the body temperature below its normal level and bring on a condition known as **hypothermia**—the rapid, progressive mental and physical collapse that accompanies the lowering of human body temperature.

The first symptom of hypothermia is exhaustion. If exposure continues, judgment and reasoning power begin to disappear. Prolonged exposure, especially at temperatures near or below freezing, produces stupor, collapse, and death when the internal body temperature drops to 26°C (79°F). Most cases of hypothermia occur when the air temperature is between 0°C and 10°C (between 32°F and 50°F). This may be because many people apparently do not realize that wet clothing in windy weather greatly enhances the loss of body heat, even when the temperature is well above freezing.

In cold weather, heat is more easily dissipated through the skin. To counteract this rapid heat loss, the peripheral blood vessels of the body constrict, cutting off the flow of blood to the outer layers of the skin. In hot weather, the blood vessels enlarge, allowing a greater loss of heat energy to the surroundings. In addition to this, we perspire. As evaporation occurs, the skin cools because it supplies the large latent heat of vaporization (about 560 cal/g). When the air contains a great deal of water vapor and it is close to being saturated, perspiration does not readily evaporate from the skin. Less evaporational cooling causes most people to feel hotter than it really is, and a number of people start to complain about the "heat and humidity." (A closer look at how we feel in hot weather will be given in Chapter 5, after we have examined the concepts of relative humidity and wet-bulb temperature.)

Measuring Air Temperature

Thermometers were developed to measure air temperature. Each thermometer has a definite scale and is calibrated so that a thermometer reading of 0°C in Vermont will indicate the same temperature as a thermometer with the same reading in North

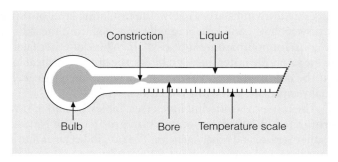

Figure 3.27
A section of a maximum thermometer.

Dakota. If a particular reading were to represent different degrees of hot or cold, depending on location, thermometers would be useless.

Liquid-in-glass thermometers are often used for measuring surface air temperature because they are easy to read and inexpensive to construct. These thermometers have a glass bulb attached to a sealed, graduated tube about 25 cm (10 in.) long. A very small opening, or bore, extends from the bulb to the end of the tube. A liquid in the bulb (usually mercury or red-colored alcohol) is free to move from the bulb up through the bore and into the tube. When the air temperature increases, the liquid in the bulb expands, and rises up the tube. When the air temperature decreases, the liquid contracts, and moves down the tube. Hence, the length of the liquid in the tube represents the air temperature. Because the bore is very narrow, a small temperature change will show up as a relatively large change in the length of the liquid column.

Maximum and minimum thermometers are liquid-in-glass thermometers used for determining daily maximum and minimum temperatures. The **maximum thermometer** looks like any other liquid-in-glass thermometer with one exception: It has a small constriction within the bore just above the bulb (see Fig. 3.27). As the air temperature increases, the mercury expands and freely moves past the constriction up the tube, until the maximum temperature occurs. However, as the air temperature begins to drop, the small constriction prevents the mercury from flowing back into the bulb. Thus, the end of the stationary mercury column indicates the maximum temperature for the day. The mercury will stay at this position until either the air warms to a higher reading or the thermometer is reset by whirling it on a special holder and pivot. Usually, the whirling is sufficient to push the mercury back into the bulb past the constriction until the end of the column indicates the present air temperature.*

A **minimum thermometer** measures the lowest temperature reached during a given period. Most minimum thermome-

---

*Liquid-in-glass thermometers that measure body temperature are maximum thermometers, which is why they are shaken both before and after you take your temperature.

ters use alcohol as a liquid, since it freezes at a temperature of –130°C compared to –39°C for mercury. The minimum thermometer is similar to other liquid-in-glass thermometers except that it contains a small barbell-shaped index marker in the bore (see Fig. 3.28). The small index marker is free to slide back and forth within the liquid. It cannot move out of the liquid because the surface tension at the end of the liquid column (the *meniscus*) holds it in.

A minimum thermometer is mounted horizontally. As the air temperature drops, the contracting liquid moves back into the bulb and brings the index marker down the bore with it. When the air temperature stops decreasing, the liquid and the index marker stop moving down the bore. As the air warms, the alcohol expands and moves freely up the tube past the stationary index marker. Because the index marker does not move as the air warms, the minimum temperature is read by observing the upper end of the marker.

To reset a minimum thermometer, simply tip it upside down. This allows the index marker to slide to the upper end of the alcohol column, which is indicating the current air temperature. The thermometer is then remounted horizontally, so that the marker will move toward the bulb as the air temperature decreases.

Highly accurate temperature measurements may be made with **electrical thermometers.** One type of electrical thermometer is the *electrical resistance thermometer,* which does not actually measure air temperature but rather the resistance of a wire, usually platinum or nickel, whose resistance increases as the temperature increases. An electrical meter measures the resistance, and is calibrated to represent air temperature.

Electrical resistance thermometers are the type of thermometers used in the measurement of air temperature at the over 900 fully automated surface weather stations (known as *ASOS* for *Automated Surface Observing System*) that exist at airports and military facilities throughout the United States. Hence, many of the liquid-in-glass thermometers have been replaced with elec-

trical thermometers. At this point it should be noted that the replacement of liquid-in-glass thermometers with electrical thermometers has raised concern among climatologists. For one thing, the response of the electrical thermometers to temperature change is faster. Thus, electrical thermometers may reach a brief extreme reading, which could have been missed by the slower-responding liquid-in-glass thermometer. In addition, many temperature readings, which were taken at airport weather offices, are now taken at ASOS locations that sit near or between runways at the airport. This change in instrumentation and relocation of the measurement site can sometimes introduce a small, but significant, temperature change at the reporting station.

Thermistors are another type of electrical thermometer. They are made of ceramic material whose resistance increases as the temperature decreases. A thermistor is the temperature-measuring device of the radiosonde—the instrument that measures air temperature from the surface up to an altitude near 30 kilometers.

Another electrical thermometer is the *thermocouple.* This device operates on the principle that the temperature difference between the junction of two dissimilar metals sets up a weak electrical current. When one end of the junction is maintained at a temperature different from that of the other end, an electrical current will flow in the circuit. This current is proportional to the temperature difference between the junctions.

Air temperature may also be obtained with instruments called *infrared sensors,* or **radiometers.** Radiometers do not measure temperature directly; rather, they measure emitted radiation (usually infrared). By measuring both the intensity of radiant energy and the wavelength of maximum emission of a particular gas, radiometers in orbiting satellites are now able to estimate the air temperature at selected levels in the atmosphere.

A **bimetallic thermometer** consists of two different pieces of metal (usually brass and iron) welded together to form a single strip. As the temperature changes, the brass expands more than the iron, causing the strip to bend. The small amount of bending is amplified through a system of levers to a pointer on a calibrated scale.

The bimetallic thermometer is usually the temperature-sensing part of the **thermograph,** an instrument that measures and records temperature. On a thermograph, the pointer is a pen that sits on a circular drum (see Fig. 3.29). The drum, which is covered with a piece of chart paper, is slowly rotated by a clock-drive. As the temperature of the air changes, the bimetallic thermometer bends accordingly, and the pen moves up or down, marking the chart paper with the current air temperature. Since the time is printed on the top of the chart paper, a continuous recording of temperature is obtained. Because bimetallic thermometers are less accurate than electrical thermometers, thermographs must be checked periodically and corrected, using an accurate thermometer.

Thermographs are gradually being replaced with *data loggers.* These small instruments have a thermistor connected to

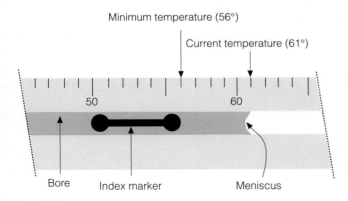

Figure 3.28
A section of a minimum thermometer showing both the current air temperature and the minimum temperature.

Focus on A SPECIAL TOPIC

Thermometers Should Be Read in the Shade

When we measure air temperature with a common liquid thermometer, an incredible number of air molecules bombard the bulb, transferring energy either to or away from it. When the air is warmer than the thermometer, the liquid gains energy, expands, and rises up the tube; the opposite will happen when the air is colder than the thermometer. The liquid stops rising (or falling) when equilibrium between incoming and outgoing energy is established. At this point, we can read the temperature by observing the height of the liquid in the tube.

It is *impossible* to measure *air temperature* accurately in direct sunlight because the thermometer absorbs radiant energy from the sun in addition to energy from the air molecules. The thermometer gains energy at a much faster rate than it can radiate it away, and the liquid keeps expanding and rising until there is equilibrium between incoming and outgoing energy. Because of the direct absorption of solar energy, the level of the liquid in the thermometer indicates a temperature much higher than the actual air temperature, and so a statement that says "today the air temperature measured 100 degrees in the sun" has no meaning. Hence, a thermometer must be kept in a shady place to measure the temperature of the air accurately.

---

a circuit board inside the logger. A computer programs the interval at which readings are taken. The loggers are not only more responsive to air temperature than are thermographs, they are less expensive.

Chances are, you may have heard someone exclaim something like, "Today the thermometer measured 90 degrees in the shade!" Does this mean that the air temperature was higher in the sun? If you are unsure of the answer, read the Focus section above before reading the next section on instrument shelters.

Thermometers and other instruments are usually housed in an **instrument shelter.** The shelter completely encloses the instruments, protecting them from rain, snow, and the sun's direct rays. It is painted white to reflect sunlight, faces north to avoid direct exposure to sunlight, and has louvered sides, so that air is free to flow through it. This construction helps to keep the air inside the shelter at the same temperature as the air outside.

The thermometers inside a standard shelter are mounted about 1.5 to 2 m (5 to 6 ft) above the ground. As we saw in an earlier section, on a clear, calm night the air at ground level may be much colder than the air at the level of the shelter. As a result, on clear winter mornings it is possible to see ice or frost on the ground even though the minimum thermometer in the shelter did not reach the freezing point.

The older instrument shelters are gradually being replaced by the *Max-Min Temperature Shelter* (see Fig. 3.30). The shelter is mounted on a pipe, and wires from the electrical temperature sensor inside are run to a building. A readout inside the building displays the current air temperature and stores the maximum and minimum temperatures for later retrieval. This type of shelter is now used with the automated (ASOS) system.

Because air temperatures vary considerably above different types of surfaces, where possible shelters are placed over grass to ensure that the air temperature is measured at the same elevation over the same type of surface. Unfortunately, some shelters are placed on asphalt, others sit on concrete, while others are located on the tops of tall buildings, making it difficult to compare air temperature measurements from different locations. In fact, if either the maximum or minimum air temperature in your area seems suspiciously different from those of nearby towns, find out where the instrument shelter is situated.

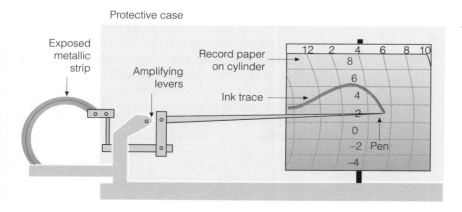

Figure 3.29
The thermograph with a bimetallic thermometer.

Figure 3.30
The max–min instrument shelter (middle box) and other weather instruments that comprise the ASOS system.

Summary

The earth has seasons because the earth is tilted on its axis as it revolves around the sun. The tilt of the earth causes a seasonal variation in both the length of daylight and the intensity of sunlight that reaches the surface. When the Northern Hemisphere is tilted toward the sun, the Southern Hemisphere is tilted away from the sun. Longer hours of daylight and more intense sunlight produce summer in the Northern Hemisphere, while, in the Southern Hemisphere, shorter daylight hours and less intense sunlight produce winter. On a more local setting, the earth's inclination influences the amount of solar energy received on the north and south side of a hill, as well as around a home.

The daily variation in air temperature near the earth's surface is controlled mainly by the input of energy from the sun and the output of energy from the surface. On a clear, calm day, the surface air warms, as long as heat input (mainly sunlight) exceeds heat output (mainly convection and radiated infrared energy). The surface air cools at night, as long as heat output exceeds input. Because the ground at night cools more quickly than the air above, the coldest air is normally found at the surface where a radiation inversion usually forms. When the air temperature in agricultural areas drops to dangerously low readings, fruit trees and grape vineyards can be protected from the cold by a variety of means, from mixing the air to spraying the trees and vines with water.

The greatest daily variation in air temperature occurs at the earth's surface. Both the diurnal and annual ranges of temperature are greater in dry climates than in humid ones. Even though two cities may have similar average annual temperatures, the range and extreme of their temperatures can differ greatly. Temperature information impacts our lives in many ways, from influencing decisions on what clothes to take on a trip to providing critical information for energy-use predictions and agricultural planning. We reviewed some of the many types of thermometers in use. Those designed to measure air temperatures near the surface are housed in instrument shelters to protect them from direct sunlight and precipitation.

Key Terms

The following terms are listed in the order they appear in the text. Define each. Doing so will aid you in reviewing the material covered in this chapter.

summer solstice
autumnal equinox
Indian summer
winter solstice
vernal equinox
radiational cooling
radiation inversion
nocturnal inversion
thermal belts
orchard heaters
wind machines
freeze

controls of temperature
isotherms
daily (diurnal) range of
   temperature
mean (average) daily
   temperature
annual range of temperature
mean (average) annual
   temperature
heating degree-day
cooling degree-day
growing degree-days

sensible temperature
wind-chill index
hypothermia
liquid-in-glass
   thermometers
maximum thermometer

minimum thermometer
electrical thermometers
radiometers
bimetallic thermometer
thermograph
instrument shelter

Questions for Review

1. In the Northern Hemisphere, why are summers warmer than winters, even though the earth is actually closer to the sun in January?
2. What are the main factors that determine seasonal temperature variations?
3. During the Northern Hemisphere's summer, the daylight hours in northern latitudes are longer than in middle latitudes. Explain why northern latitudes are not warmer.
4. If it is winter and January in New York City, what is the season in Sydney, Australia?
5. Explain why Southern Hemisphere summers are not warmer than Northern Hemisphere summers.
6. Explain why the vegetation on the north-facing side of a hill is frequently different from the vegetation on the south-facing side of the same hill.
7. Look at Figures 3.13 and 3.16, which show vertical profiles of air temperature during different times of the day. Explain why the temperature curves are different.
8. What are some of the factors that determine the daily fluctuation of air temperature just above the ground?
9. Explain how incoming energy and outgoing energy regulate the daily variation in air temperature.
10. On a calm, sunny day, why is the air next to the ground normally much warmer than the air just above?
11. Explain why the warmest time of the day is usually in the afternoon, even though the sun's rays are most direct at noon.
12. Explain how radiational cooling at night produces a radiation temperature inversion.
13. What weather conditions are best suited for the formation of a cold night and a strong radiation inversion?
14. Explain why thermal belts are found along hillsides at night.
15. List some of the measures farmers use to protect their crops against the cold. Explain the physical principle behind each method.
16. Why are the lower tree branches most susceptible to damage from low temperatures?
17. Describe each of the controls of temperature.
18. Look at Fig. 3.21 (temperature map for January) and explain why the isotherms dip southward (equatorward) over the Northern Hemisphere continents.
19. Explain why the daily range of temperature is normally greater (a) in dry regions than in humid regions and (b) on clear days than on cloudy days.

20. Why is the largest annual range of temperatures normally observed over continents away from large bodies of water?
21. Two cities have the same mean annual temperature. Explain why this fact does not mean that their temperatures throughout the year are similar.
22. During a cold, calm, sunny day, why do we usually feel warmer than a thermometer indicates?
23. What atmospheric conditions can bring on hypothermia?
24. During the winter, frost can form on the ground when the minimum thermometer indicates a low temperature above freezing. Explain.
25. Why do daily temperature ranges decrease as you increase in altitude?
26. Why do the first freeze in autumn and the last freeze in spring occur in low-lying areas?
27. Someone says, "The air temperature today measured 99°F in the sun." Why does this statement have no meaning?

Questions for Thought

1. Explain (with the aid of a diagram) why the morning sun shines brightly through a south-facing bedroom window in December, but not in June.
2. Consider these two scenarios: (a) The tilt of the earth decreased to 10°. (b) The tilt of the earth increased to 40°. How would this change the summer and winter temperatures in your area? Explain, using a diagram.
3. At the top of the earth's atmosphere during the early summer (Northern Hemisphere), above what latitude would you expect to receive the most solar radiation in one day? During the same time of year, where would you expect to receive the most solar radiation at the surface? Explain why the two locations are different. (If you are having difficulty with this question, refer to Fig. 3.5, p. 59.)
4. If a construction company were to build a solar-heated home in middle latitudes in the Southern Hemisphere, in which direction should the solar panels on the roof be directed for maximum daytime heating?
5. Aside from the aesthetic appeal (or lack of such), explain why painting the outside north-facing wall of a middle latitude house one color and the south-facing wall another color is not a bad idea.
6. How would the lag in daily temperature experienced over land compare to the daily temperature lag over water?
7. Where would you expect to experience the smallest variation in temperature from year to year and from month to month? Why?
8. The average temperature in San Francisco, California, for December, January, and February is 11°C (52°F). During the same three-month period the average temperature in Richmond, Virginia, is 4°C (39°F). Yet, San Francisco and Richmond have nearly the same yearly total of heating degree-days. Explain why. (Hint: See Fig. 3.24, p. 74.)

9. On a warm summer day, one city experienced a daily range of 22°C (40°F), while another had a daily range of 10°C (18°F). One of these cities is located in New Jersey and the other in New Mexico. Which location most likely had the highest daily range, and which one had the smallest? Explain.

10. Minimum thermometers are usually read during the morning, yet they are reset in the afternoon. Explain why.

11. If clouds arrive at 2 A.M. in the middle of a calm, clear night it is quite common to see temperatures rise after 2 A.M. How does this happen?

12. In the Northern Hemisphere, south-facing mountain slopes normally have a greater diurnal range in temperature than north-facing slopes. Why?

13. If the poles have 24 hours of sunlight during the summer, why is the average summer temperature still below 0°F?

Problems and Exercises

1. Draw a graph similar to Figs. 3.5 (p. 59) and 3.7 (p. 61). Include in it the amount of solar radiation reaching the earth's surface at each latitude on the equinox.

2. Each day past the winter solstice the noon sun is a little higher above the southern horizon. (a) Determine how much change takes place each day at your latitude. (b) Does the same amount of change take place at each latitude in the Northern Hemisphere? Explain.

3. On approximately what dates will the sun be overhead at noon at latitudes: (a) 10°N? (b) 15°S?

4. Design a solar-heated home that sits on the north side of an east-west running street. If the home is located at 40°N, draw a proper roof angle for maximum solar heating. Design windows, doors, overhangs, and rooms with the intent of reducing heating and cooling costs. Place trees around the home that will block out excess summer sunlight and yet let winter sunlight inside. Choose a paint color for the house that will add to the home's energy efficiency.

5. Suppose peas are planted in Indiana on May 1. If the peas need 1200 growing degree-days before they can be picked,

and if the average maximum temperature for May and June is 80°F and the average minimum is 60°F, on about what date will the peas be ready to pick? (Assume a base temperature of 55°F.)

6. What is the wind-chill equivalent temperature when the air temperature is 5°F and the wind speed is 35 mi/hr? (Use Table 3.3, p. 77.)

 Questions for Exploration

On the Blue Skies: College Edition CD-ROM go to the **Atmospheric Basics** section of the CD and click on "**Energy Balance**."

1. Explore the model of energy exchange. This time modify only the time of day in three-hour increments. (a) For each time step note the values of energy flow to and from the earth's surface and plot total gains and total losses versus time. (b) Based on this information when would you expect the temperature to reach its peak for the day?

2. Historical Weather Data (http://www.wunderground.com): Enter the name of any city in the United States and find the current weather forecast for that city. Using the "Historical Conditions" section of the page, find the record high and low temperatures for three different dates.

3. World Climate Data (http://www.worldclimate.com/climate/index.htm): Enter the name of any city and find the average monthly temperatures for that location. Compare the average monthly temperatures for a coastal city with those of a city located in the interior of a large continent. Discuss the differences you find.

Go to the Brooks/Cole Earth Sciences Resource Center (http://earthscience.brookscole.com) for critical thinking exercises, articles, and additional readings from InfoTrac College Edition, Brooks/Cole's online student library.

Sunlight bending through ice crystals in cirri-form clouds produces bands of color called sundogs, or parhelia, on both sides of the sun on this cold winter day in Minnesota. (Photo © 2002 STAR TRIBUNE/Minneapolis-St. Paul.)

Global Climate

CONTENTS

The climate is unbearable . . . At noon today the highest temperature measured was −33°C. We really feel that it is late in the season. The days are growing shorter, the sun is low and gives no warmth, katabatic winds blow continuously from the south with gales and drifting snow. The inner walls of the tent are like glazed parchment with several millimeters thick ice-armour . . . Every night several centimeters of frost accumulate on the walls, and each time you inadvertently touch the tent cloth a shower of ice crystals falls down on your face and melts. In the night huge patches of frost from my breath spread around the opening of my sleeping bag and melt in the morning. The shoulder part of the sleeping bag facing the tent-side is permeated with frost and ice, and crackles when I roll up the bag . . . For several weeks now my fingers have been permanently tender with numb fingertips and blistering at the nails after repeated frostbites. All food is frozen to ice and it takes ages to thaw out everything before being able to eat. At the depot we could not cut the ham, but had to chop it in pieces with a spade. Then we threw ourselves hungrily at the chunks and chewed with the ice crackling between our teeth. You have to be careful with what you put in your mouth. The other day I put a piece of chocolate from an outer pocket directly in my mouth and promptly got frostbite with blistering of the palate.

Ove Wilson (Quoted in David M. Gates, *Man and His Environment*)

Our opening comes from a report by Norwegian scientists on their encounter with one of nature's cruelest climates—that of Antarctica. Their experience illustrates the profound effect that climate can have on even ordinary events, such as eating a piece of chocolate. Though we may not always think about it, climate profoundly affects nearly everything in the middle latitudes, too. For instance, it influences our housing, clothing, the shape of landscapes, agriculture, how we feel and live, and even where we reside, as most people will choose to live on a sunny hillside rather than in a cold, dark, and foggy river basin. Entire civilizations have flourished in favorable climates and have moved away from, or perished in, unfavorable ones. We learned early in this text that *climate* is the average of the day-to-day weather over a long duration. But the concept of climate is much larger than this, for it encompasses, among other things, the daily and seasonal extremes of weather within specified areas.

When we speak of climate, then, we must be careful to specify the spatial location we are talking about. For example, the Chamber of Commerce of a rural town may boast that its community has mild winters with air temperatures seldom below freezing. This may be true several meters above the ground in an instrument shelter, but near the ground the temperature may drop below freezing on many winter nights. This small climatic region near or on the ground is referred to as a **microclimate.** Because a much greater extreme in daily air temperatures exists near the ground than several meters above, the microclimate for small plants is far more harsh than the thermometer in an instrument shelter would indicate.

When we examine the climate of a small area of the earth's surface, we are looking at the **mesoclimate.** The size of the area may range from a few acres to several square kilometers. Mesoclimate includes regions such as forests, valleys, beaches, and towns. The climate of a much larger area, such as a state or a country, is called **macroclimate.** The climate extending over the entire earth is often referred to as **global climate.**

In this chapter, we will concentrate on the larger scales of climate. We will begin with the factors that regulate global climate; then we will discuss how climates are classified. Finally, we will examine the different types of climate.

A World with Many Climates

The world is rich in climatic types. From the teeming tropical jungles to the frigid polar "wastelands," there seems to be an almost endless variety of climatic regions. The factors that produce the climate in any given place—the **climatic controls**—are the same that produce our day-to-day weather. Briefly, the controls are the:

1. intensity of sunshine and its variation with latitude
2. distribution of land and water
3. ocean currents
4. prevailing winds
5. positions of high- and low-pressure areas
6. mountain barriers
7. altitude

We can ascertain the effect these controls have on climate by observing the global patterns of two weather elements—temperature and precipitation.

Global Temperatures   Figure 18.1 shows mean annual temperatures for the world. To eliminate the distorting effect of topography, the temperatures are corrected to sea level.* Notice that in both hemispheres the isotherms are oriented east-west, reflecting the fact that locations at the same latitude receive nearly the same amount of solar energy. In addition, the annual solar heat that each latitude receives decreases from low to high latitude; hence, annual temperatures tend to decrease from equatorial toward polar regions.†

The bending of the isotherms along the coastal margins is due in part to the unequal heating and cooling properties of land and water, and to ocean currents and upwelling. For example, along the west coast of North and South America, ocean currents transport cool water equatorward. In addition to this, the wind in both regions blows toward the equator, parallel to the coast. This situation favors upwelling of cold water (see Chapter 11), which cools the coastal margins. In the area of the eastern North Atlantic Ocean (north of 40°N), the poleward bending of the isotherms is due to the Gulf Stream and the North Atlantic Drift, which carry warm water northward.

The fact that land masses heat up and cool off more quickly than do large bodies of water means that variation in temperature between summer and winter will be far greater over continental interiors than along the west coastal margins of continents. By the same token, the climates of interior continental regions will be more extreme, as they have (on the average) higher summer temperatures and lower winter temperatures than their west-coast counterparts. In fact, west-coast climates are typically quite mild for their latitude.

The highest mean temperatures do not occur in the tropics, but rather in the subtropical deserts of the Northern Hemisphere. Here, the subsiding air associated with the subtropical anticyclones produces generally clear skies and low humidity. In summer, the high sun beating down upon a relatively barren landscape produces scorching heat.

The lowest mean temperatures occur over large land masses at high latitudes. The coldest area of the world is the Antarctic. During part of the year, the sun is below the horizon; when it is above the horizon, it is low in the sky and its rays do not effectively warm the surface. Consequently, the land remains snow- and ice-covered year-round. The snow and ice reflect perhaps 80 percent of the sunlight that reaches the surface. Much of the unreflected solar energy is used to transform the ice and snow into water vapor. The relatively dry air and the Antarctic's high

---

*This correction is made by adding to each station above sea level an amount of temperature that would correspond to the normal (standard) temperature lapse rate of 6.5°C per 1000 m (3.6°F per 1000 ft).

†Average global temperatures for January and July are given in Figs. 3.21 and 3.22, respectively, on p. 71.

elevation permit rapid radiational cooling during the dark winter months, producing extremely cold surface air. The extremely cold Antarctic helps to explain why, overall, the Southern Hemisphere is cooler than the Northern Hemisphere. Other contributing factors for a cooler Southern Hemisphere include the fact that polar regions of the Southern Hemisphere reflect more incoming sunlight, and the fact that less land area is found in tropical and subtropical areas of the Southern Hemisphere.

The Hottest and Coldest Places on Earth   Most people are aware of the extreme heat that exists during the summer in the desert southwest of the United States. But how hot does it get there? On July 10, 1913, Greenland Ranch in Death Valley, California, reported the highest temperature ever observed in North America: 57°C, or 134°F. Here, air temperatures are persistently hot throughout the summer, with the average maximum for July being 47°C (116°F). During the summer of 1917, there was an incredible period of 43 consecutive days when the maximum temperature reached 49°C (120°F) or higher.

Probably the hottest urban area in the United States is Yuma, Arizona. Located along the California–Arizona border, Yuma's high temperature during July averages 42°C (108°F). In 1937, the high reached 38°C (100°F) or more for 101 consecutive days.

In a more humid climate, the maximum temperature rarely climbs above 41°C (106°F). However, during the record heat wave of 1936, the air temperature reached 49°C (121°F) near

Weather Watch

The coldest place on earth. In 1912, during the Antarctic summer, Robert Scott of Great Britain not only lost the race to the South Pole to Norway's Roald Amundsen, but perished in a blizzard trying to return. Temperature data taken by Scott and his crew showed that the winter of 1912 was unusually cold, with air temperatures remaining below −34°C (−30F°) for nearly a month. These exceptionally low temperatures eroded the men's health. They also created an increase in frictional drag on the sleds the men were pulling. Just before Scott's death, he wrote in his journal that "no one in the world would have expected the temperatures and surfaces which we encountered at this time of year."

Alton, Kansas. And during the heat wave of 1983, which destroyed about $7 billion in crops and increased the nation's air-conditioning bill by an estimated $1 billion, Fayetteville reported North Carolina's all-time record high temperature when the mercury hit 43°C (110°F).

These readings, however, do not hold a candle to the hottest place in the world. That distinction probably belongs to Dallol, Ethiopia. Dallol is located south of the Red Sea, near latitude 12°N, in the hot, dry Danakil Depression. A prospecting company kept weather records at Dallol from 1960 to 1966. During

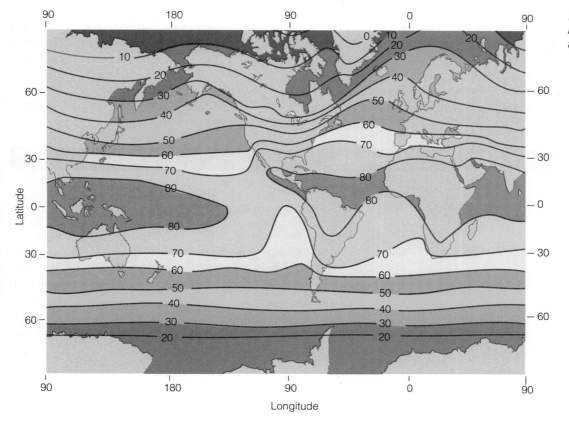

Figure 18.1
Average annual sea-level temperatures throughout the world (°F).

this time, the average daily maximum temperature exceeded 38°C (100°F) every month of the year, except during December and January, when the average maximum lowered to 37°C (98°F) and 36°C (97°F), respectively. On many days, the air temperature exceeded 49°C (120°F). The average annual temperature for the six years at Dallol was 34°C (94°F). In comparison, the average annual temperature in Yuma is 23°C (74°F) and at Death Valley, 24°C (76°F). The highest temperature reading on earth (under standard conditions) occurred about 3500 km northeast of Dallol at El Azizia, Libya (32°N), when, on September 13, 1922, the temperature reached a scorching 58°C (136°F). Table 18.1 gives record high temperatures throughout the world.

One of the coldest spots in the United States is International Falls, Minnesota, where the average temperature for January is −16°C (3°F). Located about 400 km to the south, Minneapolis–St. Paul, with an average temperature of −9°C (16°F) for the three winter months, is the coldest major urban area in the nation. For duration of extreme cold, Minneapolis reported 186 consecutive hours of temperatures below −18°C (0°F) during the winter of 1911–1912. Within the 48 adjacent states, however, the record for the longest duration of severe cold belongs to Langdon, North Dakota, where the thermometer remained below −18°C (0°F) for 41 consecutive days during the winter of 1936. The official record for the lowest temperature in the 48 adjacent states belongs to Rogers Pass, Montana, where on the morning of January 20, 1954, the mercury dropped to −57°C (−70°F). The lowest official temperature for Alaska, −62°C (−80°F), occurred at Prospect Creek on January 23, 1971.

The coldest areas in North America are found in the Yukon and Northwest Territories of Canada. Resolute, Canada (latitude 75°N), has an average temperature of −32°C (−26°F) for the month of January.

The coldest winters in the Northern Hemisphere are found in the interior of Siberia and Greenland. For example, the average January temperature in Yakutsk, Siberia (latitude 62°N), is −43°C (−46°F). There, the mean temperature for the entire year is a bitter cold −11°C (12°F). At Eismitte, Greenland, the average temperature for February (the coldest month) is −47°C (−53°F), with the mean annual temperature being a frigid −30°C (−22°F). Even though these temperatures are extremely low, they do not come close to the coldest area of the world: the Antarctic.

At the geographical South Pole, nearly 2800 m (9200 ft) above sea level, where the Amundsen-Scott scientific station has been keeping records for more than 25 years, the average temperature for the month of July (winter) is −59°C (−74°F) and the mean annual temperature is −49°C (−57°F). The lowest temperature ever recorded there (−83°C, or −117°F) occurred under clear skies with a light wind on the morning of June 23, 1983. Cold as it was, it was not the record low for the world. That belongs to the Russian station at Vostok, Antarctica (latitude 78°S), where the temperature plummeted to −89°C (−129°F) on July 21, 1983. See Table 18.2 for record low temperatures throughout the world.

Global Precipitation   Appendix L, pp. A-18 and A-19, shows the worldwide general pattern of annual precipitation, which varies from place to place. There are, however, certain regions that stand out as being wet or dry. For example, equatorial regions are typically wet, while the subtropics and the polar regions are relatively dry. The global distribution of precipitation is closely tied to the general circulation of the atmosphere (Chapter 11) and to the distribution of mountain ranges and high plateaus.

Figure 18.2 shows in simplified form how the general circulation influences the north-to-south distribution of precipitation to be expected on a uniformly water-covered earth. Precipitation is most abundant where the air rises; least abundant where it sinks. Hence, one expects a great deal of precipitation in the tropics and along the polar front, and little near subtropical highs and at the poles. Let's look at this in more detail.

In tropical regions, the trade winds converge along the Intertropical Convergence Zone (ITCZ), producing rising air, towering clouds, and heavy precipitation all year long. Poleward of

Table 18.1   Some Record High Temperatures Throughout the World

LOCATION (LATITUDE)	RECORD HIGH TEMPERATURE (°C)	RECORD HIGH TEMPERATURE (°F)	RECORD FOR:	DATE
El Azizia, Libya (32°N)	58	136	The world	September 13, 1922
Death Valley, CA (36°N)	57	134	Western Hemisphere	July 10, 1913
Tirat Tsvi, Israel (32°N)	54	129	Middle East	June 21, 1942
Cloncurry, Queensland (21°S)	53	128	Australia	January 16, 1889
Seville, Spain (37°N)	50	122	Europe	August 4, 1881
Rivadavia, Argentina (35°S)	49	120	South America	December 11, 1905
Midale, Saskatchewan (49°N)	45	113	Canada	July 5, 1937
Fort Yukon, Alaska (66°N)	38	100	Alaska	June 27, 1915
Pahala, Hawaii (19°N)	38	100	Hawaii	April 27, 1931
Esperanza, Antarctica (63°S)	14	58	Antarctica	October 20, 1956

the equator, near latitude 30°, the sinking air of the subtropical highs produces a "dry belt" around the globe. The Sahara Desert of North Africa is in this region. Here, annual rainfall is exceedingly light and varies considerably from year to year. Because the major wind belts and pressure systems shift with the season—northward in July and southward in January—the area between the rainy tropics and the dry subtropics is influenced by both the ITCZ and the subtropical highs.

In the cold air of the polar regions there is little moisture, so there is little precipitation. Winter storms drop light, powdery snow that remains on the ground for a long time because of the low evaporation rates. In summer, a ridge of high pressure tends to block storm systems that would otherwise travel into the area; hence, precipitation in polar regions is meager in all seasons.

There are exceptions to this idealized pattern. For example, in middle latitudes the migrating position of the subtropical anticyclones also has an effect on the west-to-east distribution of precipitation. The sinking air associated with these systems is more strongly developed on their eastern side. Hence, the air along the eastern side of an anticyclone tends to be more stable; it is also drier, as cooler air moves equatorward because of the circulating winds around these systems. In addition, along coastlines, cold upwelling water cools the surface air even more, adding to the air's stability. Consequently, in summer, when the Pacific high moves to a position centered off the California coast, a strong, stable subsidence inversion forms above coastal regions. With the strong inversion and the fact that the anticyclone tends to steer storms to the north, central and southern California areas experience little, if any, rainfall during the summer months.

On the western side of subtropical highs, the air is less stable and more moist, as warmer air moves poleward. In summer, over the North Atlantic, the Bermuda high pumps moist tropical air northward from the Gulf of Mexico into the eastern two-thirds of the United States. The humid air is conditionally unstable to begin with, and by the time it moves

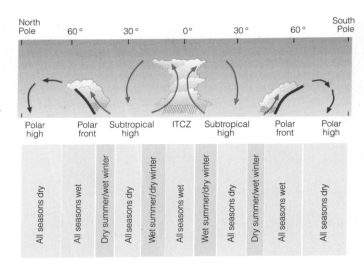

Figure 18.2
A vertical cross section along a line running north to south illustrates the main global regions of rising and sinking air and how each region influences precipitation.

over the heated ground, it becomes even more unstable. If conditions are right, the moist air will rise and condense into cumulus clouds, which may build into towering thunderstorms.

In winter, the subtropical North Pacific high moves south, allowing storms traveling across the ocean to penetrate the western states, bringing much needed rainfall to California after a long, dry summer. The Bermuda high also moves south in winter. Across much of the United States, intense winter storms develop and travel eastward, frequently dumping heavy precipitation as they go. Usually, however, the heaviest precipitation is concentrated in the eastern states, as moisture from the Gulf of Mexico moves northward ahead of these systems. Therefore, cities on the plains typically receive more rainfall in summer and

Table 18.2	Some Record Low Temperatures Throughout the World			

LOCATION (LATITUDE)	RECORD LOW TEMPERATURE (°C)	(°F)	RECORD FOR:	DATE
Vostok, Antarctica (78°S)	−89	−129	The world	July 21, 1983
Verkhoyansk, Russia (67°N)	−68	−90	Northern Hemisphere	February 7, 1892
Northice, Greenland (72°N)	−66	−87	Greenland	January 9, 1954
Snag, Yukon (62°N)	−63	−81	North America	February 3, 1947
Prospect Creek, Alaska (66°N)	−62	−80	Alaska	January 23, 1971
Rogers Pass, Montana (47°N)	−57	−70	United States (excluding Alaska)	January 20, 1954
Sarmiento, Argentina (34°S)	−33	−27	South America	June 1, 1907
Ifrane, Morocco (33°N)	−24	−11	Africa	February 11, 1935
Charlotte Pass, Australia (36°S)	−22	−8	Australia	July 22, 1949
Mt. Haleakala, Hawaii (20°N)	−10	14	Hawaii	January 2, 1961

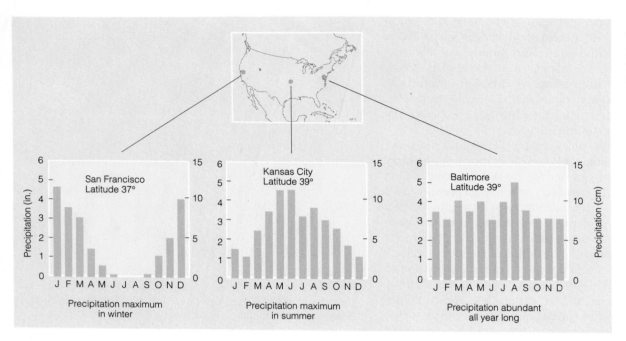

Figure 18.3
Variation in annual precipitation for three Northern Hemisphere cities.

those on the west coast have maximum precipitation in winter, whereas cities in the midwest and east usually have abundant precipitation all year long. The contrast in seasonal precipitation among a west coast city (San Francisco), a central plains city (Kansas City), and an eastern city (Baltimore) is clearly shown in Fig. 18.3.

Mountain ranges disrupt the idealized pattern of global precipitation (1) by promoting convection (because their slopes are warmer than the surrounding air) and (2) by forcing air to rise along their windward slopes *(orographic uplift)*. Consequently, the windward side of mountains tends to be "wet." As air descends and warms along the leeward side, there is less likelihood of clouds and precipitation. Thus, the leeward side of mountains tends to be "dry." As Chapter 7 points out, a region on the leeward side of a mountain where precipitation is noticeably less is called a *rain shadow*.

A good example of the rain shadow effect occurs in the northwestern part of Washington State. Situated on the western side at the base of the Olympic Mountains, the Hoh River Valley annually receives an average 380 cm (150 in.) of precipitation. On the eastern (leeward) side of this range, only about 100 km (62 mi) from the Hoh rain forest, the mean annual precipitation is less than 43 cm (17 in.), and irrigation is necessary to grow certain crops. Figure 18.4 shows a classic example of how topography produces several rain shadow effects. (Additional information on precipitation extremes is given in the Focus section on p. 496.)

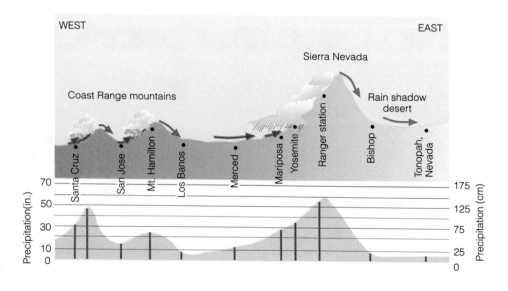

Figure 18.4
The effect of topography on average annual precipitation along a line running from the Pacific Ocean through central California into western Nevada.

Brief Review   Before going on to the section on climate classification, here is a brief review of some of the facts we have covered so far:

- The climate controls are the factors that govern the climate of any given region.

- The hottest places on earth tend to occur in the subtropical deserts of the Northern Hemisphere, where clear skies and sinking air, coupled with low humidity and a high summer sun beating down upon a relatively barren landscape, produce extreme heat.

- The coldest places on earth tend to occur in the interior of high-latitude land masses. The coldest areas of the Northern Hemisphere are found in the interior of Siberia and Greenland, whereas the coldest area of the world is the Antarctic.

- The wettest places in the world tend to be located on the windward side of mountains where warm, humid air rises upslope. On the downwind (leeward) side of a mountain there often exists a "dry" region, known as a *rain shadow*.

Climatic Classification

The climatic controls interact to produce such a wide array of different climates that no two places experience exactly the same climate. However, the similarity of climates within a given area allows us to divide the earth into climatic regions.

The Ancient Greeks   By considering temperature and worldwide sunshine distribution, the ancient Greeks categorized the world into three climatic regions:

1. A low-latitude *tropical* (or *torrid*) *zone;* bounded by the northern and southern limit of the sun's vertical rays ($23\frac{1}{2}°$N and $23\frac{1}{2}°$S); here, the noon sun is always high, day and night are of nearly equal length, and it is warm year-round.
2. A high-latitude *polar* (or *frigid*) *zone;* bounded by the Arctic or Antarctic Circle; cold all year long due to long periods of winter darkness and a low summer sun.
3. A middle-latitude *temperate zone;* sandwiched between the other two zones; has distinct summer and winter, so exhibits characteristics of both extremes.

Such a sunlight, or temperature-based, climatic scheme is, of course, far too simplistic. It excludes precipitation, so there is no way to differentiate between wet and dry regions. The best classification of climates would take into account as many meteorological factors as can possibly be obtained.

The Köppen System   A widely used classification of world climates based on the annual and monthly averages of temperature and precipitation was devised by the famous German scientist Waldimir Köppen (1846–1940). Initially published in 1918, the original **Köppen classification system** has since been modified and refined. Faced with the lack of adequate observing

Weather Watch

Wynoochee Oxbow, Washington, on the Olympic Peninsula, is considered the wettest weather station in the continental United States, with an average rainfall of 366 cm (144 in.)—a total 86 times greater than the average 4.3 cm (1.7 in.) for Death Valley, California.

stations throughout the world, Köppen related the distribution and type of native vegetation to the various climates. In this way, climatic boundaries could be approximated where no climatological data were available.

Köppen's scheme employs five major climatic types; each type is designated by a capital letter:

A   *Tropical moist climates:* All months have an average temperature above 18°C (64°F). Since all months are warm, there is no real winter season.

B   *Dry climates:* Deficient precipitation most of the year. Potential evaporation and transpiration exceed precipitation.

C   *Moist mid-latitude climates with mild winters:* Warm-to-hot summers with mild winters. The average temperature of the coldest month is below 18°C (64°F) and above −3°C (27°F).

D   *Moist mid-latitude climates with severe winters:* Warm summers and cold winters. The average temperature of the warmest month exceeds 10°C (50°F), and the coldest monthly average drops below −3°C (27°F).

E   *Polar climates:* Extremely cold winters and summers. The average temperature of the warmest month is below 10°C (50°F). Since all months are cold, there is no real summer season.

Each group contains subregions that describe special regional characteristics, such as seasonal changes in temperature and precipitation. In mountainous country, where rapid changes in elevation bring about sharp changes in climatic type, delineating the climatic regions is impossible. These regions are designated by the letter H, for highland climates. (Köppen's climate classification system, including the criteria for the various subdivisions, is given in Appendix K on p. A-17.)

Köppen's system has been criticized primarily because his boundaries (which relate vegetation to monthly temperature and precipitation values) do not correspond to the natural boundaries of each climatic zone. In addition, the Köppen system implies that there is a sharp boundary between climatic zones, when in reality there is a gradual transition.

The Köppen system has been revised several times, most notably by the German climatologist Rudolf Geiger, who worked with Köppen on amending the climatic boundaries of certain regions. A popular modification of the Köppen system was developed by the American climatologist Glenn T. Trewartha, who redefined some of the climatic types and altered the climatic

Focus on A SPECIAL TOPIC

Precipitation Extremes

Most of the "rainiest" places in the world are located on the windward side of mountains. For example, Mount Waialeale on the island of Kauai, Hawaii, has the greatest annual average rainfall on record: 1168 cm (460 in.). Cherrapunji, on the crest of the southern slopes of the Khasi Hills in northeastern India, receives an average of 1080 cm (425 in.) of rainfall each year, the majority of which falls during the summer monsoon, between April and October. Cherrapunji, which holds the greatest twelve-month rainfall total of 2647 cm (1042 in.), once received 380 cm (150 in.) of rain in just five days.

Record rainfall amounts are often associated with tropical storms. On the island of La Réunion (about 650 km east of Madagascar in the Indian Ocean), a tropical cyclone dumped 135 cm (53 in.) of rain on Belouve in twelve hours. Heavy rains of short duration often occur with severe thunderstorms that move slowly or stall over a region. On July 4, 1956, 3 cm (1.2 in.) of rain fell from a thunderstorm on Unionville, Maryland, in one minute.

Snowfalls tend to be heavier where cool, moist air rises along the windward slopes of mountains. One of the snowiest places in North America is located at the Paradise Ranger Station in Mt. Rainier National Park, Washington. Situated at an elevation of 1646 m (5400 ft) above sea level, this station receives an average 1575 cm (620 in.) of snow annually. However, a record annual snowfall amount of 2896 cm (1140 in.) was recorded at Mt. Baker ski area during the winter of 1998–1999.

As we noted earlier, the driest regions of the world lie in the frigid polar region, the leeward side of mountains, and in the belt of subtropical high pressure, between 15° and 30° latitude. Arica in northern Chile holds the world record for lowest annual rainfall, 0.08 cm (0.03 in.). In the United States, Death Valley, California, averages only 4.5 cm (1.78 in.) of precipitation annually. Figure 1 gives additional information on world precipitation records.

KEY TO MAP

❶	World's greatest annual average rainfall	1168 cm (460 in.)	Mt. Waialeale, Hawaii
❷	Greatest 1-month rainfall total	930 cm (366 in.)	Cherrapunji, India, July, 1861
❸	Greatest 12-hour rainfall total	135 cm (53 in.)	Belouve, La Réunion Island, February 28, 1964
❹	Greatest 24-hour rainfall total in United States	109 cm (43 in.)	Alvin, Texas, July 25, 1979
❺	Greatest 42-minute rainfall total	30 cm (12 in.)	Holt, Missouri, June 22, 1947
❻	Greatest 1-minute rainfall total in United States	3 cm (1.2 in.)	Unionville, MD, July 4, 1956
❼	Lowest annual average rainfall in Northern Hemisphere	3 cm (1.2 in.)	Bataques, Mexico
❽	Lowest annual average rainfall in the world	0.08 cm (0.03 in.)	Arica, Chile
❾	Greatest annual snowfall in United States	2896 cm (1140 in.)	Mt. Baker ski area, WA, 1998
❿	Greatest snowfall in 1 month	991 cm (390 in.)	Tamarack, CA, January, 1911
⓫	Greatest snowfall in 24 hours	193 cm (76 in.)	Silverlake, Boulder, CO April 14–15, 1921
⓬	Longest period without measurable precipitation in U.S. (993 days)	0.0 cm (0.0 in.)	Bagdad, CA August 1909 to May 1912

world map by putting more emphasis on the lengths of growing seasons and average summer temperatures.

Thornthwaite's System   To correct some of the Köppen deficiencies, the American climatologist C. Warren Thornthwaite (1899–1963) devised a new classification system in the early 1930s. Both systems utilized temperature and precipitation measurements and both related natural vegetation to climate. However, to emphasize the importance of precipitation (P) and evaporation (E) on plant growth, Thornthwaite developed a *P/E ratio,* which is essentially monthly precipitation divided by monthly evaporation. The annual sum of the P/E ratios gives the **P/E index.** Using this index, the Thornthwaite system defines five major humidity provinces and their characteristic vegetations: rain forest, forest, grassland, steppe, and desert.

To better describe the moisture available for plant growth, Thornthwaite proposed a new classification system in 1948 and slightly revised it in 1955. His new scheme emphasized the con-

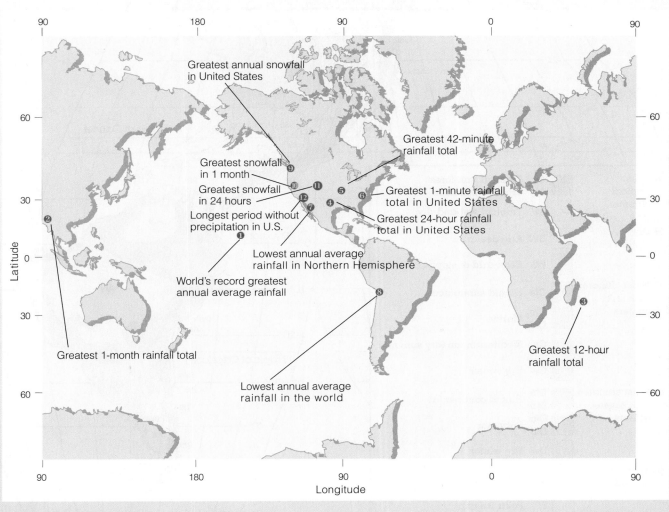

Figure 1
Some precipitation records throughout the world.

cept of *potential evapotranspiration** (PE), which is the amount of moisture that would be lost from the soil and vegetation if the moisture were available.

Thornthwaite incorporated potential evapotranspiration into a moisture index that depends essentially on the differences between precipitation and PE. The index is high in moist climates and negative in arid climates. An index of 0 marks the boundary between wet and dry climates.

The Global Pattern of Climate

Figure 18.5 (pp. 498–499) displays how the major climatic regions of the world are distributed, based mainly on the work of Köppen. (The major climatic types along with their subdivisions are given in Appendix K, p. A-17.) We will first examine humid

*Evapotranspiration refers to the evaporation from soil and transpiration of plants.

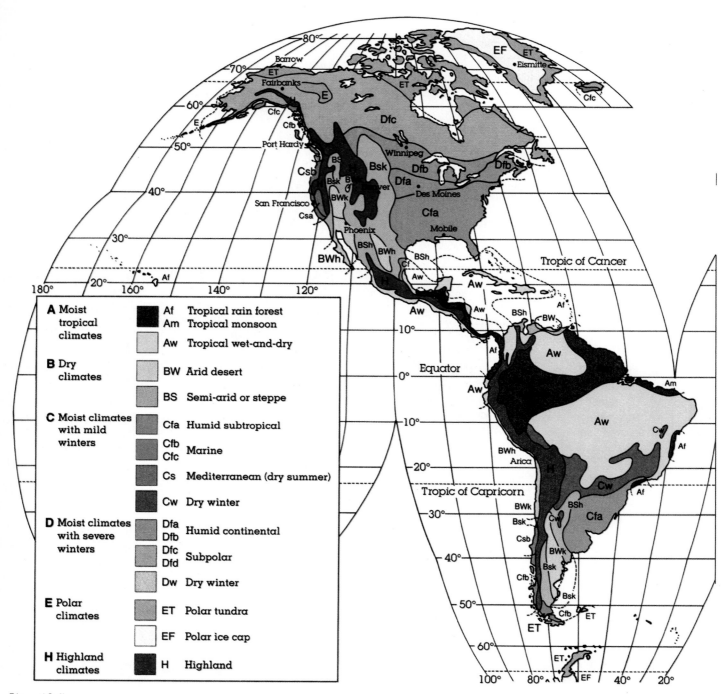

Figure 18.5
Worldwide distribution of climatic regions (after Köppen).

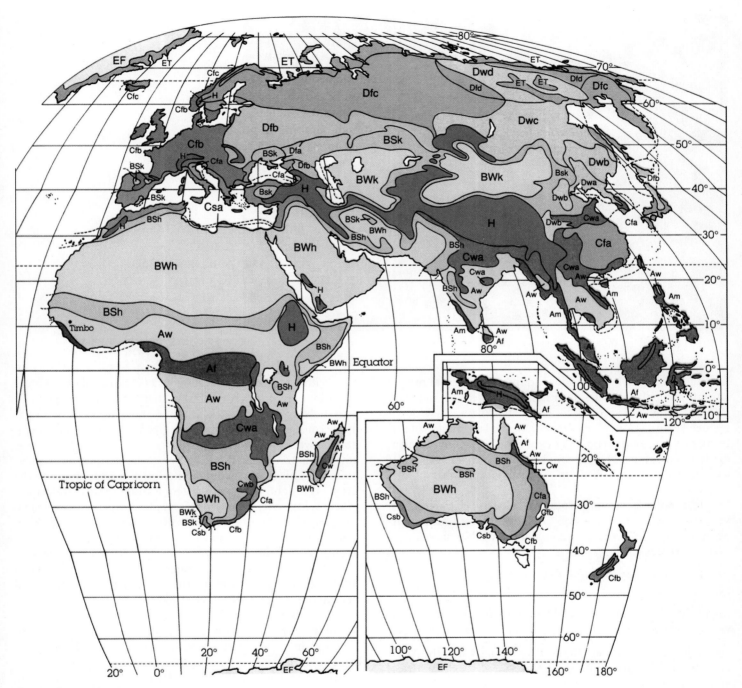

Figure 18.5, continued

Figure 18.6
Tropical rain forest near Iquitos, Peru. (Climatic information for this region is presented in Fig. 18.7.)

tropical climates in low latitudes and then we'll look at middle latitude and polar climates. Bear in mind that each climatic region has many subregions of local climatic differences wrought by such factors as topography, elevation, and large bodies of water. Remember, too, that boundaries of climatic regions represent gradual transitions. Thus, the major climatic characteristics of a given region are best observed away from its periphery.

Tropical Moist Climates (Group A)

General characteristics: year-round warm temperatures (all months have a mean temperature above 18°C, or 64°F); abundant rainfall (typical annual average exceeds 150 cm, or 59 in.).

Extent: northward and southward from the equator to about latitude 15° to 25°.

Major types (based on seasonal distribution of rainfall): *tropical wet* (Af), *tropical monsoon* (Am), and *tropical wet and dry* (Aw).

At low elevations near the equator, in particular the Amazon lowland of South America, the Congo River Basin of Africa, and the East Indies from Sumatra to New Guinea, high temperatures and abundant yearly rainfall combine to produce a dense, broadleaf, evergreen forest called a **tropical rain forest.** Here, many different plant species, each adapted to differing light intensity, present a crudely layered appearance of diverse vegetation. In the forest, little sunlight is able to penetrate to the ground through the thick crown cover. As a result, little plant growth is found on the forest floor. However, at the edge of the forest, or where a clearing has been made, abundant sunlight allows for the growth of tangled shrubs and vines, producing an almost impenetrable *jungle* (see Fig. 18.6).

Within the **tropical wet climate*** (Af), seasonal temperature variations are small (normally less than 3°C) because the noon sun is always high and the number of daylight hours is relatively constant. However, there is a greater variation in temperature between day (average high about 32°C) and night (average low about 22°C) than there is between the warmest and coolest months. This is why people remark that winter comes to the tropics at night. The weather here is monotonous and sultry. There is little change in temperature from one day to the next. Furthermore, almost every day, towering cumulus clouds form and produce heavy, localized showers by early afternoon. As evening approaches, the showers usually end and skies clear. Typical annual rainfall totals are greater than 150 cm (59 in.) and, in some cases, especially along the windward side of hills and mountains, the total may exceed 400 cm (157 in.).

The high humidity and cloud cover tend to keep maximum temperatures from reaching extremely high values. In fact, summer afternoon temperatures are normally higher in middle latitudes than here. Nighttime cooling can produce saturation and, hence, a blanket of dew and—occasionally—fog covers the ground.

An example of a station with a tropical wet climate (Af) is Iquitos, Peru (see Fig. 18.7). Located near the equator (latitude 4°S), in the low basin of the upper Amazon River, Iquitos has an average annual temperature of 25°C (77°F), with an annual temperature range of only 2.2°C (4°F). Notice also that the monthly rainfall totals vary more than do the monthly temperatures. This is due primarily to the migrating position of the

---

*The tropical wet climate is also known as the *tropical rain forest climate*.

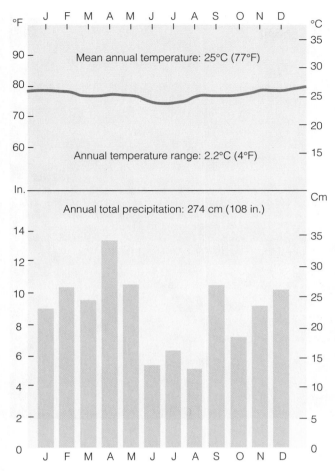

Figure 18.7
Temperature and precipitation data for Iquitos, Peru, latitude 4°S. A station with a tropical wet climate (Af). (This type of diagram is called a *climograph*. It shows monthly mean temperatures with a solid red line and monthly mean precipitation with bar graphs.)

Intertropical Convergence Zone (ITCZ) and its associated wind-flow patterns. Although monthly precipitation totals vary considerably, the average for each month exceeds 6 cm, and consequently no month is considered deficient of rainfall.

Take a minute and look back at Fig. 18.6. From the photo, one might think that the soil beneath the forest's canopy would be excellent for agriculture. Actually, this is not true. As heavy rain falls on the soil, the water works its way downward, removing nutrients in a process called *leaching*. Strangely enough, many of the nutrients needed to sustain the lush forest actually come from dead trees that decompose. The roots of the living trees absorb this matter before the rains leach it away. When the forests are cleared for agricultural purposes, or for the timber, what is left is a thick red soil called **laterite.** When exposed to the intense sunlight of the tropics, the soil may harden into a bricklike consistency, making cultivation almost impossible.

Köppen classified tropical wet regions, where the monthly precipitation totals drop below 6 cm for perhaps one or two months, as **tropical monsoon climates** (Am). Here, yearly rainfall totals are similar to those of the tropical wet climate, usually exceeding 150 cm a year. Because the dry season is brief and copious rains fall throughout the rest of the year, there is sufficient soil moisture to maintain the tropical rain forest through the short dry period. Tropical monsoon climates can be seen in Fig. 18.5 along the coasts of Southeast Asia, India, and in northeastern South America.

Poleward of the tropical wet region, total annual rainfall diminishes, and there is a gradual transition from the tropical wet climate to the **tropical wet-and-dry climate** (Aw), where a distinct dry season prevails. Even though the annual precipitation usually exceeds 100 cm, the dry season, where the monthly rainfall is less than 6 cm (2.4 in.), lasts for more than two months. Because tropical rain forests cannot survive this "drought," the jungle gradually gives way to tall, coarse **savanna grass,** scattered with low, drought-resistant deciduous trees (see Fig. 18.8). The dry season occurs during the winter (low sun period), when the region is under the influence of the subtropical highs. In summer, the ITCZ moves poleward, bringing with it heavy precipitation, usually in the form of showers. Rainfall is enhanced by slow moving shallow lows that move through the region.

Tropical wet-and-dry climates not only receive less total rainfall than the tropical wet climates, but the rain that does occur is much less reliable, as the total rainfall often fluctuates widely from one year to the next. In the course of a single year, for example, destructive floods may be followed by serious droughts. As with tropical wet regions, the daily range of temperature usually exceeds the annual range, but the climate here is much less monotonous. There is a cool season in winter when the maximum temperature averages 30°C to 32°C (86°F to 90°F). At night, the low humidity and clear skies allow for rapid radiational cooling and, by early morning, minimum temperatures drop to 20°C (68°F) or below.

From Fig. 18.5, pp. 498–499, we can see that the principal areas having a tropical wet-and-dry climate (Aw) are those located in western Central America, in the region both north and south of the Amazon Basin (South America), in southcentral and eastern Africa, in parts of India and Southeast Asia, and in northern Australia. In many areas (especially within India and Southeast Asia), the marked variation in precipitation is associated with the *monsoon*—the seasonal reversal of winds.

As we saw in Chapter 10, the monsoon circulation is due in part to differential heating between land masses and oceans. During winter in the Northern Hemisphere, winds blow outward, away from a cold, shallow high-pressure area centered over continental Siberia. These downslope, relatively dry northeasterly winds from the interior provide India and Southeast Asia with generally fair weather and the dry season. In summer, the wind-flow pattern reverses as air flows into a developing thermal low over the continental interior. The humid air from the water rises and condenses, resulting in heavy rain and the wet season.

Figure 18.8
Acacia trees illustrate typical trees of the East African grassland savanna, a region with a tropical wet-and-dry climate (Aw).

An example of a station with a tropical wet-and-dry climate (Aw) is given in Fig. 18.9. Located at latitude 11°N in west Africa, Timbo, Guinea, receives an annual average 163 cm (64 in.) of rainfall. Notice that the rainy season is during the summer when the ITCZ has migrated to its most northern position. Note also that practically no rain falls during the months of December, January, and February, when the region comes under the domination of the subtropical high-pressure area and its sinking air.

The monthly temperature patterns at Timbo are characteristic of most tropical wet-and-dry climates. As spring approaches, the noon sun is slightly higher, and the more intense sunshine produces greater surface heating and higher afternoon temperatures—usually above 32°C (90°F) and occasionally above 38°C (100°F)—creating hot, dry desertlike conditions. After this brief hot season, a persistent cloud cover and the evaporation of rain tends to lower the temperature during the summer. The warm, muggy weather of summer often resembles that of the tropical wet climate (Af). The rainy summer is followed by a warm, relatively dry period, with afternoon temperatures usually climbing above 30°C (86°F).

Poleward of the tropical wet-and-dry climate, the dry season becomes more severe. Clumps of trees are more isolated and

the grasses dominate the landscape. When the potential annual water loss through evaporation and transpiration exceeds the annual water gain from precipitation, the climate is described as dry.

Dry Climates (Group B) *General characteristics:* deficient precipitation most of the year; potential evaporation and transpiration exceed precipitation.

Extent: the subtropical deserts extend from roughly 20° to 30° latitude in large continental regions of the middle latitudes, often surrounded by mountains.

Major types: arid (BW)—the "true desert"—and semi-arid (BS).

A quick glance at Fig. 18.5, pp. 498–499, reveals that, according to Köppen, the dry regions of the world occupy more land area (about 26 percent) than any other major climatic type. Within these dry regions, a deficiency of water exists. Here, the potential annual loss of water through evaporation is greater than the annual water gained through precipitation. Thus, classifying a climate as dry depends not only on precipitation totals but also on temperature, which greatly influences evaporation. For example,

35 cm (14 in.) of precipitation in a hot climate will support only sparse vegetation, while the same amount of precipitation in northcentral Canada will support a conifer forest. In addition, a region with a low annual rainfall total is more likely to be classified as dry if the majority of precipitation is concentrated during the warm summer months, when evaporation rates are greater.

Precipitation in a dry climate is both meager and irregular. Typically, the lower the average annual rainfall, the greater its variability. For example, a station that reports an annual rainfall of 5 cm (2 in.) may actually measure no rainfall for two years; then, in a single downpour, it may receive 10 cm (4 in.).

The major dry regions of the world can be divided into two primary categories. The first includes the area of the subtropics (between latitude 15° and 30°), where the sinking air of the subtropical anticyclones produces generally clear skies. The second is found in the continental areas of the middle latitudes. Here, far removed from a source of moisture, areas are deprived of precipitation. Dryness here is often accentuated by mountain ranges that produce a rain shadow effect.

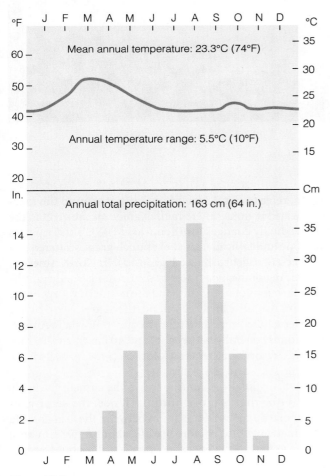

Figure 18.9
Climatic data for Timbo, Guinea, latitude 11°N. A station with a tropical wet-and-dry climate (Aw).

Köppen divided dry climates into two types based on their degree of dryness: the *arid* (BW)* and the *semi-arid,* or steppe (BS). These two climatic types can be divided even further. For example, if the climate is hot and dry with a mean annual temperature above 18°C (64°F), it is either BWh or BSh (the *h* is for *heiss,* meaning "hot" in German). On the other hand, if the climate is cold (in winter, that is) and dry with a mean annual temperature below 18°C, then it is either BWk or BSk (where the *k* is for *kalt,* meaning "cold" in German).

The **arid climates** (BW) occupy about 12 percent of the world's land area. From Fig. 18.5, pp. 498–499, we can see that this climatic type is found along the west coast of South America and Africa and over much of the interior of Australia. Notice, also, that a swath of arid climate extends from northwest Africa all the way into central Asia. In North America, the arid climate extends from northern Mexico into the southern interior of the United States and northward along the leeward slopes of the Sierra Nevada. This region includes both the Sonoran and Mojave deserts and the Great Basin.

The southern desert region of North America is dry because it is dominated by the subtropical high most of the year, and winter storm systems tend to weaken before they move into the area. The northern region is in the rain shadow of the Sierra Nevada. These regions are deficient in precipitation all year long, with many stations receiving less than 13 cm (5 in.) annually. As noted earlier, the rain that does fall is spotty, often in the form of scattered summer afternoon showers. Some of these showers can be downpours that change a gentle gully into a raging torrent of water. More often than not, however, the rain evaporates into the dry air before ever reaching the ground, and the result is rain-streamers (virga) dangling beneath the clouds (see Fig. 18.10).

Contrary to popular belief, few deserts are completely without vegetation. Although meager, the vegetation that does exist must depend on the infrequent rains. Thus, most of the native plants are **xerophytes**—those capable of surviving prolonged periods of drought (see Fig. 18.11). Such vegetation includes various forms of cacti and short-lived plants that spring up during the rainy periods.

In low-latitude deserts (BWh), intense sunlight produces scorching heat on the parched landscape. Here, air temperatures are as high as anywhere in the world. Maximum daytime readings during the summer can exceed 50°C (122°F), although 40°C to 45°C (104°F to 113°F) are more common. In the middle of the day, the relative humidity is usually between 5 and 25 percent. At night, the air's relatively low water vapor content allows for rapid radiational cooling. Minimum temperatures often drop below 25°C (77°F). Thus, arid climates have large daily temperature ranges, often between 15°C and 25°C (27°F and 45°F) and occasionally higher.

During the winter, temperatures are more moderate, and minimums may, on occasion, drop below freezing. The variation

---

*The letter *W* is for *Wüste,* the German word for "desert."

Figure 18.10
Rain streamers (virga) are common in dry climates, as falling rain evaporates into the drier air before ever reaching the ground.

in temperature from summer to winter produces large annual temperature ranges. We can see this in the climate record for Phoenix, Arizona (see Fig. 18.12), a city in the southwestern United States with a BWh climate. Notice that the average annual temperature in Phoenix is 22°C (72°F), and that the average temperature of the warmest month (July) reaches a sizzling 32°C (90°F). As we would expect, rainfall is meager in all months. There is, however, a slight maximum in July and August. This is due to the summer monsoon, when more humid, southerly winds are likely to sweep over the region and develop into afternoon showers and thunderstorms (see Fig. 10.26, p. 270).

In middle-latitude deserts (BWk), average annual temperatures are lower. Summers are typically warm to hot, with afternoon temperatures frequently reaching 40°C (104°F). Winters are usually extremely cold, with minimum temperatures sometimes dropping below −35°C (−31°F). Many of these deserts lie in the rainshadow of an extensive mountain chain, such as the Sierra Nevada and the Cascade mountains in North America, the Himalayan Mountains in Asia, and the Andes in South America. The meager precipitation that falls comes from an occasional summer shower or a passing mid-latitude cyclone in winter.

Again, refer to Fig. 18.5 and notice that around the margins of the arid regions, where rainfall amounts are greater, the climate gradually changes into **semi-arid** (BS). This region is called **steppe** and typically has short bunch grass, scattered low bushes, trees, or sagebrush (see Fig. 18.13). In North America, this climatic region includes most of the Great Plains, the southern coastal sections of California, and the northern valleys of the Great Basin. As in the arid region, northern areas experience lower winter temperatures and more frequent snowfalls. Annual precipitation is generally between 20 and 40 cm (8 and 16 in.). The climatic record for Denver, Colorado (see Fig. 18.14), exemplifies the semi-arid (BSk) climate.

As average rainfall amounts increase, the climate gradually changes to one that is more humid. Hence, the semi-arid (steppe) climate marks the transition between the arid and the humid climatic regions. (Before reading about moist climates, you may wish to read the Focus section on p. 507 about deserts that experience drizzle but little rainfall.)

Moist Subtropical Mid-Latitude Climates (Group C) *General characteristics:* humid with mild winters (i.e., average temperature of the coldest month below 18°C, or 64°F, and above −3°C, or 27°F).

Extent: on the eastern and western regions of most continents, from about 25° to 40° latitude.

Major types: humid subtropical (Cfa), marine (Cfb), and dry-summer subtropical, or Mediterranean (Cs).

The Group C climates of the middle latitudes have distinct summer and winter seasons. Additionally, they have ample precipitation to keep them from being classified as dry. Although winters can be cold, and air temperatures can change appreciably from one day to the next, no month has a mean temperature below −3°C (27°F), for if it did, it would be classified as a D climate—one with severe winters.

The first C climate we will consider is the **humid subtropical climate** (Cfa). Notice in Fig. 18.5, pp. 498–499, that Cfa cli-

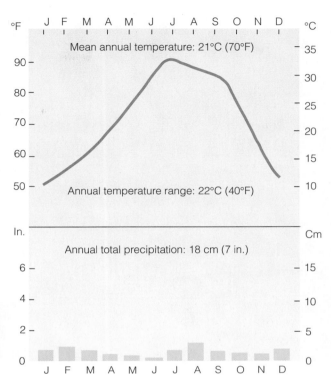

Figure 18.12
Climatic data for Phoenix, Arizona, latitude 33.5°N. A station with an arid climate (BWh).

Figure 18.11
Creosote bushes and cactus are typical of the vegetation found in the arid southwestern American deserts (BWh).

mates are found principally along the east coasts of continents, roughly between 25° and 40° latitude. They dominate the southeastern section of the United States, as well as eastern China and southern Japan. In the Southern Hemisphere, they are found in southeastern South America and along the southeastern coasts of Africa and Australia.

A trademark of the humid subtropical climate is its hot, muggy summers. This sultry summer weather occurs because Cfa climates are located on the western side of subtropical highs, where maritime tropical air from lower latitudes is swept poleward into these regions. Generally, summer dew-point temperatures are high (often exceeding 23°C, or 73°F) and so is the relative humidity, even during the middle of the day. The high humidity combines with the high air temperature (usually above 32°C, or 90°F) to produce more oppressive conditions than are found in equatorial regions. Summer morning low temperatures often range between 21°C and 27°C (70°F and 81°F). Occasionally, a weak summer cool front will bring temporary relief from the sweltering conditions. However, devastating heat waves, sometimes lasting many weeks, can occur when an upper-level ridge moves over the area.

Winters tend to be relatively mild, especially in the lower latitudes, where air temperatures rarely dip much below freezing. Poleward regions experience winters that are colder and harsher. Here, frost, snow, and ice storms are more common, but heavy snowfalls are rare. Winter weather can be quite

Figure 18.13
Cumulus clouds forming over the steppe grasslands of western North America, a region with a semi-arid climate (BS).

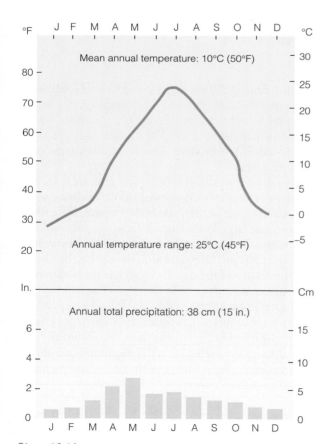

Figure 18.14
Climatic data for Denver, Colorado, latitude 40°N. A station with a semi-arid climate (BSk).

changeable, as almost summerlike conditions can give way to cold rain and wind in a matter of hours when a middle-latitude storm and its accompanying fronts pass through the region.

Humid subtropical climates experience adequate and fairly well-distributed precipitation throughout the year, with typical annual averages between 80 and 165 cm (31 and 65 in.). In summer, when thunderstorms are common, much of the precipitation falls as afternoon showers. Tropical storms entering the United States and China can substantially add to their summer and autumn rainfall totals. Winter precipitation most often occurs with eastward-trekking middle-latitude storms. In the southeastern United States, the abundant rainfall supports a thick pine forest that becomes mixed with oak at higher latitudes. The climate data for Mobile, Alabama, a city with a Cfa climate, is given in Fig. 18.15.

Glance back at Fig. 18.5, pp. 498–499, and observe that C climates extend poleward along the western side of most continents from about latitude 40° to 60°. These regions are dominated by prevailing winds from the ocean that moderate the climate, keeping winters considerably milder than stations located at the same latitude farther inland. In addition to this, summers are quite cool. When the summer season is both short and cool, the climate is designated as Cfc.* Equatorward, where summers are longer (but still cool), the climate is classified as *west coast marine,* or simply **marine,** Cfb.

Where mountains parallel the coastline, such as along the west coasts of North and South America, the marine influence is restricted to narrow belts. Unobstructed by high mountains, pre-

*Appendix K, p. A-17, details the necessary criteria for each climatic type.

Focus on A SPECIAL TOPIC

A Desert with Clouds and Drizzle

We already know that not all deserts are hot. By the same token, not all deserts are sunny. In fact, some coastal deserts experience considerable cloudiness, especially low stratus and fog.

Amazingly, these coastal deserts are some of the driest places on earth. They include the Atacama Desert of Chile and Peru, the coastal Sahara Desert of northwest Africa, the Namib Desert of southwestern Africa, and a portion of the Sonoran Desert in Baja, California (see Fig. 2). On the Atacama Desert, for example, some regions go without measurable rainfall for decades. And Arica, in northern Chile, has an annual rainfall of only 0.08 cm (0.03 in.).

The cause of this aridity is, in part, due to the fact that each region is adjacent to a large body of relatively cool water. Notice in Fig. 2 that these deserts are located along the western coastal margins of continents, where a subtropical high-pressure area causes prevailing winds to move cool water from higher latitudes along the coast. In addition, these winds help to accentuate the water's coldness by initiating *upwelling*—the rising of cold water from lower levels. The combination of these conditions tends to produce coastal water temperatures between 10°C and 15°C (50°F and 59°F), which is quite cool for such low latitudes. As surface air sweeps across the cold water, it is chilled to its dew point, often

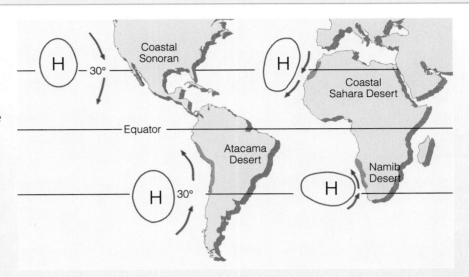

Figure 2
Location of coastal deserts that experience frequent fog, drizzle, and low clouds.

producing a blanket of fog and low clouds, from which drizzle falls. The drizzle, however, accounts for very little rainfall. In most regions, it is only enough to dampen the streets with a mere trace of precipitation.

As the cool stable air moves inland, it warms, and the water droplets evaporate. Hence, most of the cloudiness and drizzle is found along the immediate coast. Although the relative humidity of this air is high, the dewpoint temperature is comparatively low (often near that of the coastal surface water). Inland, further warming causes the air to rise. However, a stable subsidence inversion, associated

with the subtropical highs, inhibits vertical motions by capping the rising air, causing it to drift back toward the ocean, where it sinks, completing a rather strong sea breeze circulation. The position of the subtropical highs, which tend to remain almost stationary, plays an additional role by preventing the Intertropical Convergence Zone with its rising, unstable air from entering the region.

And so we have a desert with clouds and drizzle—a desert that owes its existence, in part, to its proximity to rather cold ocean water and, in part, to the position and air motions of the subtropical high.

vailing westerly winds pump ocean air over much of western Europe and thus provide this region with a marine climate (Cfb).

During much of the year, marine climates are characterized by low clouds, fog, and drizzle. The ocean's influence produces adequate precipitation in all months, with much of it falling as light or moderate rain associated with maritime polar air masses. Snow does fall, but frequently it turns to slush after only a day or so. In some locations, topography greatly enhances precipitation totals. For example, along the west coast of North America, coastal mountains not only force air upward enhanc-

Weather Watch

Which city experiences colder winters—Bergen, Norway, near the Arctic Circle, or Philadelphia, Pennsylvania, with a humid subtropical climate near latitude 40°N? Actually, the warm water of the Gulf Stream helps Bergen maintain a marine climate and an average winter temperature about 0.6°C (about 1°F) higher than the average winter temperature in Philadelphia.

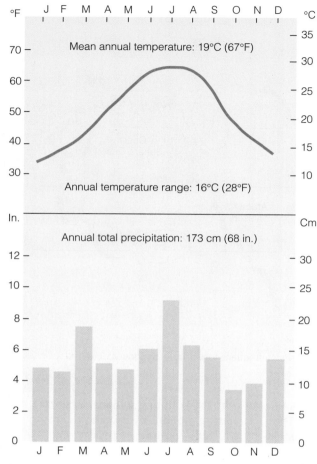

Figure 18.15
Climatic data for Mobile, Alabama, latitude 30°N. A station with a humid subtropical climate (Cfa).

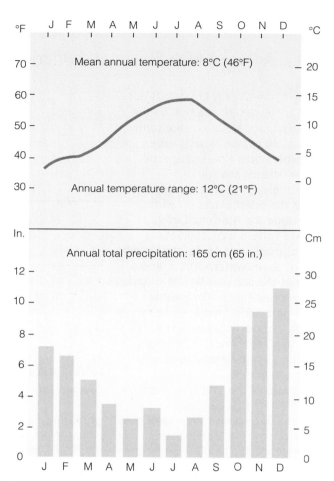

Figure 18.16
Climatic data for Port Hardy, Canada, latitude 51°N. A station with a marine climate (Cfb).

ing precipitation, they also slow the storm's eastward progress, which enables the storm to drop more precipitation on the area.

Along the northwest coast of North America, rainfall amounts decrease in summer. This phenomenon is caused by the northward migration of the subtropical Pacific high, which is located southwest of this region. The summer decrease in rainfall can be seen by examining the climatic record of Port Hardy (see Fig. 18.16), a station situated along the coast of Canada's Vancouver Island. The data illustrate another important characteristic of marine climates: the low annual temperature range for such a high-latitude station. The ocean's influence keeps daily temperature ranges low as well. In this climate type, it rains on many days and when it is not raining, skies are usually overcast. The heavy rains produce a dense forest of Douglas fir.

Moving equatorward of marine climates, the influence of the subtropical highs becomes greater, and the summer dry period more pronounced. Gradually, the climate changes from marine to one of **dry-summer subtropical** (Cs), or **Mediterranean,** because it also borders the coastal areas of the Mediterranean Sea. Along

the west coast of North America, Portland, Oregon, because it has rather dry summers, marks the transition between the marine climate and the dry-summer subtropical climate to the south.

The extreme summer aridity of the Mediterranean climate, which in California may exist for five months, is caused by the sinking air of the subtropical highs. In addition, these anticyclones divert summer storm systems poleward. During the winter, when the subtropical highs move equatorward, mid-latitude storms from the ocean frequent the region, bringing with them much needed rainfall. Consequently, Mediterranean climates are characterized by mild, wet winters, and mild-to-hot, dry summers.

Where surface winds parallel the coast, upwelling of cold water helps keep the water itself and the air above it cool all summer long. In these coastal areas, which are often shrouded in low clouds and fog, the climate is called *coastal Mediterranean* (Csb). Here, summer daytime maximum temperatures usually reach about 21°C (70°F), while overnight lows often drop below 15°C (59°F). Inland, away from the ocean's influence, summers are hot and winters are a little cooler than coastal areas. In this

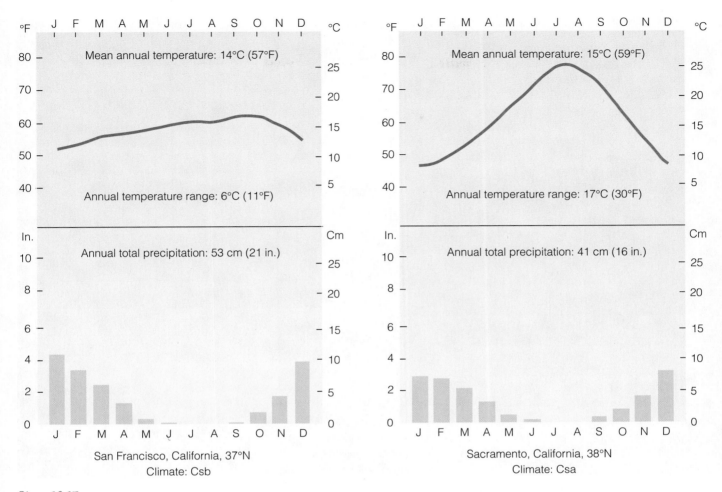

Figure 18.17
Comparison of a coastal Mediterranean climate, Csb (San Francisco, at left), with an interior
Mediterranean climate, Csa (Sacramento, at right).

interior Mediterranean climate (Csa), summer afternoon temperatures usually climb above 34°C (93°F) and occasionally above 40°C (104°F).

Figure 18.17 contrasts the coastal Mediterranean climate of San Francisco, California, with the interior Mediterranean climate of Sacramento, California. While Sacramento is only 130 km (80 mi) inland from San Francisco, Sacramento's average July temperature is 9°C (16°F) higher. As we would expect, Sacramento's annual temperature range is considerably higher, too. Although Sacramento and San Francisco both experience an occasional frost, snow in these areas is a rarity.

In Mediterranean climates, yearly precipitation amounts range between 30 and 90 cm (12 and 35 in.). However, much more precipitation falls on surrounding hillsides and mountains. Because of the summer dryness, the land supports only a scrubby type of low-growing woody plants and trees called *chaparral* (see Fig. 18.18).

At this point, we should note that summers are not as dry along the Mediterranean Sea as they are along the west coast of North America. Moreover, coastal Mediterranean areas are also warmer, due to the lack of upwelling in the Mediterranean Sea.

Before leaving our discussion of C climates, note that when the dry season is in winter, the climate is classified as Cw. Over northern India and portions of China, the relatively dry winters are the result of northerly winds from continental regions circulating southward around the cold Siberian high. Many lower-latitude regions with a Cw climate would be tropical if it were not for the fact they are too high in elevation and, consequently, too cool to be designated as tropical.

Moist Continental Climates (Group D)   *General characteristics:* warm-to-cool summers and cold winters (i.e., average temperature of warmest month exceeds 10°C, or 50°F, and the coldest monthly average drops below −3°C, or 27°F); winters are severe with snowstorms, blustery winds, bitter cold; climate controlled by large continent.

Extent: north of moist subtropical mid-latitude climates.

Figure 18.18
In the Mediterranean-type climates of North America, typical chaparral vegetation includes chamise, manzanita, and foothill pine.

Major types: humid continental with hot summers (Dfa), humid continental with cool summers (Dfb), and subpolar (Dfc).

The D climates are controlled by large land masses. Therefore, they are found only in the Northern Hemisphere. Look at the climate map, Fig. 18.5, pp. 498–499, and notice that D climates extend across North America and Eurasia, from about latitude 40°N to almost 70°N. In general, they are characterized by cold winters and warm-to-cool summers.

As we know, for a station to have a D climate, the average temperature of its coldest month must dip below −3°C (27°F). This is not an arbitrary number. Köppen found that, in Europe, this temperature marked the southern limit of persistent snow cover in winter.* Hence, D climates experience a great deal of winter snow that stays on the ground for ex-

tended periods. When the temperature drops to a point such that no month has an average temperature of 10°C (50°F), the climate is classified as polar (E). Köppen found that the average monthly temperature of 10°C tended to represent the minimum temperature required for tree growth. So no matter how cold it gets in a D climate (and winters can get extremely cold), there is enough summer warmth to support the growth of trees.

There are two basic types of D climates: the **humid continental** (Dfa and Dfb) and the **subpolar** (Dfc). Humid continental climates are observed from about latitude 40°N to 50°N (60°N in Europe). Here, precipitation is adequate and fairly evenly distributed throughout the year, although interior stations experience maximum precipitation in summer. Annual precipitation totals usually range from 50 to 100 cm (20 to 40 in.). Native vegetation in the wetter regions includes forests of spruce, fir, pine, and oak. In autumn, nature's pageantry unveils itself as the leaves of deciduous trees turn brilliant shades of red, orange, and yellow (see Fig. 18.19).

---

*In North America, studies suggest that an average monthly temperature of 0°C (32°F) or below for the coldest month seems to correspond better to persistent winter snow cover.

Humid continental climates are subdivided on the basis of summer temperatures. Where summers are long and hot,* the climate is described as *humid continental with hot summers* (Dfa). Here summers are often hot and humid, especially in the southern regions. Midday temperatures often exceed 32°C (90°F) and occasionally 40°C (104°F). Summer nights are usually warm and humid, as well. The frost-free season normally lasts from five to six months, long enough to grow a wide variety of crops. Winters tend to be windy, cold, and snowy. Farther north, where summers are shorter and not as hot,† the climate is described as *humid continental with long cool summers* (Dfb). In Dfb climates, summers are not only cooler but much less

___

*"Hot" means that the average temperature of the warmest month is above 22°C (72°F) and at least four months have a monthly mean temperature above 10°C (50°F).
†"Not as hot" means that the average temperature of the warmest month is below 22°C (72°F) and at least four months have a monthly mean temperature above 10°C (50°F).

humid. Temperatures may exceed 35°C (95°F) for a time, but extended hot spells lasting many weeks are rare. The frost-free season is shorter than in the Dfa climate, and normally lasts between three and five months. Winters are long, cold, and windy. It is not uncommon for temperatures to drop below −30°C (−22°F) and stay below −18°C (0°F) for days and sometimes weeks. Autumn is short, with winter often arriving right on the heels of summer. Spring, too, is short, as late spring snowstorms are common, especially in the more northern latitudes.

Figure 18.20 compares the Dfa climate of Des Moines, Iowa, with the Dfb climate of Winnipeg, Canada. Notice that both cities experience a large annual temperature range. This is characteristic of climates located in the northern interior of continents. In fact, as we move poleward, the annual temperature range increases. In Des Moines, it is 31°C (56°F), while 950 km (590 mi) to the north in Winnipeg, it is 38°C (68°F). The summer precipitation maximum expected for these interior

Figure 18.19
The leaves of deciduous trees burst into brilliant color during autumn over the countryside of Adirondack Park, a region with a humid continental climate.

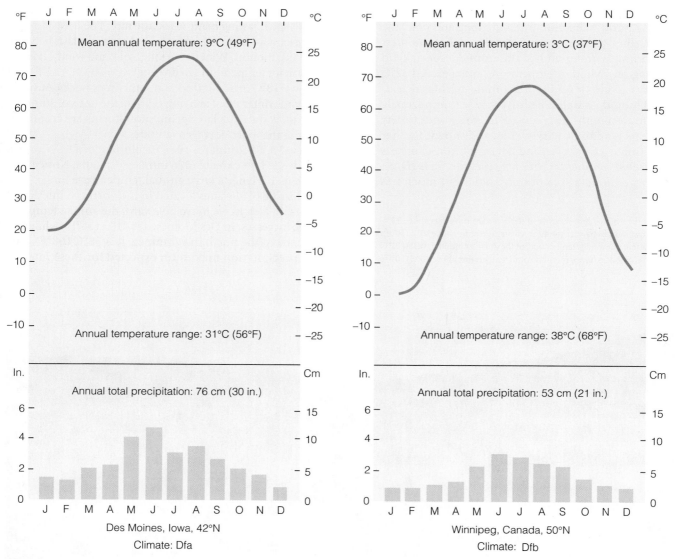

Figure 18.20

Comparison of a humid continental hot summer climate, Dfa (Des Moines, at left), with a humid continental cool summer climate, Dfb (Winnipeg, at right).

continental locations shows up well in Fig. 18.20. Most of the summer rain is in the form of convective showers, although an occasional weak frontal system can produce more widespread precipitation, as can a cluster of thunderstorms—the Mesoscale Convective Complex described in Chapter 15. The weather in both climatic types can be quite changeable, especially in winter, when a brief warm spell is replaced by blustery winds and temperatures plummeting well below −30°C (−22°F).

When winters are severe and summers short and cool, with only one to three months having a mean temperature exceeding 10°C (50°F), the climate is described as *subpolar* (Dfc). From Fig. 18.5 we can see that, in North America, this climate occurs in a broad belt across Canada and Alaska; in Eurasia, it

stretches from Norway over much of Siberia. The exceedingly low temperatures of winter account for these areas being the primary source regions for continental polar and arctic air masses. Extremely cold winters coupled with cool summers produce large annual temperature ranges, as exemplified by the climate data in Fig. 18.21 for Fairbanks, Alaska.

Precipitation is comparatively light in the subpolar climates, especially in the interior regions, with most places receiving less than 50 cm (20 in.) annually. A good percentage of the precipitation falls when weak cyclonic storms move through the region in summer. The total snowfall is usually not large but the cold air prevents melting, so snow stays on the ground for months at a time. Because of the low temperatures, there is a

Weather Watch

Which city has experienced the highest temperature—Prospect Creek, Alaska, situated near the Arctic Circle with a polar climate, or Belem, Brazil, situated near the equator with a tropical climate? The highest temperature ever measured in Prospect Creek (100°F) is exactly 2°F higher than the highest temperature ever measured in Belem.

low annual rate of evaporation that ensures adequate moisture to support the boreal forests of conifers and birches known as **taiga** (see Fig. 18.22). Hence, the subpolar climate is known also as a *boreal climate* and as a *taiga climate*.

In the taiga region of northern Siberia and Asia, where the average temperature of the coldest month drops to a frigid −38°C (−36°F) or below, the climate is designated Dfd. Where the winters are considered dry, the climate is designated Dwd.

Polar Climates (Group E)   *General characteristics:* year-round low temperatures (i.e., average temperature of the warmest month is below 10°C, or 50°F).

Extent: northern coastal areas of North America and Eurasia; Greenland and Antarctica.

Major types: polar tundra (ET) and polar ice caps (EF).

In the **polar tundra** (ET), the average temperature of the warmest month is below 10°C (50°F), but above freezing. (See Fig. 18.23, the climate data for Barrow, Alaska.) Here, the ground is permanently frozen to depths of hundreds of meters, a condition known as **permafrost.** Summer weather, however, is just warm enough to thaw out the upper meter or so of soil. Hence,

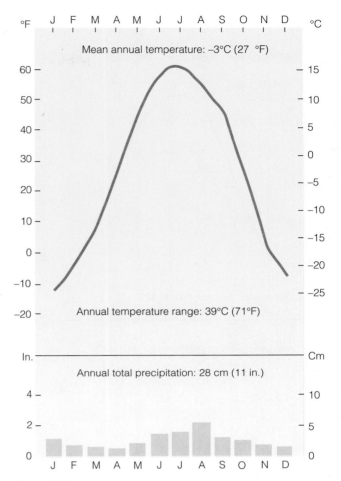

Figure 18.21
Climatic data for Fairbanks, Alaska, latitude 65°N. A station with a subpolar climate (Dfc).

Figure 18.22
Coniferous forests (taiga) such as this occur where winter temperatures are low and precipitation is abundant.

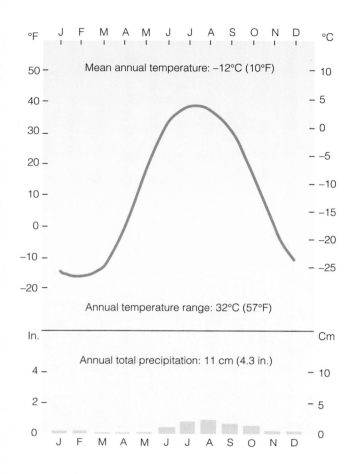

Mean annual temperature: –12°C (10°F)

Annual temperature range: 32°C (57°F)

Annual total precipitation: 11 cm (4.3 in.)

Figure 18.23
Climatic data for Barrow, Alaska, latitude 71°N. A station with a polar tundra climate (ET).

during the summer, the tundra turns swampy and muddy. Annual precipitation on the tundra is meager, with most stations receiving less than 20 cm (8 in.). In lower latitudes, this would constitute a desert, but in the cold polar regions evaporation rates are very low and moisture remains adequate. Because of the extremely short growing season, *tundra vegetation* consists of mosses, lichens, dwarf trees, and scattered woody vegetation, fully grown and only several centimeters tall (see Fig. 18.24).

Even though summer days are long, the sun is never very high above the horizon. Additionally, some of the sunlight that reaches the surface is reflected by snow and ice, while some is used to melt the frozen soil. Consequently, in spite of the long hours of daylight, summers are quite cool. The cool summers and the extremely cold winters produce large annual temperature ranges.

When the average temperature for every month drops below freezing, plant growth is impossible, and the region is perpetually covered with snow and ice. This climatic type is known as **polar ice cap** (EF). It occupies the interior ice sheets of Greenland and Antarctica, where the depth of ice in some places measures thousands of meters. In this region, temperatures are never much above

Figure 18.24
Tundra vegetation in Alaska. This type of tundra is composed mostly of sedges and dwarfed wildflowers that bloom during the brief growing season.

freezing, even during the middle of "summer." The coldest places in the world are located here. Precipitation is extremely meager with many places receiving less than 10 cm (4 in.) annually. Most precipitation falls as snow during the "warmer" summer. Strong downslope katabatic winds frequently whip the snow about, adding to the climate's harshness. The data in Fig. 18.25 for Eismitte, Greenland, illustrate the severity of an EF climate.

Highland Climates (Group H)   It is not necessary to visit the polar regions to experience a polar climate. Because temperature decreases with altitude, climatic changes experienced when climbing 300 m (1000 ft) in elevation are about equivalent in high latitudes to horizontal changes experienced when traveling 300 km (186 mi) northward. (This distance is equal to about 3° latitude.) Therefore, when ascending a high mountain, one can travel through many climatic regions in a relatively short distance.

Figure 18.26 shows how the climate and vegetation change along the western slopes of the central Sierra Nevada. (See Fig. 18.4, p. 494, for the precipitation patterns for this region.) Notice that, at the base of the mountains, the climate and vegetation represent semi-arid conditions, while in the foothills the climate becomes Mediterranean and the vegetation changes to chaparral. Higher up, thick fir and pine forests prevail. At still higher elevations, the climate is subpolar and the taiga gives way to dwarf trees and tundra vegetation. Near the summit there are permanent patches of ice and snow, with some small glaciers nestled in protected areas. Hence, in less than 13,000 vertical feet, the climate has changed from semi-arid to polar.

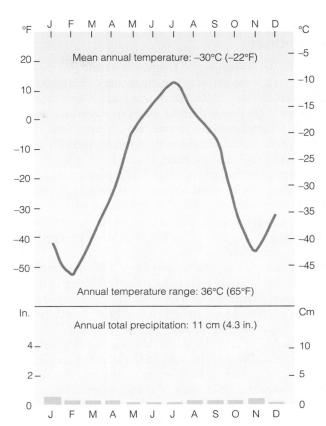

Figure 18.25
Climatic data for Eismitte, Greenland, latitude 71°N. Located in the interior of Greenland at an elevation of 3030 m (9941 ft), Eismitte has a polar ice cap climate (EF).

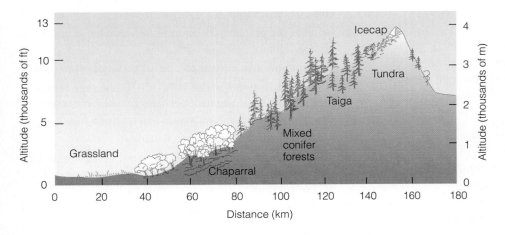

Figure 18.26
Vertical view of changing vegetation and climate due to elevation in the central Sierra Nevada.

Summary

In this chapter, we examined global temperature and precipitation patterns, as well as the various climatic regions throughout the world. Tropical climates are found in low latitudes, where the noon sun is always high, day and night are of nearly equal length, every month is warm, and no real winter season exists. Some of the rainiest places in the world exist in the tropics, especially where warm, humid air rises upslope along mountain ranges.

Dry climates prevail where potential evaporation and transpiration exceed precipitation. Some deserts, such as the Sahara, are mainly the result of sinking air associated with the subtropical highs, while others, due to the rain shadow effect, are found on the leeward side of mountains. Many deserts form in response to both of these effects.

Middle latitudes are characterized by a distinct winter and summer season. Winters tend to be milder in lower latitudes and more severe in higher latitudes. Along the east coast of some continents, summers tend to be hot and humid as moist air sweeps poleward around the subtropical highs. The air often rises and condenses into afternoon thunderstorms in this humid subtropical climate. The west coasts of many continents tend to be drier, especially in summer, as the combination of cool ocean water and sinking air of the subtropical highs, to a large degree, inhibit the formation of cumuliform clouds.

In the middle of large continents, such as North America and Eurasia, summers are usually wetter than winters. Winter temperatures are generally lower than those experienced in coastal regions. As one moves northward, summers become shorter and winters longer and colder. Polar climates prevail at high latitudes, where winters are severe and there is no real summer. When ascending a high mountain, one can travel through many climatic zones in a relatively short distance.

Key Terms

The following terms are listed in the order they appear in the text. Define each. Doing so will aid you in reviewing the material covered in this chapter.

microclimate	xerophytes
mesoclimate	semi-arid climate
macroclimate	steppe
global climate	humid subtropical climate
climatic controls	marine climate
Köppen classification system	dry-summer subtropical
P/E index	(Mediterranean)
tropical rain forest	humid continental climate
tropical wet climate	subpolar climate
laterite	taiga
tropical monsoon climate	polar tundra climate
tropical wet-and-dry climate	permafrost
savanna grass	polar ice cap climate
arid climate	

Questions for Review

1. Describe as many factors as you can that influence the global pattern of precipitation.

2. Explain why, in North America, precipitation typically is a maximum along the west coast in winter, a maximum on the central plains in summer, and fairly evenly distributed between summer and winter along the east coast.

3. What climatic information did Köppen use in classifying climates?

4. According to Köppen's climatic system (Fig. 18.5, p. 498–499), what major climatic type is most abundant in each of the following areas:
   (a) in North America
   (b) in South America, and
   (c) throughout the world.

5. What constitutes a dry climate?

6. In which climatic region would each of the following be observed: tropical rain forest, xerophytes, steppe, taiga, tundra, and savanna?

7. How do C-type climates differ from D-type climates?

8. Why are large annual temperature ranges characteristic of D-type climates?

9. Why are D climates found in the Northern Hemisphere but not in the Southern Hemisphere?

10. Explain why a tropical rain forest climate will support a tropical rain forest, while a tropical wet-and-dry climate will not.

11. Why are marine climates (Cs) usually found on the west coast of continents?

12. What is the primary distinction between a Cfa and a Dfa climate?

13. Explain how arid deserts can be found adjacent to oceans.

14. Why did Köppen use the 10°C (50°F) average temperature for July to distinguish between D and E climates?

15. What accounts for the existence of a BWk climate in the western Great Basin of North America?

16. Barrow, Alaska, receives a mere 11 cm (4.3 in.) of precipitation annually. Explain why its climate is not classified as arid or semi-arid.

17. Explain why subpolar climates are also known as boreal climates and taiga climates.

Questions for Thought

1. Why do cities directly east of the Rockies (such as Denver, Colorado) receive much more precipitation than cities east of the Sierra Nevada (such as Reno and Lovelock, Nevada)?

2. What climatic controls affect the climate in your area?

3. Los Angeles, Seattle, and Boston are all coastal cities, yet Boston has a continental rather than a marine climate. Explain why.

4. Why are many structures in polar regions built on pilings.

5. Why are summer afternoon temperatures in a humid subtropical climate (Cfa) often higher than in a tropical wet climate (Af)?

6. Why are humid subtropical climates (Cfa) found in regions bounded by 20° and 40° (N or S) latitudes, and nowhere else?

7. In which of the following climate types is virga likely to occur most frequently: humid continental, arid desert, or polar tundra? Explain why.

8. As shown in Figure 18.17, San Francisco and Sacramento, California, have similar mean annual temperatures but different annual temperature ranges. What factors control the annual temperature ranges at these two locations?

9. Why is there a contrast in climate types on either side of the Rocky Mountains, but not on either side of the Appalachian Mountains?

Problems and Exercises

1. Suppose a city has the mean annual precipitation and temperature given in Table 18.3. Based on Köppen's climatic types, how would this climate be classified? On a map of North America, approximately where would this city be located? What type of vegetation would you expect to see there? Answer these same questions for the data in Table 18.4.

2. Compare the following climate classifications for your area:
   (a) Ancient Greeks
   (b) Köppen system
   (c) Thornthwaite's system
   Which classification system is best for your area's mesoclimate? Macroclimate?

 ## Questions for Exploration

1. Use the Weather Forecasting/Forecasting section of the Blue Skies CD-ROM to identify weather conditions in four of the major Köppen climatic regions. (Use the World Weather button to examine weather conditions throughout the globe.)

2. U.S. Climate Data (http://www.cdc.noaa.gov/USclimate/states.fast.html): Compare graphs of maximum and minimum temperature and precipitation for three cities in different parts of the United States. Describe the differences in climate.

3. Current Global Temperatures (http://www.ssec.wisc.edu/data/composites.html): Look at the current global pattern of surface temperatures. How does it compare to the average conditions? Are there any areas experiencing significant anomalies (differences from average conditions)? What might be causing these anomalies?

 Go to the Brooks/Cole Earth Sciences Resource Center (http://earthscience.brookscole.com) for critical thinking exercises, articles, and additional readings from InfoTrac College Edition, Brooks/Cole's online student library.

Table 18.3

	JAN.	FEB.	MAR.	APR.	MAY	JUNE	JULY	AUG.	SEPT.	OCT.	NOV.	DEC.	YEAR
Temperature (°F)	40	42	50	60	68	77	80	79	73	62	49	42	60
Precipitation (in.)	4.9	4.2	5.3	3.7	3.8	3.2	4.0	3.3	2.7	2.5	3.4	4.1	45

Table 18.4

	JAN.	FEB.	MAR.	APR.	MAY	JUNE	JULY	AUG.	SEPT.	OCT.	NOV.	DEC.	YEAR
Temperature (°F)	18	18	29	42	55	65	70	68	60	48	36	23	44
Precipitation (in.)	1.9	1.5	2.2	2.6	2.9	3.6	3.8	3.0	3.1	2.9	2.8	1.9	32

Twenty thousand years ago, glaciers covered three times more land than they do today. Over portions of North America, the ice was thousands of meters thick and extended well into the eastern half of the United States. Today, the ice over North America is gone except for the relatively small alpine glaciers that still exist in high mountain valleys. (Photo © Stephen J. Krasemann/Photo Researchers.)

Climate Change

CONTENTS

A change in our climate however is taking place very sensibly. Both heats and colds are becoming much more moderate within the memory even of the middle-aged. Snows are less frequent and less deep. They do not often lie, below the mountains, more than one, two, or three days, and very rarely a week. They are remembered to have been formerly frequent, deep, and of long continuance. The elderly inform me the earth used to be covered with snow about three months in every year. The rivers, which then seldom failed to freeze over in the course of the winter, scarcely ever do now. This change has produced an unfortunate fluctuation between heat and cold, in the spring of the year, which is very fatal to fruits. In an interval of twenty-eight years, there was no instance of fruit killed by the frost in the neighborhood of Monticello. The accumulated snows of the winter remaining to be dissolved all together in the spring, produced those overflowings of our rivers, so frequent then, and so rare now.

Thomas Jefferson, *Notes on the State of Virginia*, 1781

he climate is always changing. Evidence shows that climate has changed in the past, and nothing suggests that it will not continue to change. In Chapter 17, we saw that as the urban environment grows, its climate differs from that of the region around it. Sometimes the difference is striking, as when city nights are warmer than the nights of the outlying rural areas. Other times, the difference is subtle, as when a layer of smoke and haze covers the city or when the climate of a relatively small area—the microclimate—becomes modified by the light and warmth of a city street lamp (see Fig. 19.1). Climate change, in the form of a persistent drought or a delay in the annual monsoon rains, can adversely affect the lives of millions. Even small changes can have an adverse effect when averaged over many years, as when grasslands once used for grazing gradually become uninhabited deserts. In this chapter, first we will investigate how the global climate has changed, then we will examine some theories on why it has changed.

The Earth's Changing Climate

Not only is the earth's climate always changing, but a mere 18,000 years ago the earth was in the grip of a cold spell, with *alpine glaciers* extending their ice fingers down river valleys and huge ice sheets (*continental glaciers*) covering vast areas of North America and Europe. The ice measured several kilometers thick and extended as far south as New York and the Ohio River Valley. Perhaps the glaciers advanced 10 times during the last 2 million years, only to retreat. In the warmer periods, between glacier advances, average global temperatures were slightly higher than at present. Hence, some scientists feel that we are still in an ice age, but in the comparatively warmer part of it.

Presently, glaciers cover only about 10 percent of the earth's land surface. The total volume of ice over the face of the earth amounts to a little more than 25 million cubic kilometers. Most of this ice is in the Greenland and Antarctic ice sheets, and its accumulation over time has allowed scientists to measure past climatic changes. If global temperatures were to rise enough so that all of this ice melted, the level of the ocean would rise about 65 m (213 ft) (see Fig. 19.2). Imagine the catastrophic results: Many major cities (such as New York, Tokyo, and London) would be inundated. Even a rise in global temperature of several degrees Celsius might be enough to raise sea level by about half a meter or so, flooding coastal lowlands.

Determining Past Climates   The study of the geological evidence left behind by advancing and retreating glaciers is one factor suggesting that global climate has undergone slow but continuous changes. To reconstruct past climates, scientists must examine and then carefully piece together all the available evidence. Unfortunately, the evidence only gives a general understanding of what the climate was like. For example, fossil pollen of a tundra plant collected in a layer of sediment in New England and dated to be 12,000 years old suggests that the climate of that region was much colder than it is today.

Other evidence of global climatic change comes from core samples taken from ocean floor sediments and ice from Greenland. A multiuniversity research project known as CLIMAP (*Cli*mate: *l*ong-range *i*nvestigation *m*apping *a*nd *p*rediction) studied the past million years of global climate. Thousands of meters of ocean sediment obtained with a hollow-centered drill were analyzed. The sediment contains the remains of calcium carbonate shells of organisms that once lived near the surface. Because certain organisms live within a narrow range of temperature, the distribution and type of organisms within the sediment indicate the surface water temperature.

In addition, the oxygen-isotope* ratio of these shells provides information about the sequence of glacier advances. For example, most of the oxygen in sea water is composed of 8 protons and 8 neutrons in its nucleus, giving it an atomic weight of 16. However, about one out of every thousand oxygen atoms contains an extra 2 neutrons, giving it an atomic weight of 18.

---

*Isotopes are atoms whose nuclei have the same number of protons but different numbers of neutrons.

Figure 19.1
Altering the microclimate. Notice in the picture that the leaves are still on the tree near the streetlight. Apparently, this sodium vapor lamp emits enough warmth and light during the night to trick the leaves into behaving as if it were September rather than the middle of November.

Figure 19.2
If all the ice locked up in glaciers and ice sheets were to melt, estimates are that this coastal area of south Florida would be under 65 m (213 ft) of water. Even a relatively small 1-m rise in sea level would threaten half of the world's population with rising seas.

When ocean water evaporates, the heavy oxygen 18 tends to be left behind. Consequently, during periods of glacier advance, the oceans, which contain less water, have a higher concentration of oxygen 18. Since the shells of marine organisms are constructed from the oxygen atoms existing in ocean water, determining the ratio of oxygen 18 to oxygen 16 within these shells yields information about how the climate may have varied in the past. A higher ratio of oxygen 18 to oxygen 16 in the sediment record suggests a colder climate, while a lower ratio suggests a warmer climate. Using data such as these, the CLIMAP project was able to reconstruct the earth's surface ocean temperature for various times during the past (see Fig. 19.3).

Vertical ice cores extracted from ice sheets in Antarctica and Greenland provide additional information on past temperature patterns. Glaciers form over land where temperatures are sufficiently low so that, during the course of a year, more snow falls than will melt. Successive snow accumulations over many years compact the snow, which slowly recrystallizes into ice. Since ice is composed of hydrogen and oxygen, examining the oxygen-isotope ratio in ancient cores provides a past record of temperature trends. Generally, the colder the air when the snow fell, the

richer the concentration of oxygen 16 in the core. Moreover, bubbles of ancient air trapped in the ice can be analyzed to determine the past composition of the atmosphere (see Fig. 19.11, p. 531).

Ice cores also record the causes of climate changes. One such cause is deduced from layers of sulfuric acid in the ice. The sulfuric acid originally came from large volcanic explosions that injected huge quantities of sulfur into the stratosphere. The resulting sulfate aerosols eventually fell to the earth in polar regions as acid snow, which was preserved in the ice sheets. The Greenland ice cores also provide a continuous record of sulfur from human sources. Moreover, ice cores at both poles record a beryllium isotope ($^{10}B_e$) that indicates solar activity. Various types of dust collected in the cores indicate whether the climate was arid or wet.

Scientists are even using the calcium carbonate material that forms into tiny stones *(otoliths)* in the inner ears of fish to reconstruct past temperatures of the Great Lakes region. As the otoliths grow, they extract oxygen from the lake water. The oxygen-isotope ratio then provides scientists with information on changes in water temperature over the life of the fish, whether it died last week or 10,000 years ago.

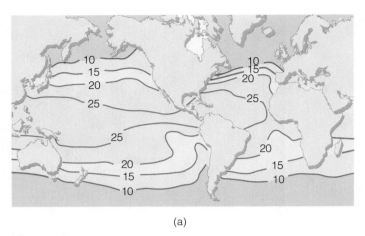

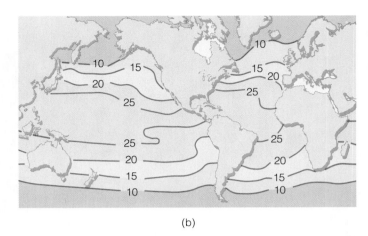

(a)   (b)

Figure 19.3
(a) Sea surface isotherms (°C) during August 18,000 years ago and (b) during August today. Apparently, during the Ice Age (diagram a) the Gulf Stream shifted to a more easterly direction, depriving northern Europe of its warmth and causing a rapid north-to-south ocean surface temperature gradient.

Still other evidence of climatic change comes from the study of annual growth rings of trees, called **dendrochronology.** As a tree grows, it produces a layer of wood cells under its bark. Each year's growth appears as a ring. The changes in thickness of the rings indicate climatic changes that may have taken place from one year to the next. The density of late growth tree rings is an even better indication of changes in climate. The presence of frost rings during particularly cold periods and the chemistry of the wood itself provide additional information about a changing climate. Tree rings are only useful in regions that experience an annual cycle and in trees that are stressed by temperature or moisture during their growing season. The growth of tree rings has been correlated with precipitation and temperature patterns for hundreds of years into the past in various regions of the world.

Other data have been used to reconstruct past climates, such as:

1. records of natural lake-bottom sediment and soil deposits
2. the study of pollen in deep ice caves, soil deposits, and sea sediments
3. certain geologic evidence (ancient coal beds, sand dunes, and fossils) and the change in the water level of closed basin lakes
4. documents concerning droughts, floods, and crop yields
5. the study of oxygen-isotope ratios of corals
6. dating calcium carbonate layers of stalactites in caves
7. borehole temperature profiles, which can be inverted to give records of past temperature change at the surface
8. deuterium (heavy hydrogen) ratios in ice cores, which indicate temperature changes

Despite all of these data, our knowledge about past climates is still incomplete. Now that we have reviewed *how* the climatologist gains information about the past, let's look at *what* this information reveals.

Climate Through the Ages   Throughout much of the earth's history, the global climate was probably between 8°C and 15°C warmer than it is today. During most of this time, the polar regions were free of ice. These comparatively warm conditions, however, were interrupted by several periods of glaciation. Geologic evidence suggests that one glacial period occurred about 700 million years ago (m.y.a.) and another about 300 m.y.a. The most recent one—the *Pleistocene epoch* or, simply, the **Ice Age**—began about 2 m.y.a. Let's summarize the climatic conditions that led up to the Pleistocene.

About 65 m.y.a., the earth was warmer than it is now; polar ice caps did not exist. Beginning about 55 m.y.a., the earth entered a long cooling trend. After millions of years, polar ice appeared. As average temperatures continued to lower, the ice grew thicker, and by about 10 m.y.a. a deep blanket of ice covered the Antarctic. Meanwhile, snow and ice began to accumulate in high mountain valleys of the Northern Hemisphere, and alpine, or valley, glaciers soon appeared.

About 2 m.y.a., continental glaciers appeared in the Northern Hemisphere, marking the beginning of the Pleistocene epoch. The Pleistocene, however, was not a period of continuous glaciation but a time when glaciers alternately advanced and retreated (melted back) over large portions of North America and Europe. Between the glacial advances were warmer periods called **interglacial periods,** which lasted for 10,000 years or more.

It was once thought that interglacial periods represented a more stable type of climate, unlike the large climate variations experienced during the colder part of the Ice Age. But analysis of Greenland ice cores suggests that the warm *Eemian interglacial period* (which lasted 19,000 years from 133,000 to 114,000 years ago) may have consisted of two major cold spells, lasting 2000 years and 6000 years. Some scientists speculate, however, that the cooling may represent a shift in the location

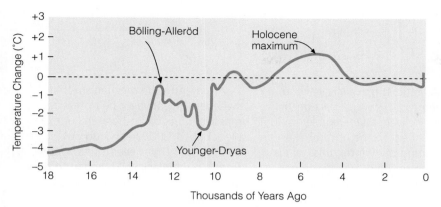

Figure 19.4
Average air-temperature variations for the past 18,000 years. These data, which represent temperature records compiled from a variety of sources, only give an approximation of temperature changes. Some regions of the world experienced a cooling and other regions a warming that either preceded or lagged behind the temperature variations shown in the diagram.

of Greenland's moisture supply (which would change the oxygen-isotope ratio) rather than actual coolings, as these cold spells do not show up in the Antarctic ice core record.

The most recent North American glaciers reached their maximum thickness and extent about 18,000 to 22,000 years ago (y.a.). At that time, the sea level was perhaps 120 m (395 ft) lower than it is now. The lower sea level exposed vast areas of land, such as the *Bering land bridge* (a strip of land that connected Siberia to Alaska), which allowed human and animal migration from Asia to North America.

The ice began to retreat about 14,000 y.a. as surface temperatures slowly rose, producing a warm spell called the *Bölling-Alleröd* period (see Fig. 19.4). Then, about 12,700 y.a., the average temperature suddenly dropped and northeastern North America and northern Europe reverted back to glacial conditions. About 1000 years later, the cold spell (known as the **Younger-Dryas***) ended abruptly and temperatures rose rapidly in many areas. Beginning about 8000 y.a. the mean temperature dropped by as much as 2°C over central Europe. During this cold period, which was not experienced worldwide, the European alpine timberline fell about 200 m (600 ft). The cold period ended, temperatures began to rise, and by about 6000 y.a. the continental ice sheets over North America were gone. This warm spell during the current interglacial period, or *Holocene epoch*, is sometimes called the **mid-Holocene maximum,** and because this warm period favored the development of plants, it is also known as the *climatic optimum*. About 5000 y.a. a cooling trend set in, during which extensive alpine glaciers returned, but not continental glaciers.

It is interesting to note that ice core data from Greenland reveal that rapid shifts in climate (from ice age conditions to a much warmer state) took place in as little as three years over

central Greenland around the end of the Younger-Dryas. The data also reveal that similar rapid shifts in climate occurred several times toward the end of the Ice Age. What could cause such rapid changes in temperature? One possible explanation is given in the Focus section on p. 526.

Climate During the Last 1000 Years   Figure 19.5 shows how the average surface air temperature changed in the Northern Hemisphere during the last 1000 years. The data needed to reconstruct the temperature profile in Fig. 19.5 comes from a variety of sources, including tree rings, corals, ice cores, historical records, and thermometers. Notice that about 1000 y.a., the Northern Hemisphere was slightly cooler than average (where

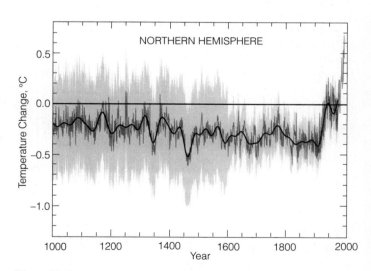

Figure 19.5
The average temperature variations over the Northern Hemisphere for the last 1000 years relative to the 1961 to 1990 average (zero line). Yearly temperature data from tree rings, corals, ice cores, and historical records are shown in blue. Yearly temperature data from thermometers are in red. The black line represents a smoothing of the data. (The gray shading represents a statistical 95 percent confidence range in the annual temperature data.) (*Source:* From Climate Change 2001: The Scientific Basis, 2001, by J.T. Houghton, et al. Copyright © 2001 Cambridge University Press. Reprinted with permission of the Intergovernmental Panel on Climate Change.)

---

*This exceptionally cold spell is named after the *Dryas*, an arctic flower.

Weather Watch

About 20,000 years ago, sea level was so low that there was no English Channel and the River Thames was actually a tributary of the Rhine River.

Focus on A SPECIAL TOPIC

The Ocean Conveyor Belt and Climate Change

During the last glacial period, the climate around Greenland (and probably other areas of the world) underwent shifts, from ice-age temperatures to much warmer conditions in a matter of years. What could bring about such large fluctuations in temperature over such a short period of time? It now appears that a vast circulation of ocean water, known as the *conveyor belt,* plays a major role in the climate picture.

Figure 1 illustrates the movement of the ocean conveyor belt, or *thermohaline circulation.** The conveyor-like circulation begins in the north Atlantic near Greenland and Iceland, where salty surface water is cooled through contact with cold Arctic air masses. The cold, dense water sinks and flows southward through the deep Atlantic Ocean, around Africa, and into the Indian and Pacific Oceans. In the North Atlantic, the sinking of cold water draws warm water northward from lower latitudes. As this water flows northward, evaporation increases the water's salinity (dissolved salt content) and density. When this salty, dense water reaches the far regions of the

_____
*Thermohaline circulations are ocean circulations produced by differences in temperature and/or salinity. Changes in ocean water temperature or salinity create changes in water density.

North Atlantic, it gradually sinks to great depths. This warm part of the conveyor delivers an incredible amount of tropical heat to the northern Atlantic. During the winter, this heat is transferred to the overlying atmosphere, and evaporation moistens the air. Strong westerly winds then carry this warmth and moisture into northern and western Europe, where it causes winters to be much warmer and wetter than one would normally expect for this latitude.

Ocean sediment records along with ice-core records from Greenland suggest that the giant conveyor belt has switched on and off during the last glacial period. Such events have apparently coincided with rapid changes in climate. For example, when the conveyor belt is strong, winters in northern Europe tend to be wet and relatively mild. However, when the conveyor belt is weak or stops altogether, winters in northern Europe appear to turn much colder. This switching from a period of milder winters to one of severe cold shows up many times in the climate record. One such event—the Younger-Dryas—illustrates how quickly climate can change and how western and northern Europe's climate can cool within a matter of decades, then quickly return back to milder conditions.

Apparently, the mechanism that switches the conveyor belt off is a massive influx of freshwater. For example, about 11,000 years ago during the Younger-Dryas event, freshwater from a huge glacial lake began to flow down the St. Lawrence River and into the North Atlantic. This massive inflow of freshwater reduced the salinity (and, hence, density) of the surface water to the point that it stopped sinking. The conveyor shut down for about 1000 years during which time severe cold engulfed much of northern Europe. The conveyor belt started up again when the influx of fresh water began to drain down the Mississippi rather than into the North Atlantic. It was during this time that milder conditions returned to northern Europe.

Will increasing levels of CO_2 have an effect on the conveyor belt? Some climate models predict that as CO_2 levels increase, more precipitation will fall over the North Atlantic. This situation reduces the density of the sea water and slows down the conveyor belt. In fact, if CO_2 levels double, computer models predict that the conveyor belt will slow by about 30 percent. If CO_2 levels quadruple, models predict that the conveyor belt will stop and severe cold will return to northern Europe, even though global temperatures will likely increase dramatically.

average represents the average temperature from 1961 to 1990). However, certain regions in the Northern Hemisphere were warmer than others. For example, during this time vineyards flourished and wine was produced in England, indicating warm, dry summers and the absence of cold springs. It was during the early part of the millennium that Vikings colonized Iceland and Greenland.*

Notice in Fig. 19.5 that the temperature curve shows a relatively warm period during the 11th to the 14th centuries—

_____
*This relatively warm, tranquil period of several hundred years over western Europe is sometimes referred to in that region as the *Medieval Climatic Optimum.*

relatively warm, but still cooler than the 20th century. During this time, the relatively mild climate of Western Europe began to show large variations. For several hundred years the climate grew stormy. Both great floods and great droughts occurred. Extremely cold winters were followed by relatively warm ones. During the cold spells, the English vineyards and the Viking settlements suffered. Europe experienced several famines during the 1300s.

Again look back at Fig. 19.5 and observe that the Northern Hemisphere experienced a slight cooling during the 15th to 19th centuries. This cooling was significant enough in certain areas to allow alpine glaciers to increase in size and advance down river canyons. In many areas in Europe, winters were long

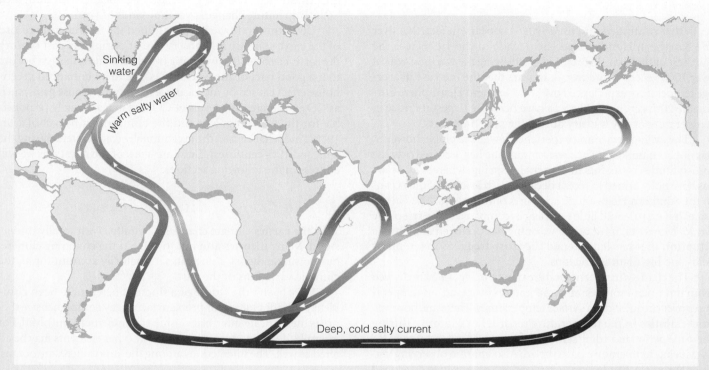

Sinking water

Warm salty water

Deep, cold salty current

Figure 1
The ocean conveyor belt. In the North Atlantic, cold, salty water sinks, drawing warm water northward from lower latitudes. The warm water provides warmth and moisture for the air above, which is then swept into northern Europe by westerly winds that keep the climate of that region milder than one would normally expect. When the conveyor belt stops, winters apparently turn much colder over northern Europe.

and severe; summers, short and wet. The vineyards in England vanished, and farming became impossible in the more northern latitudes. Cut off from the rest of the world by an advancing ice pack, the Viking colony in Greenland perished.

There is no evidence that this cold spell existed worldwide. However, over Europe, this cold period has come to be known as the **Little Ice Age.** During these colder times, one particular year stands out: 1816. In Europe that year, bad weather contributed to a poor wheat crop, and famine spread across the land. In Northern America, unusual blasts of cold arctic air moved through Canada and the northeastern United States between May and September. The cold spells brought heavy snow in June

and killing frosts in July and August. In the warmer days that followed each cold snap, farmers replanted, only to have another cold outbreak damage the planting. The year 1816 has come to be known as "the year without a summer" or "eighteen hundred and froze-to-death." The unusually cold summer was followed by a bitterly cold winter.

In the early 1900s, the average global surface temperature began to rise (see Fig. 19.6). Notice that, from about 1900 to 1945, the average temperature rose nearly 0.5°C. Following the warmer period, the earth began to cool slightly over the next 25 years or so. In the late 1960s and 1970s, the cooling trend ended over most of the Northern Hemisphere. In the mid-1970s, a warming trend

Weather Watch

During the 1700s, winters were much colder over North America than they are today. Those cold winters, in fact, allowed soldiers during the Revolutionary War to drag cannons from Staten Island to Manhattan across the frozen Upper New York Bay.

set in that continued into the 1990s. It appears, in fact, that over the Northern Hemisphere, the decade of the 1990s was the warmest of the 20th century, with 1998 being the warmest year in over 1000 years.* Moreover, it appears that the increase in average temperature experienced over the Northern Hemisphere during the 20th century is likely to have been the largest increase in temperature of any century during the past 1000 years.

The average warming experienced over the globe, however, has not been uniform. The greatest warming has occurred over the mid-latitude continents in winter and spring, whereas a few areas have not warmed in recent decades, such as areas of the oceans in the Southern Hemisphere and parts of Antarctica. The United States has experienced little warming as compared to the rest of the world. Moreover, most of the warming has occurred at night—a situation that has lengthened the frost-free seasons in many mid- and high-latitude regions.

The changes in air temperature shown in Fig. 19.6 are derived from three main sources: air temperatures over land, air temperatures over ocean, and sea surface temperatures. There are, however, uncertainties in the temperature record. For example, during this time period recording stations have moved, and techniques for measuring temperature have varied. Also, marine observing stations are scarce. In addition, urbanization (especially in developed nations) tends to artificially raise average temperatures as cities

grow (the urban heat island effect). When urban warming is taken into account, and improved sea surface temperature information is incorporated into the data, the warming over the past 100 years measures about 0.6°C (about 1°F).

A global increase in temperature of 0.6°C may seem small, but in Fig. 19.4, p. 525, we can see that global temperatures have varied no more than 2°C during the past 10,000 years. Consequently, an increase of 0.6°C becomes significant when compared with temperature changes over thousands of years.

Up to this point we have examined the temperature record of the earth's surface and observed that during the past century the earth has been in a warming trend. Climate scientists believe that a good part of the warming is due to an enhanced greenhouse effect caused by increasing levels of greenhouse gases, such as CO_2.† If increasing levels of CO_2 are at least partly responsible for the warming, why did the climate begin to cool after 1940? And what caused the exceptionally cold winters during the 14th and 19th centuries? These are a few of the questions we will address in the following sections.

Possible Causes of Climatic Change

Why the earth's climate changes naturally is not totally understood. Many theories attempt to explain the changing climate, but no single theory alone can satisfactorily account for *all* the climatic variations of the past.

Why hasn't the riddle of a fluctuating climate been completely solved? One major problem facing any comprehensive theory is the intricate interrelationship of the elements involved. For example, if temperature changes, many other elements may be altered as well. The interactions among the atmosphere, the oceans,

---

*The exceptionally warm year of 1998 happened to coincide with a major El Niño warming of the tropical Pacific Ocean.

†The earth's atmospheric greenhouse effect is due mainly to the absorption and emission of infrared radiation by gases, such as water vapor, CO_2, methane, nitrous oxide, and chlorofluorocarbons. Refer back to Chapter 2 for additional information on this topic.

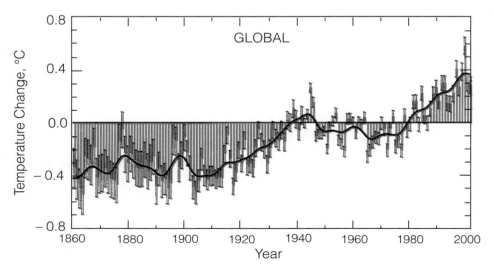

Figure 19.6
Average temperature variations over the globe (land and sea) from 1860 to 1999. The red bars represent yearly temperature changes; the solid black curve represents a smoothing of the data. The zero line represents the average surface temperature from 1961 to 1990. (*Source:* From Climate Change 2001: The Scientific Basis, 2001, by J.T. Houghton, et al. Copyright © 2001 Cambridge University Press. Reprinted with permission of the Intergovernmental Panel on Climate Change.)

and the ice are extremely complex and the number of possible interactions among these systems is enormous. No climatic element within the system is isolated from the others. With this in mind, we will first investigate how feedback systems work; then we will consider some of the current theories of climatic change.

Climate Change and Feedback Mechanisms

In Chapter 2, we learned that the earth-atmosphere system is in a delicate balance between incoming and outgoing energy. If this balance is upset, even slightly, global climate can undergo a series of complicated changes.

Let's assume that the earth-atmosphere system has been disturbed to the point that the earth has entered a slow warming trend. Over the years the temperature slowly rises, and water from the oceans rapidly evaporates into the warmer air. The increased quantity of water vapor absorbs more of the earth's infrared energy, thus strengthening the atmospheric greenhouse effect. This strengthening of the greenhouse effect raises the air temperature even more, which, in turn, allows more water vapor to evaporate into the atmosphere. The greenhouse effect becomes even stronger and the air temperature rises even more. This situation is known as the **water vapor-greenhouse feedback.** (Also called the *water vapor-temperature rise* feedback.) It represents a **positive feedback mechanism** because the initial increase in temperature is reinforced by the other processes. If this feedback were left unchecked, the earth's temperature would increase until the oceans evaporated away. Such a chain reaction is called a *runaway greenhouse effect.* Another positive feedback mechanism is the **snow-albedo feedback,** where an increase in global surface air temperature might cause snow and ice to melt in polar latitudes. This melting would reduce the albedo (reflectivity) of the surface, allowing more solar energy to reach the surface, which would further raise the temperature.

Helping to counteract the positive feedback mechanisms are **negative feedback mechanisms**—those that tend to weaken the interactions among the variables rather than reinforce them. For example, as the surface warms, it emits more infrared radiation.* This increase in radiant energy from the surface would greatly slow the rise in temperature and help to stabilize the climate. The increase in radiant energy from the surface with increasing surface temperature is the strongest negative feedback in the climate system, and greatly lowers the possibility of a runaway greenhouse effect. Consequently, there is no evidence that a runaway greenhouse effect ever occurred on earth, and it is not very likely that it will occur in the future.

Another negative feedback on a warming planet might come from clouds. Suppose, for example, that as the surface warms, more water evaporates from the oceans and global low cloudiness increases. Low clouds tend to reflect a large per-

centage of incoming sunlight, and with less solar energy to heat the surface, the warming slows.

All feedback mechanisms work simultaneously and in both directions. Earlier, we saw that the snow-albedo feedback produces a positive feedback on a warming planet, but it produces a positive feedback on a cooling planet as well. For example, suppose the earth were in a slow global cooling trend that lasted for hundreds or even thousands of years. Lower temperatures might allow for a greater snow cover in middle and high latitudes, which would increase the albedo of the surface so that much of the incident sunlight would be reflected back to space. Less sunlight absorbed at the surface might cause a further drop in temperature. This action might further increase the snow cover, lowering the temperature even more.† If left unchecked, the snow-albedo feedback would produce a *runaway ice age* which, of course, is not likely on earth because other feedback mechanisms in the atmospheric system are constantly working to moderate the magnitude of the cooling. In summary, the earth-atmosphere system has a number of checks and balances that help it to counteract tendencies of climate change.

Climate Change, Plate Tectonics, and Mountain Building

During the geologic past, the earth's surface has undergone extensive modifications. One involves the slow shifting of the continents and the ocean floors. This motion is explained in the widely accepted **theory of plate tectonics** (formerly called the *theory of continental drift*). According to this theory, the earth's outer shell is composed of huge plates that fit together like pieces of a jigsaw puzzle. The plates, which slide over a partially molten zone below them, move in relation to one another. Continents are embedded in the plates and move along like luggage riding piggyback on a conveyor belt. The rate of motion is extremely slow, only a few centimeters per year.

Besides providing insights into many geological processes, plate tectonics also helps to explain past climates. For example, we find glacial features near sea level in Africa today, suggesting that the area underwent a period of glaciation hundreds of millions of years ago. Were temperatures at low elevations near the equator ever cold enough to produce ice sheets? Probably not. The ice sheets formed when this land mass was located at a much higher latitude. Over the many millions of years since then, the land has slowly moved to its present position. Along the same line, we can see how the fossil remains of tropical vegetation can be found under layers of ice in polar regions today.

According to plate tectonics, the now existing continents were at one time joined together in a single huge continent, which broke apart. Its pieces slowly moved across the face of the earth, thus changing the distribution of continents and ocean basins, as illustrated in Fig. 19.7. Some scientists feel that, when land masses are concentrated in middle and high lati-

---

*Recall from Chapter 2, p. 36, that the outgoing infrared radiation from the surface increases at a rate proportional to the fourth power of the surface's absolute temperature. This relationship is called the Stefan-Boltzmann law. In effect, doubling the surface temperature results in 16 times more energy emitted.

---

†This snow-albedo positive feedback on a cooling planet operates on all time scales, including seasonal temperature cycles.

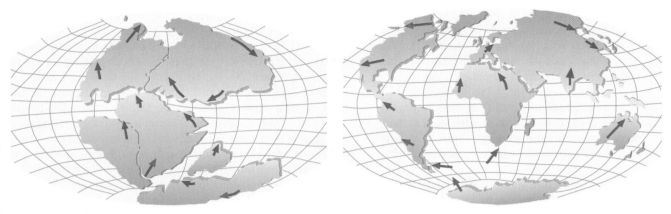

Figure 19.7
Geographical distribution of (a) land masses about 180 million years ago, and (b) today. Arrows show the relative direction of continental movement.

tudes, ice sheets are more likely to form. During these times, there is a greater likelihood that more sunlight will be reflected back into space and that the snow-albedo feedback mechanism mentioned earlier will amplify the cooling.

The various arrangements of the continents may also influence the path of ocean currents, which, in turn, could not only alter the transport of heat from low to high latitudes but could also change both the global wind system and the climate in middle and high latitudes. As an example, suppose that plate movement "pinches off" a rather large body of high-latitude ocean water such that the transport of warm water into the region is cut off. In winter, the surface water would eventually freeze over with ice. This freezing would, in turn, reduce the amount of sensible and latent

heat given up to the atmosphere. Furthermore, the ice allows snow to accumulate on top of it, thereby setting up conditions that could lead to even lower temperatures.

There are other mechanisms by which tectonic processes* may influence climate. In Fig. 19.8, notice that the formation of oceanic plates (plates that lie beneath the ocean) begins at a *ridge*, where dense, molten material from inside the earth wells up to the surface, forming new sea floor material as it hardens. Spreading (on the order of several centimeters a year) takes place at the ridge center, where two oceanic plates move away from one another. When an oceanic plate encounters a lighter continental

*Tectonic processes are large-scale processes that deform the earth's crust.

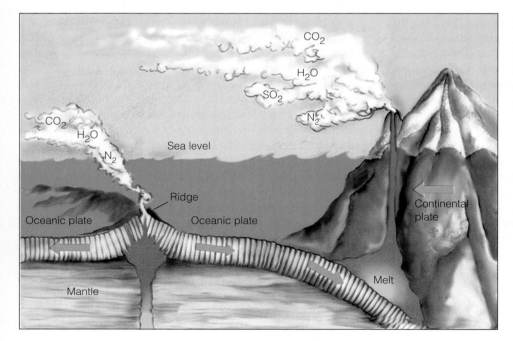

Figure 19.8
The earth is composed of a series of moving plates. The rate at which plates move (spread) may influence global climate. During times of rapid spreading, increased volcanic activity may promote global warming by enriching the CO_2 content of the atmo-sphere.

plate, it responds by diving under it, in a process called *subduction*. Heat and pressure then melt a portion of the subducting rock, which usually consists of volcanic rock and calcium-rich ocean sediment. The molten rock may then gradually work its way to the surface, producing volcanic eruptions that spew water vapor, carbon dioxide, and minor amounts of other gases into the atmosphere. The release of these gases (called *degassing*) usually takes place at other locations as well (for instance, at ridges where new crustal rock is forming.)

Some scientists speculate that climatic change, taking place over millions of years, might be related to the rate at which the plates move and, hence, related to the amount of CO_2 in the air. For example, during times of rapid spreading, a relatively wide ridge forms, causing sea level to rise relative to the continents. At the same time, an increase in volcanic activity vents large quantities of CO_2 into the atmosphere, which enhances the atmospheric greenhouse effect, causing global temperatures to rise. Moreover, a higher sea level means that there is less exposed landmass and, presumably, less chemical weathering of rocks*— a process that removes CO_2 from the atmosphere. However, as global temperatures climb, increasing temperatures promote chemical weathering that removes atmospheric CO_2 at a faster rate.

Millions of years later, when spreading rates decrease, less volcanic activity means less degassing. The changing shape of the underwater ridge causes the sea level to drop relative to the continents, exposing more rocks for chemical attack and the removal of CO_2 from the air. A reduction in CO_2 levels weakens the greenhouse effect, which causes global temperatures to drop. The accumulation of ice and snow over portions of the continents may promote additional cooling by reflecting more sunlight back to space. The cooling, however, will not go unchecked, as lower temperatures retard both the chemical weathering of rocks and the depletion of atmospheric CO_2.

A chain of volcanic mountains forming above a subduction zone may disrupt the airflow over them. By the same token, mountain-building that occurs when two continental plates collide (like that which presumably formed the Himalayan mountains and Tibetan highlands) can have a marked influence on global circulation patterns and, hence, on the climate of an entire hemisphere.

Climate Change and Variations in the Earth's Orbit

A theory ascribing climatic changes to variations in the earth's orbit is the **Milankovitch theory,** named for the astronomer Milutin Milankovitch, who first proposed the idea in the 1930s. The basic premise of this theory is that, as the earth travels through space, three separate cyclic movements combine to produce variations in the amount of solar energy that falls on the earth.

The first cycle deals with changes in the shape (**eccentricity**) of the earth's orbit as the earth revolves about the sun. Notice in Fig. 19.9 that the earth's orbit changes from being el-

Figure 19.9
For the earth's orbit to stretch from nearly a circle (solid line) to an elliptical orbit (dashed line) and back again takes nearly 100,000 years. (Diagram is highly exaggerated and is not to scale.)

liptical to being nearly circular. To go from less elliptical to more elliptical and back again takes about 100,000 years. The greater the eccentricity of the orbit (that is, the more eccentric the orbit), the greater the variation in solar energy received by the earth between its closest and farthest approach to the sun.

Presently, we are in a period of low eccentricity. The earth is closer to the sun in January and farther away in July (see Chapter 3, p. 56). The difference in distance (which only amounts to about 3 percent) is responsible for a nearly 7 percent increase in the solar energy received at the top of the atmosphere from July to January. When the difference in distance is 9 percent (a highly eccentric orbit), the difference in solar energy received will be on the order of 20 percent. In addition, the more eccentric orbit will change the length of seasons in each hemisphere by changing the length of time between the vernal and autumnal equinoxes.†

The second cycle takes into account the fact that, as the earth rotates on its axis, it wobbles like a spinning top. This wobble, known as the **precession** of the earth's axis, occurs in a cycle of about 23,000 years. Presently, the earth is closer to the sun in January and farther away in July. Due to precession, the reverse will be true in about 11,000 years (see Fig. 19.10). In about 23,000 years we will be back to where we are today. This means, of course, that if everything else remains the same, 11,000 years from now seasonal variations in the Northern Hemisphere should be greater than at present. The opposite would be true for the Southern Hemisphere.

The third cycle takes about 41,000 years to complete and relates to the changes in tilt (**obliquity**) of the earth as it orbits the sun. Presently, the earth's orbital tilt is $23\frac{1}{2}°$, but during the 41,000-year cycle the tilt varies from about 22° to $24\frac{1}{2}°$. The smaller the tilt, the less seasonal variation there is between summer and winter in middle and high latitudes. Thus, winters

---

*Chemical weathering is the process by which rocks decompose.

†Although rather large percentage changes in solar energy can occur between summer and winter, the globally and annually averaged change in solar energy received by the earth (due to orbital changes) hardly varies at all. It is the distribution of incoming solar energy that changes, not the totals.

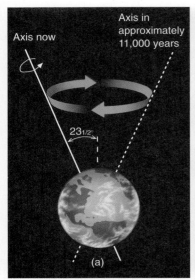

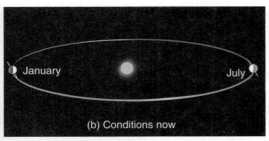

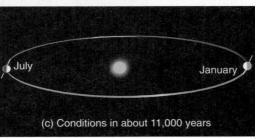

Figure 19.10
(a) Like a spinning top, the earth's axis of rotation slowly moves and traces out the path of a cone in space. (b) Presently the earth is closer to the sun in January, when the Northern Hemisphere experiences winter. (c) In about 11,000 years, due to precession, the earth will be closer to the sun in July, when the Northern Hemisphere experiences summer.

tend to be milder and summers cooler. During the warmer winters, more snow would probably fall in polar regions due to the air's increased capacity for water vapor. And during the cooler summers, less snow would melt. As a consequence, the periods of smaller tilt would tend to promote the formation of glaciers in high latitudes. In fact, when all of the cycles are taken into account, the present trend should be toward a cooler climate over the Northern Hemisphere.

In summary, the Milankovitch cycles that combine to produce variations in solar radiation received at the earth's surface include:

1. changes in the shape *(eccentricity)* of the earth's orbit about the sun
2. *precession* of the earth's axis of rotation, or wobbling
3. changes in the tilt *(obliquity)* of the earth's axis

In the 1970s, scientists of the CLIMAP project found strong evidence in deep-ocean sediments that variations in climate during the past several hundred thousand years were closely associated with the Milankovitch cycles. More recent studies have strengthened this premise. For example, studies conclude that during the past 800,000 years, ice sheets have peaked about every 100,000 years. This conclusion corresponds naturally to variations in the earth's eccentricity. Superimposed on this situation are smaller ice advances that show up at intervals of about 41,000 years and 23,000 years. It appears, then, that eccentricity is the *forcing factor*—the external cause—for the frequency of glaciation, as it appears to control the severity of the climatic variation.

But orbital changes alone are probably not totally responsible for ice buildup and retreat. Evidence (from trapped air bubbles in the ice sheets of Greenland and Antarctica representing thousands of years of snow accumulation) reveals that CO_2 levels were about 30 percent lower during colder glacial periods than during warmer interglacial periods. Analysis of air bubbles in Antarctic ice cores reveals that methane follows a pattern similar to that of CO_2 (see Fig. 19.11). This knowledge suggests that lower atmospheric CO_2 levels may have had the effect of amplifying the cooling initiated by the orbital changes. Likewise, increasing CO_2 levels at the end of the glacial period may have accounted for the rapid melting of the ice sheets. Just why atmospheric CO_2 levels have varied as glaciers expanded and contracted is not clear, but it appears to be due to changes in biological activity taking place in the oceans.

Perhaps, also, changing levels of CO_2 indicate a shift in ocean circulation patterns. Such shifts, brought on by changes in precipitation and evaporation rates, may alter the distribution of heat energy around the world. Alteration wrought in this manner could, in turn, affect the global circulation of winds, which may explain why alpine glaciers in the Southern Hemisphere expanded and contracted in tune with Northern Hemisphere glaciers during the last ice age, even though the Southern Hemisphere (according to the Milankovitch cycles) was not in an orbital position for glaciation.

Still other factors may work in conjunction with the earth's orbital changes to explain the temperature variations between glacial and interglacial periods. Some of these are

1. the amount of dust and other aerosols in the atmosphere
2. the reflectivity of the ice sheets
3. the concentration of other trace gases, such as methane
4. the changing characteristics of clouds
5. the rebounding of land, having been depressed by ice

Hence, the Milankovitch cycles, in association with other natural factors, may explain the advance and retreat of ice over periods of 10,000 to 100,000 years. But what caused the Ice Age to begin in the first place? And why have periods of glaciation been so infrequent during geologic time? The Milankovitch theory does not attempt to answer these questions.

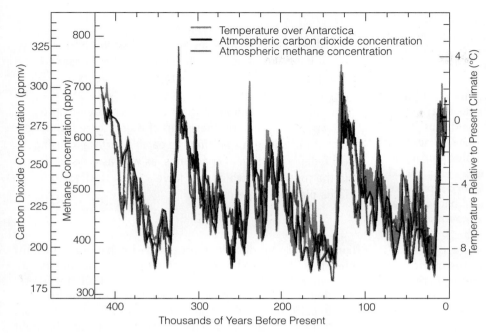

Figure 19.11
Variations of temperature (red line, °C), carbon dioxide (black line, ppmv), and methane (blue line, ppbv). Concentrations of gases are derived from air bubbles trapped within the ice sheets of Antarctica and extracted from ice cores. Temperatures are derived from the analysis of oxygen isotopes. (Note: ppmv represents parts per million by volume, and ppbv represents parts per billion by volume.) (*Source:* From Climate Change 2001: The Scientific Basis, 2001, by J.T. Houghton, et al. Copyright © 2001 Cambridge University Press. Reprinted with permission of the Intergovernmental Panel on Climate Change.)

Climate Change and Atmospheric Particles   Microscopic liquid and solid particles *(aerosols)* that enter the atmosphere from both human-induced (anthropogenic) and natural sources can have an effect on climate. The effect, however, is exceedingly complex and depends upon a number of factors, such as the particle's size, shape, color, chemical composition, and vertical distribution above the surface. In this section, we will first examine aerosols in the lower atmosphere. Then we will examine the effect that volcanic aerosols in the stratosphere have on climate.

Aerosols in the Troposphere   Aerosols enter the lower atmosphere in a variety of ways—from factory and auto emissions, agricultural burning, wildland fires, and dust storms. Some particles (such as soil dust and sulfate particles) mainly reflect and scatter incoming sunlight, while others (such as smoky soot) readily absorb sunlight, which warms the air around them. Many aerosols that reduce the amount of sunlight reaching the earth's surface tend to cause net cooling of the surface air during the day. Certain aerosols also selectively absorb and emit infrared energy back to the surface, producing a net warming of the surface air at night. However, the overall net effect of human-induced (anthropogenic) aerosols on climate is to *cool the surface.*

In recent years, the effect of highly reflective **sulfate aerosols** on climate has been extensively researched. In the lower atmosphere, the majority of these particles come from the combustion of sulfur-containing fossil fuels but emissions from smoldering volcanoes can also be a significant source of tropospheric sulfate aerosols. Sulfur pollution, which has more than doubled globally since preindustrial times, enters the atmosphere mainly as sulfur dioxide gas. There, it transforms into tiny sulfate droplets or particles. Since these aerosols usually remain in the atmosphere for only a few days, they do not have time to spread around the globe. Hence, they are not well mixed and their effect is felt mostly over the Northern Hemisphere, especially over polluted regions. Over the oceans, a major source of sulfate aerosols comes from tiny drifting aquatic plants—phytoplankton—that produce *dimethylsulphide* (DMS). The DMS slowly diffuses into the atmosphere where it oxidizes to form sulfur dioxide, which in turn converts to sulfate aerosols.

Sulfate aerosols not only scatter incoming sunlight back to space, but they also serve as cloud condensation nuclei. Consequently, they have the potential for altering the physical characteristics of clouds. For example, if the number of sulfate aerosols and, hence, condensation nuclei inside a cloud should increase, the cloud would have to share its available moisture with the added nuclei, a situation that should produce many more (but smaller) cloud droplets. The greater number of droplets would reflect more sunlight and have the effect of brightening the cloud and reducing the amount of sunlight that reaches the surface.

In summary, sulfate aerosols reflect incoming sunlight, which tends to lower the earth's surface temperature during the day. Sulfate aerosols may also modify clouds by increasing their reflectivity. Because sulfate pollution has increased significantly over industrialized areas of eastern Europe, northeastern North America and China, the cooling effect brought on by these particles may explain: (1) why the Northern Hemisphere has warmed less than the Southern Hemisphere during the past several decades, (2) why the United States has experienced little warming compared to the rest of the world, and (3) why most of the global warming has occurred at night and not during the day, especially over polluted areas. Research is still being done, and the overall effect of tropospheric aerosols on the climate system is not totally understood. (Information regarding the possible effect on climate from particles injected into the atmosphere during nuclear war is given in the Focus section on p. 533.)

Volcanic Eruptions and Aerosols in the Stratosphere Volcanic eruptions can have a definitive impact on climate. During volcanic eruptions, fine particles of ash and dust (as well as gases) can be ejected into the stratosphere (see Fig. 19.12). Scientists agree that the volcanic eruptions having the greatest impact on climate are those rich in sulfur gases. These gases, over a period of about two months, combine with water vapor in the presence of sunlight to produce tiny, reflective sulfuric acid particles that grow in size, forming a dense layer of haze. The haze may reside in the stratosphere for several years, absorbing and reflecting back to space a portion of the sun's incoming energy. The absorption of the sun's energy along with the absorption of infrared energy from the earth, warms the stratosphere. The reflection of incoming sunlight by the haze tends to cool the air at the earth's surface, especially in the hemisphere where the eruption occurs.

Two of the largest volcanic eruptions of the 20th century in terms of their sulfur-rich veil, were that of El Chichón in Mexico during April, 1982, and Mount Pinatubo in the Philippines during June, 1991.* Mount Pinatubo ejected an estimated 20 mil-

---

*The eruption of Mount Pinatubo in 1991 was many times greater than that of Mount St. Helens in the Pacific Northwest in 1980. In fact, the largest eruption of Mount St. Helens was a lateral explosion that pulverized a portion of the volcano's north slope. The ensuing dust and ash (and very little sulfur) had virtually no effect on global climate as the volcanic material was confined mostly to the lower atmosphere and fell out quite rapidly over a large area of the northwestern United States.

Weather Watch

Could atmospheric particles and a nuclear winter-type event have contributed to the demise of the dinosaurs? One theory proposes that about 65 million years ago a giant meteorite slammed into the earth with such impact that it sent billions of tons of dust and debris into the upper atmosphere. These particles greatly reduced the amount of sunlight reaching the earth's surface, causing cold, dark, and dismal conditions, as well as a disruption in the food chain, which may have adversely affected large plant-eating dinosaurs.

lion tons of sulfur dioxide (more than twice that of El Chichón) that gradually worked its way around the globe (see Fig. 19.13). For major eruptions such as this one, mathematical models predict that average hemispheric temperatures can drop by about 0.2° to 0.5°C or more for one to three years after the eruption. Model predictions agreed with temperature changes brought on by the Pinatubo eruption, as in early 1992 the mean global surface temperature had decreased by about 0.5°C (see Fig. 19.14). The cooling might even have been greater had the eruption not coincided with a major El Niño event that began in 1990 and lasted until early 1995 (see Chapter 11, p. 303, for information on El Niño).

As previously noted, volcanic eruptions rich in sulfur warm the lower stratosphere. During the winter, the tropical stratosphere can become much warmer than the polar stratosphere. This situation produces a strong horizontal pressure gradient

Figure 19.12
Large volcanic eruptions rich in sulfur can affect climate. As sulfur gases in the stratosphere transform into tiny reflective sulfuric acid particles, they prevent a portion of the sun's energy from reaching the surface. Here, the Philippine volcano Mount Pinatubo erupts during June, 1991.

Focus on A SPECIAL TOPIC

Nuclear Winter—Climate Change Induced by Nuclear War

A number of studies indicate that a nuclear war involving hundreds or thousands of nuclear detonations would drastically modify the earth's climate.

Researchers assume that a nuclear war would raise an enormous pall of thick, sooty smoke from massive fires that would burn for days, even weeks, following an attack. The smoke would drift higher into the atmosphere, where it would be caught in the upper-level westerlies and circle the middle latitudes of the Northern Hemisphere. Unlike soil dust, which mainly scatters and reflects incoming solar radiation, soot particles readily absorb sunlight. Hence, for several weeks after the war, sunlight would virtually be unable to penetrate the smoke layer, bringing darkness or, at best, twilight at midday.

Such reduction in solar energy would cause surface air temperatures over landmasses to drop below freezing, even during the summer, resulting in extensive damage to plants and crops and the death of millions (or perhaps billions) of people. The dark, cold, and gloomy conditions that would be brought on by nuclear war are often referred to as **nuclear winter.**

As the lower troposphere cools, the solar energy absorbed by the smoke particles in the upper troposphere would cause this region to warm. The end result would be a strong, stable temperature inversion extending from the surface up into the higher atmosphere. A strong inversion would lead to a number of adverse effects, such as suppressing convection, altering precipitation processes, and causing major changes in the general wind patterns.

The heating of the upper part of the smoke cloud would cause it to rise upward into the stratosphere, where it would then drift southward. Thus, about one-third of the smoke would remain in the atmosphere for a year or longer. The other two-thirds would be washed out in a month or so by precipitation. This smoke lofting, combined with persisting sea ice formed by the initial cooling, would produce climatic change that would remain for several years.

Virtually all research on nuclear winter, including models and analog studies, confirms this gloomy scenario. Observations of forest fires show lower temperatures under the smoke, confirming part of the theory. A three-year study involving more than 300 scientists from more than 30 countries conducted by the Scientific Committee On Problems of the Environment (SCOPE) of the International Council of Scientific Unions has detailed the climatic, environmental, and agricultural effects of nuclear winter. The implications of nuclear winter are clear: A nuclear war would drastically alter global climate and would devastate our living environment.

Even with improved global superpower relations, and the end of the Cold War, the danger of nuclear winter remains a possibility. Presently, the current global nuclear arsenal is more than that needed to produce the effects of a nuclear winter. As other nations develop nuclear capability, the potential for nuclear winter remains with us. It will not disappear until the global nuclear weapons arsenal numbers in the hundreds, not in the thousands.

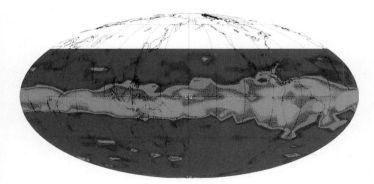

Figure 19.13
Sulfur dioxide plume (dark red and green areas) from the eruption of Mount Pinatubo as measured by the Upper Atmosphere Research Satellite on September 21, 1991. Only three months after the eruption, the plume girdles the equator in the stratosphere at an altitude near 25 km.

and strong west-to-east (zonal) stratospheric winds. These winds apparently work their way down into the upper troposphere, where they direct milder maritime surface air from off the ocean onto the continents. The milder ocean air produces warmer winters over Northern Hemisphere continents during the first or second winter after the eruption occurs.

An infamous cold spell often linked to volcanic activity occurred during the year 1816, "the year without a summer" mentioned earlier. Apparently, a rather stable longwave pattern in the atmosphere produced unseasonably cold summer weather over eastern North America and western Europe. The cold weather followed the massive eruption in 1815 of Mount Tambora in Indonesia. In addition to this, major volcanic eruptions occurred in the four years preceding Tambora. If, indeed, the cold weather pattern was brought on by volcanic eruptions, it was probably an accumulation of several volcanoes loading the stratosphere with particles—particles that probably remained there for several years.

Weather Watch

The year without a summer (1816) even had its effect on literature. Inspired (or perhaps dismayed) by the cold, gloomy, summer weather along the shores of Lake Geneva, Mary Shelley wrote the novel *Frankenstein*.

In an attempt to correlate sulfur-rich volcanic eruptions with long-term trends in global climate, scientists are measuring the acidity of annual ice layers in Greenland and Antarctica. Generally, the greater the concentration of sulfuric acid particles in the atmosphere, the greater the acidity of the ice layer. Relatively acidic ice has been uncovered from about A.D. 1350 to about 1700, a time that corresponds to a cooling trend. Such findings suggest that sulfur-rich volcanic eruptions may have played an important role in triggering this comparatively cool period and, perhaps, other cool periods during the geologic past. Moreover, recent core samples taken from the northern Pacific Ocean reveal that volcanic eruptions in the northern Pacific were at least 10 times larger 2.6 million years ago (a time when Northern Hemisphere glaciation began) than previous volcanic events recorded elsewhere in the sediment.

Climate Change and Variations in Solar Output

In the past, it was thought that solar energy did not vary by more than a fraction of a percent over many centuries. However, measurements made by sophisticated radiometers aboard satellites suggest that the sun's energy output may vary more than was thought. Moreover, the sun's energy output appears to change slightly with sunspot activity.

Sunspots are huge magnetic storms on the sun that show up as cooler (darker) regions on the sun's surface. They occur in cycles, with the number and size reaching a maximum approximately every 11 years. During periods of maximum sunspots, the sun emits more energy (about 0.1 percent more) than during periods of sunspot minimums (see Fig. 19.15). Ev-

idently, the greater number of bright areas *(faculae)* around the sunspots radiate more energy, which offsets the effect of the dark spots.

It appears that the 11-year sunspot cycle has not always prevailed. Apparently, between 1645 and 1715, during the period known as the **Maunder minimum,*** there were few, if any, sunspots. It is interesting to note that the minimum occurred during a cool spell in the temperature record shown in Fig. 19.5, p. 523. Some scientists suggest that a reduction in the sun's energy output was, in part, responsible for this cold spell.

In an attempt to better understand the sun's behavior, solar researchers are examining stars that are similar in age and mass to our sun. Recent observations suggest that, in some of these stars, energy output may vary by as much as 0.4 percent, leading some scientists to speculate that changes in the sun's brightness might account for part of the global warming during the last century.

The sun's magnetic field varies with sunspot activity and actually reverses every 11 years. Because it takes 22 years to return to its original state, the sun's *magnetic cycle* is 22 years, rather than 11. Some researchers point to the fact that periodic 20-year droughts on the Great Plains of the United States seem to correlate with this 22-year solar cycle. More recently, scientists have found a relationship between the 11-year sunspot cycle and weather patterns across the Northern Hemisphere. It appears that winter warmings might be related to variations in sunspots and to a pattern of reversing stratospheric winds over the tropics, known as the *quasi-biennial oscillation* (because it takes about 2 years for the winds to complete the cycle).

Earlier, we learned that the total energy output of the sun varies over an 11-year sunspot cycle by only about 0.1 percent. However, most of this variation is in the ultraviolet wavelength, which is absorbed by stratospheric ozone. But ozone varies with the sunspot cycle, reaching a maximum during sunspot maxi-

---

*This period is named after E. W. Maunder, the British solar astronomer who first discovered the low sunspot period sometime in the late 1880s.

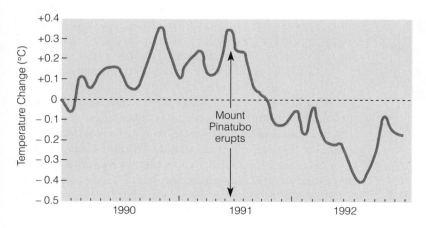

Figure 19.14

Changes in average global air temperature from 1990 to 1992. After the eruption of Mount Pinatubo in June, 1991, the average global temperature by July, 1992, decreased by almost 0.5°C (0.9°F) from the 1981 to 1990 average (dashed line).

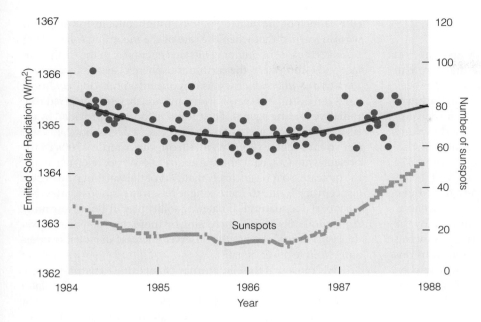

Figure 19.15
Changes in solar energy output (upper curve) in watts per square meter as measured by the *Earth Radiation Budget Satellite.* Bottom curve represents the yearly average number of sunspots. As sunspot activity increases from minimum to maximum, the sun's energy output increases by about 0.1 percent.

mum. Consequently, during sunspot maximum, more ozone is able to absorb the excess ultraviolet radiation. This absorption warms the stratosphere, producing temperature gradients and winds that appear to influence the circulation in the troposphere, especially the tropical Hadley cell (see Chapter 11) and the mid-latitude storm track.

To sum up, fluctuations in solar output may account for climatic changes over time scales of decades and centuries. To date, many theories have been proposed linking solar variations to climate change, but none have been proven. However, instruments aboard satellites and solar telescopes on the earth are monitoring the sun to observe how its energy output may vary. Because many years of data are needed, it may be some time before we fully understand the relationship between solar activity and climate change on earth.

Brief Review   Before going on to the next section, here is a brief review of some of the facts and concepts we covered so far:

- The earth's climate is constantly undergoing change. Evidence suggests that throughout much of the earth's history, the earth's climate was much warmer than it is today.

- The most recent glacial period (or Ice Age) began about 2 million years ago. During this time, glacial advances were interrupted by warmer periods called *interglacial periods.* In North America, glaciers reached their maximum thickness and extent about 18,000 to 22,000 years ago and disappeared completely from North America by about 6000 years ago.

- The Younger-Dryas event represents a time about 12,000 years ago when northeastern North America and northern Europe reverted back to glacier conditions.

- Over the last 100 years or so, the earth's surface temperature has increased by about 0.6°C (about 1°F).

- The shifting of continents, along with volcanic activity and mountain building, are possible causes of climate change.

- The Milankovitch theory (in association with other natural forces) proposes that altering glacial and interglacial episodes during the past 2 million years are the result of small variations in the tilt of the earth's axis and in the geometry of the earth's orbit around the sun.

- Trapped air bubbles in the ice sheets of Greenland and Antarctica reveal that CO_2 levels and methane levels were lower during colder glacial periods and higher during warmer interglacial periods.

- Sulfate aerosols in the troposphere reflect incoming sunlight, which tends to lower the earth's surface temperature during the day. Sulfate aerosols may also modify clouds by increasing the cloud's reflectivity.

- Volcanic eruptions, rich in sulfur, may be responsible for cooler periods that span years and decades in the geologic past.

- Fluctuation in solar output (brightness) may account for climatic changes over time scales of decades and centuries.

In previous sections, we saw how increasing levels of CO_2 may have contributed to changes in global climate spanning thousands and even millions of years. Today, we are undertaking a global scientific experiment by injecting vast quantities of greenhouse gases into our atmosphere without fully understanding the long-term consequences. The next section describes how CO_2 and other trace gases appear to be enhancing the earth's greenhouse effect, producing global warming.

Global Warming

We know from Chapter 2 that CO_2 is a greenhouse gas that strongly absorbs infrared radiation and plays a major role in warming the lower atmosphere. We also know that CO_2 has been increasing steadily in the atmosphere, primarily due to the burning of fossil fuel (see Fig. 1.4, p. 6). However, deforestation is also adding to this increase as tropical rain forests are cut down and replaced with plants less efficient in removing CO_2 from the atmosphere. In 2001, the annual average of CO_2 was about 374 parts per million, and present estimates are that if CO_2 levels continue to increase at the same rate that they have been (about 1.5 parts per million per year), atmospheric concentrations will rise to between 540 and 970 parts per million by the end of this century. To complicate the picture, trace gases such as methane (CH_4), nitrous oxide (N_2O), and chlorofluorocarbons (CFCs), all of which readily absorb infrared radiation, have been increasing in concentration over the past century.* Collectively, the increase in these gases is about equal to CO_2 in their ability to enhance the atmospheric greenhouse effect.

Numerical climate models (mathematical models that simulate climate) predict that by the end of this century increasing concentrations of greenhouse gases will result in a mean global warming of surface air between 1.4° and 5.8°C (between about 2.5° and 10.5°F) above the average surface air temperature of 1990. The newest, most sophisticated models take into account a number of important relationships, including the interactions between the oceans and the atmosphere, the processes by which CO_2 is removed from the atmosphere, and the cooling effect produced by sulfate aerosols in the lower atmosphere. The models also predict that as the air warms, additional water vapor will evaporate from the oceans into the air. The added water vapor (which is the most abundant greenhouse gas) will produce a positive feedback by enhancing the atmospheric greenhouse effect and accelerating the temperature rise. (This is the *water vapor-greenhouse effect feedback* described on p. 527.) Without this feedback produced by the added water vapor, the models predict that the warming will be much less.

The Recent Warming   Earlier in this chapter we saw that, since the beginning of the 20th century, the average global surface air temperature has risen about 0.6°C. Is this warming due to increasing greenhouse gases and an enhanced greenhouse effect? Before we can address this question, we need to review a few concepts we learned in Chapter 2.

Radiative Forcing Agents   We know from Chapter 2 that our world without water vapor, CO_2, and other greenhouse gases would be a colder world—about 33°C (59°F) colder than at present. With an average surface temperature of about −18°C

(0°F), much of the planet would be uninhabitable. In Chapter 2, we also learned that when the rate of the incoming solar energy balances the rate of outgoing infrared energy from the earth's surface and atmosphere, the earth-atmosphere system is in a state of *radiative equilibrium.* Increasing concentrations of greenhouse gases can disturb this equilibrium and are, therefore, referred to as **radiative forcing agents.** The **radiative forcing**† provided by extra CO_2 and other greenhouse gases increased by about 2.43 watts per square meter (2.43 W/m²) from the middle 1700s to the present, with CO_2 contributing about 1.46 W/m², or 60 percent of the increase. So it is very likely that part of the warming during the last century is due to increasing levels of greenhouse gases. But what part does natural climate variability play in global warming? And with levels of CO_2 increasing by more than 30 percent over the last century, why has the observed increase in global temperature been relatively small?

We know that the climate may change due to natural events. For example, changes in the sun's energy output (called *solar irradiance*) and volcanic eruptions rich in sulfur are two major natural radiative forcing agents. Studies show that since the middle 1700s, changes in the sun's energy output may have contributed a small positive forcing (about 0.3 W/m²) on the climate system, most of which occurred during the first half of the 20th century. On the other hand, volcanic eruptions that inject sulfur-rich particles into the stratosphere produce a negative forcing, which lasts for a few years after the eruption. Because several major eruptions occurred between 1880 and 1920, as well as between 1960 and 1991, the combined change in radiative forcing due to both volcanic activity and solar activity over the past 20 to 40 years appears to be negative. (The combined effect is that of cooling.) Recall that sulfur-rich aerosols near the surface also have a net cooling effect on the climate.

Climate Models and Recent Temperature Trends   How, then, does the temperature change observed over the last century compare with temperature changes derived from climate models? Before we look at what climate models reveal, it is important to realize that the interactions between the earth and its atmosphere are so complex that it is difficult to unequivocally *prove* that the warming trend during the past 100 years has been primarily to increasing concentrations of greenhouse gases. The problem is that any human-induced signal of climate change is superimposed on a background of natural climatic variations ("noise"), such as the El Niño-Southern Oscillation (ENSO) phenomenon (discussed in Chapter 11). Moreover, in the temperature observations, it is difficult to separate a signal from the noise of natural climate variability. However, today's more sophisticated climate models are much better at filtering out this

---

*Refer back to Chapter 1 and to Table 1.1, p. 3 for additional information on the concentration of these gases.

†Radiative forcing is interpreted as an increase (positive) or a decrease (negative) in net radiant energy observed over an area at the tropopause. All factors being equal, an *increase in radiative forcing* may induce surface *warming*, whereas a *decrease* may induce surface *cooling.*

noise while at the same time taking into account those forcing agents that are both natural and human-induced.

Figure 19.16 shows the predicted changes in surface air temperature from 1860 to 2000 made by different climate models using various scenarios (different forcing agents). The gray line presents the actual changes in surface air temperature from 1860 to 2000. Notice that when only increasing levels of greenhouse gases are plugged into the model (yellow line), the model shows a surface temperature increase in excess of 1°C. When greenhouse gases and aerosols are both added to the model (blue line), the increase in surface temperature is much less; in fact, it is less than the temperature increase observed over the past 100 years. However, when greenhouse gases, sulfate aerosols, and changes in solar radiation are *all* added to the model (red line), the projected temperature change and the observed temperature change closely match.

It is climate studies using computer models such as these that have led scientists to conclude that some of the warming during the 20th century is very likely due to increasing levels of greenhouse gases. In fact, the Intergovernmental Panel on Climate Change (IPCC), a committee of over 2000 leading earth scientists, considered the issues of climate change in a report published in 1990 and updated in 1992, in 1995, and again in

2001. The 2001 report, called the IPCC, TAR (Third Assessment Report), states that:

> In the light of new evidence and taking into account the remaining uncertainties, most of the observed warming over the last 50 years is likely to have been due to the increase in greenhouse gas concentrations.

Future Warming—Projections, Questions and Uncertainties

Today's climate models project that, due to increasing levels of greenhouse gases, the surface air temperature will increase between 1.4°C and 5.8°C from the year 1990 to the year 2100 (see Fig. 19.17). Notice that the smallest projected increase in temperature of 1.4°C is still twice that experienced during the 20th century. An increase of 5.8°C would have potentially devastating effects worldwide. Consequently, it is likely that the warming over this century will be much larger than the warming experienced during the 20th century and probably greater than any warming during the past 10,000 years.

There are, however, uncertainties in the climate picture. For example, it is not known how fast CO_2 levels will increase. Currently, the oceans and vegetation on land absorb about half of the CO_2 emitted by human sources. As a result, the

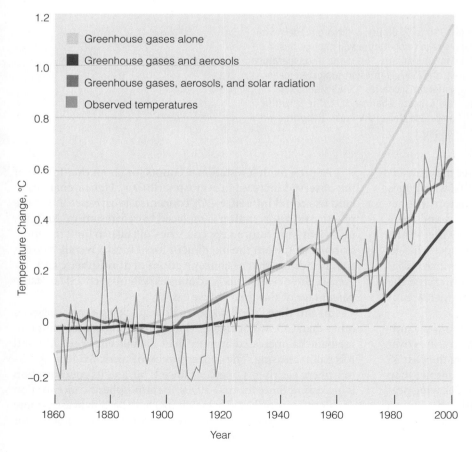

Figure 19.16

Projected surface air temperature changes, 1860 to 2000, using different climate models. Model input from greenhouse gases only is shown in yellow; input from greenhouse gases plus aerosols is shown in blue; input from greenhouse gases, sulfate aerosols, and solar energy changes is shown in red. The gray line shows observed surface temperatures. The dashed line is the 1860 to 1999 mean temperature. (Redrawn from "The Science of Climate Change" by Tom M. L. Wigley, published by the Pew Center of Global Climate Change.)

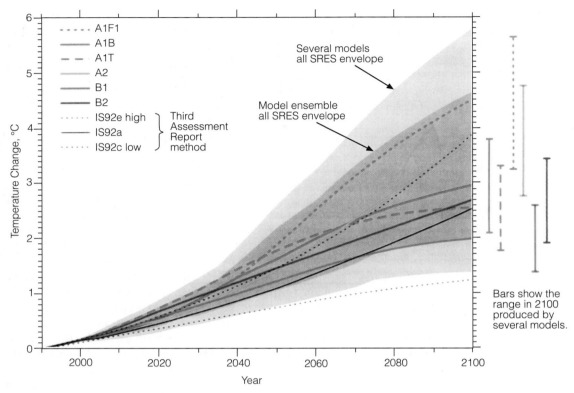

Figure 19.17

Global average projected temperature changes (°C) from 1990 to 2100 using climate models with six different scenarios. Each scenario describes how the average temperature will change based on different concentrations of greenhouse gases and various forcing agents. The range in temperature change for each model is shown on the left—IS92a, IS92c, and IS92e represent projected mean temperatures based on a 1992 climate model with three different scenarios. (SRES stands for "IPCC Special Report on Emission Scenarios") (*Source:* From Climate Change 2001: The Scientific Basis, 2001, by J.T. Houghton, et al. Copyright © 2001 Cambridge University Press. Reprinted with permission of the Intergovernmental Panel on Climate Change.)

oceans play a major role in the climate system, yet the exact effect they will have on rising levels of CO_2 and global warming is not totally clear. Microscopic plants (phytoplankton) extract CO_2 from the atmosphere during photosynthesis and store some of it below the ocean's surface, where they die. Will a warming earth trigger a large blooming of these tiny plants, in effect reducing the rate at which atmospheric CO_2 is increasing? Or would a gradual rise in ocean temperature increase the amount of CO_2 in the air due to the fact that warmer oceans can't hold as much CO_2 as colder ones?

In addition, rising temperatures may alter the way landmasses absorb and emit CO_2. For example, temperatures over the Alaskan tundra have risen dramatically during the past 35 years to the point where more frozen soil melts in summer than it used to. During warmer months, deep layers of decaying peat release CO_2 into the atmosphere. Until recently, this region absorbed more CO_2 than it released. Now, however, much of the tundra acts as a source for CO_2.

At present, deforestation accounts for about one-fourth of the observed increase in atmospheric CO_2. Hence, changes in land use could influence CO_2 concentrations, especially if the practice of deforestation is replaced by reforestation. And it is unknown what future steps countries will take to limit the emissions of CO_2 from the burning of fossil fuels. Overall, present trends indicate that as concentrations of atmospheric CO_2 increase, the oceans and landmasses will absorb a *decreasing* percentage of this greenhouse gas.

At this time, it is not known how quickly greenhouse gases other than CO_2 will increase. The atmospheric concentration of methane has increased by more than 150 percent since 1750, and it is still increasing. The concentration of nitric oxide in the atmosphere has risen 17 percent since 1750, and its concentration is increasing. Since the mid-1990s, the atmospheric concentration of chlorofluorocarbons (halocarbons) have been increasing more slowly or even decreasing. However, the substitute compounds for chlorofluorocarbons, which are also greenhouse gases, have been increasing. Moreover, the total amount of surface ozone probably increased by more than 30 percent since 1750. The concentration of this gas varies greatly from region to region, and depends upon the production of photochemical smog described in Chapter 17. The increase in surface ozone has probably led to a small increase in radiative forcing.

As the atmosphere warms and more water vapor is added to the air, global cloudiness might increase as well. How, then, would clouds—which come in a variety of shapes and sizes and form at different altitudes—affect the climate system? Clouds reflect incoming sunlight back to space, a process that tends to cool the climate, but they also absorb infrared radiation from the earth, which tends to warm it. Just how the climate will respond to changes in cloudiness will probably depend on the type of clouds that form and their physical properties, such as liquid water (or ice) content and droplet size distribution. For example, high, thin cirriform clouds (composed mostly of ice) tend to promote a net warming effect: They allow a good deal of sunlight to pass through (which warms the earth's surface), yet because they are cold, they warm the atmosphere by absorbing more infrared radiation from the earth than they emit upward. Low stratified clouds, on the other hand, tend to promote a net cooling effect. Composed mostly of water droplets, they reflect much of the sun's incoming energy, and, because their tops are relatively warm, they radiate away much of the infrared energy they receive from the earth. Satellite data from the Earth Radiation Budget Experiment confirm that, overall, clouds presently have a *net cooling effect* on our planet, which means that, without clouds, our atmosphere would be warmer.

Additional clouds in a warmer world would not necessarily have a net cooling effect, however. Their influence on the average surface air temperature would depend on their extent and on whether low or high clouds dominate the climate scene. Consequently, the feedback from clouds could potentially enhance or reduce the warming produced by increasing greenhouse gases. Most models show that as the surface air warms, there will be more convection, more convective-type clouds, and an increase in cirrus clouds. This situation would tend to provide a positive feedback on the climate system, and the effect of clouds on cooling the earth would be diminished.*

Some scientists speculate that an increase in towering cumuliform clouds, brought on by enhanced convection, will promote a negative feedback on global warming. They contend that as cumulus clouds develop, much of their water vapor will condense and fall to the surface as rain, leaving the upper part of the clouds relatively dry. Additionally, sinking air filling the space around the clouds produces warmer and dryer air aloft. Less water vapor, they feel, will diminish the effect of greenhouse warm-

ing. All modeling and observational studies, however, do not support these ideas, as convection generally moistens rather than dries the middle and upper troposphere.

Critics of global warming point to the fact that, even though the surface has warmed dramatically over the past two decades, the overall troposphere has not. Since 1979, satellite measurements indicate that, within the troposphere, the air has warmed 0° to 0.2°C, whereas surface stations during the same period show a warming of 0.25°C to 0.4°C. If an enhanced atmospheric greenhouse effect is in fact causing the surface warming, why hasn't the atmosphere warmed in tandem? Although this question has not been totally resolved, one answer may be that perhaps natural events, such as the ocean warming during El Niño and the cooling induced by large volcanic eruptions, may account for part of the temperature differences. Also, it could well be the case that the thinning of ozone in the stratosphere may be partly responsible for a cooler upper troposphere. In fact, studies indicate that, from 1979 to 2000, the depletion of ozone in the stratosphere caused a small negative radiative forcing. As the ozone layer recovers, it is likely that this negative forcing will diminish.

Possible Consequences of Global Warming   If the world warms as predicted by climate computer models, what will the warmer world be like? Climate models predict that land areas will warm more rapidly than the global average, particularly in the northern high latitudes in winter (see Fig. 19.18). In the high latitudes of the Northern Hemisphere, the dark green boreal forests absorb up to three times as much solar energy as the snow-covered tundra. Consequently, the winter temperatures in subarctic regions are, on the average, about 11.5°C (21°F) higher than they would be without trees. If warming allows the boreal forests to expand into the tundra, the forests may accelerate the warming in that region. As the temperature rises, organic matter in the soil should decompose at a faster rate, adding more CO_2 to the air, which might accelerate the warming even more. Moreover, trees that grow in a climate zone defined by temperature may become especially hard hit as rising temperatures place them in an inhospitable environment. In a weakened state, they may become more susceptible to insects and disease.

In a warmer world, enhanced evaporation of water should lead to greater worldwide average precipitation. During the warming of the 20th century, there appears to have been an increase in precipitation by as much as 10 percent over the middle- and high-latitude land areas of the Northern Hemisphere. In contrast, it appears that over subtropical land areas, a decrease in precipitation has occurred. Moreover, it appears that there has been an increase in the frequency of heavy precipitation events during the last half of the 20th century.

As the warming continues, some models predict that the jet stream will weaken and global winds will shift from their "normal" position. The shifting upper-level winds might reduce precipitation over certain areas, which, in turn, would put added stress on certain agricultural regions. These same models indi-

---

*In addition to the amount of distribution of clouds, the way in which climate models calculate the optical properties of a cloud (such as albedo) can have a large influence on the model's calculations. Also, there is much uncertainty as to how clouds will interact with aerosols, and what the net effect will be.

Focus on A SPECIAL TOPIC

The Sahel—An Example of Climatic Variability and Human Existence

The Sahel is in North Africa, located between about 14° and 18°N latitude (see Fig. 2). Bounded on the north by the dry Sahara and on the south by the grasslands of the Sudan, the Sahel is a semi-arid region of variable rainfall. Precipitation totals may exceed 50 cm (20 in.) in the southern portion while in the north, rainfall is scanty. Yearly rainfall amounts are also variable as a year with adequate rainfall can be followed by a dry one.

During the winter, the Sahel is dry but, as summer approaches, the Intertropical Convergence Zone (ITCZ) with its rain usually moves into the region. The inhabitants of the Sahel are mostly nomadic people who migrate to find grazing land for their cattle and goats. In the early and middle 1960s, adequate rainfall led to improved pasture lands; herds grew larger and so did the population. However, in 1968, the annual rains did not reach as far north as usual, marking the beginning of a series of dry years and a severe drought.

Rain fell in 1969, but the totals were far below those of the favorable years in the mid-1960s. The decrease in rainfall, along with overgrazing, turned thousands of square kilometers of pasture into barren wasteland. By 1973, when the severe drought reached its climax, rainfall totals were 50 percent of the long-term average, and perhaps 50 percent of the cattle and goats had died. The Sahara Desert had migrated southward into the northern fringes of the region, and a great famine had taken the lives of more than 100,000 people.

Although low rainfall years have been followed by wetter ones, relatively dry conditions have persisted over the region for the past 30 years or so. The wetter years of the 1950s and 1960s appear to be due to the northward displacement of the ITCZ. The drier years, however, appear to be more related to the intensity of rain that falls during the so-called rainy season. But what causes the lack of intense rain? Some scientists feel that this situation is due to a *biogeophysical*

feedback mechanism wherein less rainfall and reduced vegetation cover modify the surface and promote a positive feedback relationship: Surface changes act to reduce convective activity, which in turn promotes or reinforces the dry conditions. As an example, when the vegetation is removed from the surface (perhaps through overgrazing or excessive cultivation), the surface albedo (reflectivity) increases, and the surface temperature drops. But studies show that less vegetation cover does not always result in a higher albedo.

Since the mid-1970s the Sahara Desert has not progressively migrated southward into the Sahel. In fact, during dry years, the desert does migrate southward, but in wet years, it retreats. By the same token, vegetation cover throughout the Sahel is more extensive during the wetter years. Consequently, desertification is not presently overtaking the Sahel, nor is the albedo of the region showing much year-to-year change.

So the question remains: Why did the Sahel go from a period of abun-

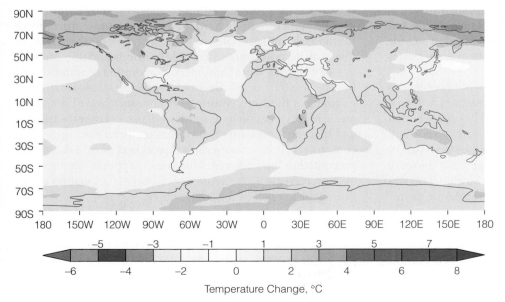

Figure 19.18
Projected changes in surface air temperature due to a doubling of CO_2 and human-induced sulfide emissions with an Atmospheric Ocean General Circulation Model (AOGCM). Notice that the greatest warming is projected for the northern polar latitudes. [After F. B. Mitchell, et al., "Transient climate response to increasing sulphate aerosols and greenhouse gases," *Nature* (1995) 376: 501–504.]

Temperature Change, °C

dant rainfall in the 1950s and early 1960s to relatively dry conditions since then? Was there a large change in the surface albedo brought on by reduced vegetation? Without adequate satellite imagery during those years, it is impossible to tell. Does this relatively dry spell indicate a long-term fluctuation in climate, or will the wetter years of the 1950s return? And if global temperatures rise into the next century, how will precipitation patterns change? At present, we have no answers.

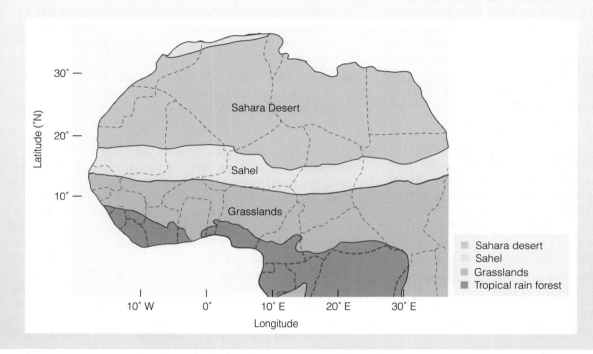

Figure 2
The semi-arid Sahel of North Africa is bounded by the Sahara Desert to the north and grasslands to the south.

cate that more precipitation will fall in winter over higher latitudes, and that precipitation intensity will increase, suggesting a possibility for more extreme rainfall events, such as floods and severe drought. In the mountainous regions of western North America, where much of the precipitation falls in winter, precipitation might fall mainly as rain, causing a decrease in snowmelt runoff that fills the reservoirs during the spring. As the planet warms, total rainfall must increase to balance the increase in evaporation. But at this point, climate models are unable to determine *exactly* how global precipitation patterns will change.

Other consequences of global warming will likely be a rise in sea level as alpine glaciers recede, polar ice melts, and the oceans continue to expand as they slowly warm. During the 20th century, sea level rose between 10 and 20 cm, and today's improved climate models estimate that sea level will rise an additional 9 to 88 cm by the end of this century, depending, of course, on how much the surface temperature increases. Rising ocean levels might have a damaging influence on coastal

ecosystems. In addition, coastal groundwater supplies might become contaminated with saltwater.

How the ice sheets in Antarctica and Greenland respond to global warming is not exactly clear. In polar regions, as elsewhere around the globe, rising temperatures produce complex interactions among temperature, precipitation, and wind patterns. Hence, it is now believed that as temperatures rise in south polar regions, more snow will fall in the warmer (but still cold) air, causing snow and ice to build up over the continent of Antarctica. Over

Weather Watch

Are you thinking of buying ocean-front property? If so, keep in mind that should the ocean level rise 50 cm (about 1.6 ft), ocean shorelines along the east coast of North America could retreat by as much as 750 m, or 2460 ft.

Greenland, where melting snow and ice are expected to exceed any increase in precipitation, the ice sheet is expected to shrink.

Increasing levels of CO_2 in a warmer world might have additional consequences. For example, higher levels of CO_2 might act as a "fertilizer" for some plants, accelerating their growth. Increased plant growth consumes more CO_2, which might retard the increasing rate of CO_2 in the environment. On the other hand, the increased plant growth might force some insects to eat more, resulting in a net loss in vegetation. It is possible that a major increase in CO_2 might upset the balance of nature, with some plant species becoming so dominant that others are eliminated. In tropical areas, where many developing nations are located, the warming may actually decrease crop yield, whereas in cold climates, where crops are now grown only marginally, the warming effect may actually increase crop yields.

Following are some conclusions about global warming and its future impact on our climate system summarized from the 2001 Third Assessment Report (TAR) of the Intergovernmental Panel on Climate Change (IPCC):

- The concentrations of the greenhouse gases methane, nitrous oxide, and carbon dioxide are all increasing. The present concentration of carbon dioxide has not been exceeded during the past 420,000 years, and it is likely not to have been during past 20 million years. The current rate of increase is unprecedented for at least the past 20,000 years.

- Emissions of long-lived greenhouse gases have a lasting effect on atmospheric composition, radiative forcing, and climate.

- The global average surface temperature has increased over the 20th century about 0.6°C (about 1°F).

- There is new and stronger evidence that most of the warming observed over the last 50 years is attributable to human activities.

- Global average temperature and sea level are projected to rise under all IPCC SRES scenarios, with the globally averaged surface temperature projected to increase by 1.4 to 5.8°C during the period 1990 to 2100.

- After greenhouse gas concentrations have stabilized, global average surface temperatures would rise at a rate of only a few tenths of a degree Celsius per century rather than the several degrees Celsius per century projected for the 21st century without stabilization.

- Global average water vapor concentration and precipitation are projected to increase during the 21st century.

- It is very likely that the 20th-century warming has, through thermal expansion of seawater and widespread loss of land ice, contributed significantly to the observed sea-level rise.

- Since 1950 it is very likely that there has been a reduction in the frequency of extreme low temperatures, with a smaller increase in the frequency of extreme high temperatures.

- It is likely that higher maximum temperatures and more hot days, along with higher minimum temperatures and fewer cold days, will occur during this century over nearly all land areas.

- Northern Hemisphere spring and summer sea-ice extent has decreased by about 10 to 15 percent since the late 1950s, and is projected to decrease further.

- It is likely that the warming associated with increasing greenhouse gas concentrations will cause an increase of Asian summer monsoon precipitation variability.

- Current projections show little change or a small increase in amplitude for El Niño events over the next 100 years.

- It is likely that over some tropical ocean, increasing water temperature may cause an increase in tropical cyclone peak winds, along with an increase in tropical cyclone mean and peak precipitation.

- Most models show weakening of the ocean thermohaline circulations, which leads to a reduction of the heat transport into high latitudes. (This phenomenon is the conveyor belt circulation described on pp. 524–525.)

In Perspective   Cutting down on the emissions of greenhouse gases and pollutants has several potentially positive benefits. For example, a reduction in greenhouse gas emissions might slow down the enhancement of the earth's greenhouse effect; a reduction in air pollutants might reduce acid rain, diminish haze, and slow the production of photochemical smog. Even if the greenhouse warming proves to be less than what modern climate models project, these measures would certainly benefit humanity.

As we look to the future of a warmer world, any modification of the earth's surface taking place right now could potentially influence the immediate climate of certain regions. For example, studies show that about half the rainfall in the Amazon River Basin is returned to the atmosphere through evaporation and through transpiration from the leaves of trees. Consequently, clearing large areas of tropical rain forests in South America to create open areas for farms and cattle ranges will most likely cause a decrease in evaporative cooling. This decrease, in turn, could lead to a warming in that area of at least several degrees Celsius. In turn, the reflectivity of the deforested area will change. Similar changes in albedo result from the overgrazing and excessive cultivation of grasslands in semi-arid regions, causing an increase in desert conditions (a process known as **desertification**).

Currently, billions of acres of the world's range and cropland, along with the welfare of millions of people, are affected by desertification. Annually, millions of acres are reduced to a state of near or complete uselessness. The main cause is overgrazing, although overcultivation, poor irrigation practices, and deforestation also play a role. The effect this will have on climate, as surface albedos increase and more dust is swept into the air, is uncertain. (For a look at how a modified surface influences the inhabitants of a region in Africa, read the Focus section on p. 540.)

Summary

In this chapter, we considered some of the many ways the earth's climate can be changed. First, we saw that the earth's climate has undergone considerable change during the geologic past. Some of the evidence for a changing climate comes from tree rings (dendrochronology), chemical analysis of oxygen isotopes in ice cores and fossil shells, and geologic evidence left behind by advancing and retreating glaciers. The evidence from these suggest that, throughout much of the geologic past (before humanity arrived on the scene), the earth was much warmer than it is today. There were cooler periods, however, during which glaciers advanced over large sections of North America and Europe.

We examined some of the possible causes of climate change, noting that the problem is extremely complex, as a change in one variable in the climate system almost immediately changes other variables. One theory suggests that the shifting of the continents, along with volcanic activity and mountain building, may account for variations in climate that take place over millions of years.

The Milankovitch theory proposes that alternating glacial and interglacial episodes during the past 2 million years are the result of small variations in the tilt of the earth's axis and in the geometry of the earth's orbit around the sun. Another theory suggests that certain cooler periods in the geologic past may have been caused by volcanic eruptions rich in sulfur. Still another theory postulates that climatic variations on earth might be due to variations in the sun's energy output.

We looked at temperature trends over the past 100 years and found that, over this span of time, the earth has warmed by about 0.6°C (about 1°F). It is likely that most of the warming during the last 50 years is due to increasing concentrations of greenhouse gases. Sophisticated climate models project that, as levels of CO_2 and other greenhouse gases continue to increase, the earth will warm by between 1.4°C and 5.8°C from 1990 to the end of this century. The models also predict that, as the earth warms, there will be a global increase in atmospheric water vapor, an increase in global precipitation, and a rise in sea level.

Key Terms

The following terms are listed in the order they appear in the text. Define each. Doing so will aid you in reviewing the material covered in this chapter.

dendrochronology
Ice Age
interglacial period
Younger-Dryas (event)
mid-Holocene maximum
Little Ice Age
water vapor-greenhouse feedback
positive feedback mechanism
snow-albedo feedback
negative feedback mechanism
theory of plate tectonics
Milankovitch theory
eccentricity
precession
obliquity
sulfate aerosols
nuclear winter
Maunder minimum
radiative forcing agents
radiative forcing
desertification

Questions for Review

1. What methods do scientists use to determine climate conditions that have occurred in the past?
2. How does the overall climate of the world today compare with the so-called "normal" climate throughout earth's history?
3. Explain how the changing climate influenced the formation of the Bering land bridge.
4. How does today's average global temperature compare with the average temperature during most of the past 1000 years?
5. What is the Younger-Dryas episode? When did it occur?
6. How does a positive feedback mechanism differ from a negative feedback mechanism? Is the water vapor-greenhouse feedback considered positive or negative? Explain.
7. How does the theory of plate tectonics explain climate change over periods of millions of years?
8. Describe the Milankovitch theory of climatic change by explaining how each of the three cycles alters the amount of solar energy reaching the earth.
9. Given the analysis of air bubbles trapped in polar ice during the past 160,000 years, were CO_2 levels generally higher or lower during colder glacial periods?
10. How do sulfate aerosols in the lower atmosphere affect surface air temperatures during the day?
11. Describe the scenario of nuclear winter.
12. Volcanic eruptions rich in sulfur warm the stratosphere. Do they warm or cool the earth's surface? Explain.
13. Explain how variations in the sun's energy output might influence global climate.
14. Climate models predict that increasing levels of CO_2 will cause the mean global surface temperature to rise by as much as 5.8°C by the year 2100. What other greenhouse gas must also increase in concentration in order for this condition to occur?
15. Describe some of the natural radiative forcing agents and their effect on climate.
16. (a) Describe how clouds influence the climate system.
    (b) Which clouds would tend to promote surface cooling: high clouds or low clouds?
17. Even though CO_2 concentrations have risen dramatically over the past 100 years, how do scientists explain the fact that global temperatures have risen by only 0.6°C?

18. Why do climate scientists now believe that at least part of the warming experienced during the 20th century was due to increasing levels of greenhouse gases?

19. List some of the consequences that increasing levels of CO_2 and other greenhouse gases might have on the atmosphere and its inhabitants.

20. Is CO_2 the only greenhouse gas we should be concerned with for anthropogenic climate change? If not, what are the other gases?

21. Why are glacial features often found in coastal Africa?

Questions for Thought

1. Ice cores extracted from Greenland and Antarctica have yielded valuable information on climate changes during the past few hundred thousands of years. What do you feel might be some of the limitations in using ice core information to evaluate past climate changes?

2. When glaciation was at a maximum (about 18,000 years ago), was global precipitation greater or less than at present? Explain your reasoning.

3. Consider the following climate change scenario. Warming global temperatures increase saturation vapor pressures over the ocean. As more water evaporates, increasing quantities of water vapor build up in the troposphere. More clouds form as the water vapor condenses. The clouds increase the albedo, resulting in decreased amounts of solar radiation reaching the earth's surface. Is this scenario plausible? What type(s) of feedback(s) is/are involved?

4. Explain why periods of glacial advance in the higher latitudes tend to occur with warmer winters and cooler summers.

5. Explain two different ways that an increase in sulfate particles might lower surface air temperatures.

6. Are ice ages in the Northern Hemisphere more likely when:
   (a) the tilt of the earth is at a maximum or a minimum?
   (b) the sun is closest to the earth during summer in the Northern Hemisphere, or during winter?
   Explain your reasoning for both (a) and (b).

7. Most climate models show that the poles will warm faster than the tropics. What effect will this have on winter storms in mid-latitudes?

8. The oceans are a major sink (absorber) of CO_2. One hypothesis states that as warming increases, less CO_2 will be dissolved in the oceans. Would you expect the earth to warm or to cool further? Why?

Problems and Exercises

1. If the annual precipitation near Hudson Bay (latitude 55°N) is 38 cm (15 in.) per year, calculate how long it would take snow falling on this region to reach a thickness of 3000 m (about 10,000 ft). (Assume that all the precipitation falls as snow, that there is no melting during the summer, and that the annual precipitation remains constant. To account for compaction of the snow, use a water equivalent of 5 to 1.)

2. On a warming planet, the snow-albedo feedback produces a positive feedback. Make a diagram (or several diagrams) to illustrate this phenomenon. Now, with another diagram, show that the snow-albedo feedback produces a positive feedback on a cooling planet.

Questions for Exploration

1. Use the Atmospheric Chemistry/Temperature Trends section of the Blue Skies CD-ROM to examine climate model predictions of future temperatures around the globe. Describe the simulated global temperature patterns 60 and 90 years into the future. What are the major differences?

2. Global Climate Change Data (http://cdiac.esd.ornl.gov/trends/trends.htm): Compare graphs of temperature trends for the Northern Hemisphere, the Southern Hemisphere, and the globe. Compare and contrast these trends. Which hemisphere has a trend that is most similar to the global trend?

3. Venus (http://qlink.queensu.ca/%7E4mr19/Venus.html): Study the climate of Venus. In what ways is it similar or dissimilar to the Earth's climate? Compare the greenhouse effect on both planets. Explain why Venus has a "runaway" greenhouse effect, while the Earth does not.

4. Paleoclimate (http://www.ngdc.noaa.gov/paleo/education.html): What is known about past climates? How does the climate change of the past 100 years compare to climate changes that have occurred in the past? When was the last glaciation? Do you think the earth could go back into a cooling trend with the formation of continental glaciers over North America? Explain your reasoning.

Go to the Brooks/Cole Earth Sciences Resource Center (http://earthscience.brookscole.com) for critical thinking exercises, articles, and additional readings from InfoTrac College Edition, Brooks/Cole's online student library.

Chapter 1

Earth Systems

Courtesy Graham R. Thompson /Jonathan Turk

Havasu Creek, a tributary of the Colorado River in
Grand Canyon

Earth Science ⊕ Now™

This icon, appearing throughout the book, indicates an opportunity to explore interactive tutorials, animations, or practice problems available on the Earth ScienceNow Web site at **http://earthscience.brookscole.com/earthsci3e**

1.1 Flowers Bloom on Earth, Venus Boils, and Mars Freezes

Earth is sometimes called the water planet or blue planet because more than two-thirds of its surface is covered by azure seas. Earth is the only planet or moon in the Solar System with rain falling from clouds, water running over the land in streams, and extensive oceans. It is also the only body in the Solar System that we know of that supports life.

Our Solar System originally evolved from a cloud of dust and gas rotating in the vast emptiness of space. Under the relentless pull of gravity, these particles condensed into discrete bodies that gradually evolved to form the Sun, the planets, and their moons. Thus, all of the planets formed from the same original mixture of materials. Yet today, the planets are distinctly different from one another. To appreciate these differences, let us briefly compare Earth with its two closest neighbors, Venus and Mars.

Of all the planets, Venus most closely resembles Earth in size, density, and distance from the Sun. Consequently, astronomers once thought that Venus might be similar to Earth, and that both water and life might be found there. However, data obtained from spacecraft reveal that Venus is extremely inhospitable (Figure 1.1). Any Earth-like life would quickly suffocate in the carbon dioxide-rich Venusian atmosphere. Caustic sulfuric acid clouds fill the sky. In addition, the surface of Venus is hot enough to melt lead, and therefore hot enough to destroy the organic molecules necessary for life.

Early in its history, Mars must have had a temperate climate somewhat like that of Earth today. Spacecraft images show extinct stream canyons, sea floors, and lake beds, indicating that flowing water must have been abundant on the planet (Figure 1.2). But today, the Martian surface is frigid and dry. Mars's winter ice caps are mostly frozen carbon dioxide, commonly called dry ice. If water is present on Mars, it lies frozen beneath the planet's surface.

If Earth, Venus, and Mars formed from the same materials, why are the three planets so different today? Why are we the only planet favored with great oceans, cascading waterfalls, blue skies, and abundant life?

Shortly after the formation of the planets, the original atmospheres of Earth, Venus, and Mars evolved into swirling mixtures of carbon dioxide, carbon monoxide, water, ammonia, methane, and other gases. To appreciate what happened next, we need to understand the behavior of carbon dioxide and water in planetary environments.

Water can be a solid, liquid, or gas. If liquid water cools, it turns to ice; when it is heated, it evaporates to form vapor. Thus water is removed from the atmosphere when it condenses or freezes whereas it is added to the atmosphere when it vaporizes. Carbon dioxide also exists in a variety of forms. At the Earth's surface, carbon dioxide occurs as an atmospheric gas, dissolves in seawater, and combines with calcium and oxygen to form a type of rock called limestone. (Carbon dioxide also exists as a liquid and a solid, but not within the Earth's natural environment). Carbon dioxide gas and water vapor are both greenhouse gases—they absorb infrared radiation and warm the atmosphere.

Because Venus is closer to the Sun than Earth is, it receives more solar radiation and was originally a bit warmer than it is now. Due to the higher temperature, water vapor never condensed, or if it did, it quickly evaporated again. Because there were no seas for carbon dioxide to dissolve into, most of the carbon dioxide also remained in the atmosphere. Both of these greenhouse gases caused Venus's atmosphere to heat up further. Heat released more water and carbon dioxide into the atmosphere and subsequently, these gases trapped more heat. The temperature spiraled higher and higher.

In contrast, Earth was cool enough so that the water vapor condensed to form vast oceans. Large amounts of carbon dioxide then dissolved in the seas or reacted to form limestone. Thus, large quantities of these two greenhouse gases were removed from the atmosphere. As a result, the atmosphere cooled. Fortunately for us, the temperature stabilized in a range favorable for the existence of liquid water and for the emergence and evolution of life. Mars is a little farther from the Sun than Earth is, and consequently it receives a little less solar energy. A carbon dioxide- and water vapor-rich Martian atmosphere probably evolved between 4.0 and 3.5 billion years ago. Both of these greenhouse gases absorbed the Sun's heat, producing a temperate climate despite the planet's greater distance from the Sun. Rain fell from clouds, rivers flowed, wind blew over shallow seas. Perhaps life evolved in this favorable environment. But because Mars is a little further from the Sun than Earth, its atmosphere cooled more than Earth's. This small initial cooling caused more water vapor to condense and more carbon dioxide to dissolve into the seas, lowering the amounts of greenhouse gases in the Martian atmosphere. The temperature spiraled downward. Today, the Martian surface occasionally becomes as warm as an autumn afternoon on Earth (20°C), but more

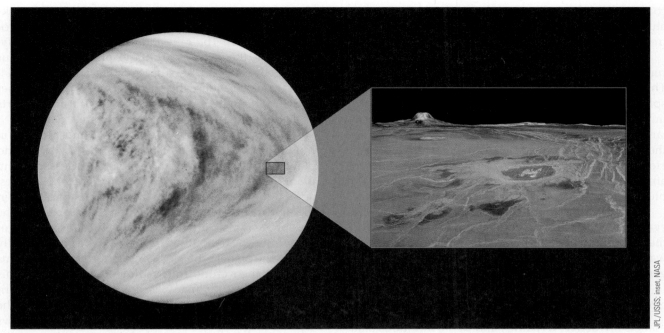

Figure 1.1 Space shot of Venus. Before astronomers could peer through the Venusian cloud cover or measure its temperature and composition, they speculated that Venus may harbor life. Today we know that the atmosphere is so hot and corrosive that living organisms could not possibly exist.

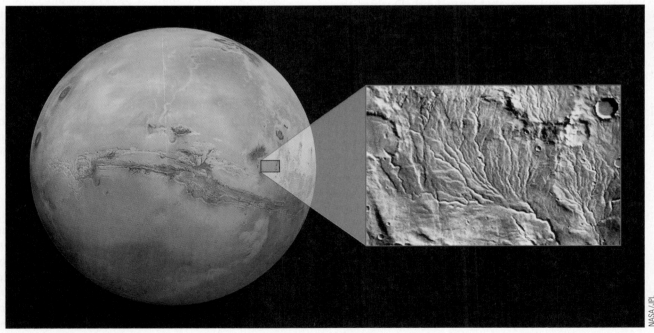

Figure 1.2 Water once flowed over the surface of Mars, eroding canyons and depositing sediment. However, today the planet is frigid and dry.

commonly, the temperature is below freezing. Temperatures as low as $-140°C$ have been recorded. At this extreme, carbon dioxide freezes into dry ice.

In summary, Venus is closer to the Sun and receives more solar radiation than either Earth or Mars. This small amount of extra solar energy initiated atmospheric changes that caused the planet to heat up much more than can be accounted for by the difference in solar energy alone. Of the three planets, Mars is the farthest from the Sun and receives the least solar energy. Here the cool initial temperatures triggered different atmospheric changes, and in this case, the temperature plummeted.

On Earth, a temperate climate prevailed. Life evolved. Then, over the course of a few billion years, the carbon dioxide- and water vapor-rich atmosphere was gradually replaced by an atmosphere rich in nitrogen and oxygen.

This example highlights the major themes summarized here:

Planets are active, dynamic, and in a continuous state of change. On Earth, a primordial poisonous atmosphere evolved into a favorable one. At the same time, continents formed in a global ocean and barren rock weathered into soil. Life formed, probably in the seas, and migrated onto land. During its history, the Earth's temperature has oscillated frequently and dramatically. At times, the planet has been warm enough to support vast tropical swamps, while at other times it has cooled sufficiently so that continental glaciers oozed from the poles and the high mountains.

Planetary changes are driven by complex interactions among the atmospheres, the seas, and the solid ground. On Earth, living organisms also alter the planet that supports them. For example, plant roots help weather rock into soil, and soil supports plants. During photosynthesis, plants produce oxygen, which plants and animals need for respiration. In many cases, small, seemingly insignificant perturbations can trigger a chain of events that will magnify the initial perturbation far beyond its initial impact. These examples illustrate how small differences in solar energy led to dramatic differences in the modern planetary environments of Earth, Venus, and Mars.

1.2 The Earth's Four Spheres

Imagine walking along a rocky coast as a storm blows in from the sea. Wind whips the ocean into whitecaps, gulls wheel overhead, and waves crash onto shore. Before you have time to escape, blowing spray has soaked your clothes. A hard rain begins as you scramble over the rocks to your car. During this adventure, you have observed the four major spheres of the Earth. The rocks and soil underfoot are the surface of the **geosphere,** or the solid Earth. The rain and sea are parts of the **hydrosphere,** the watery part of our planet. The gaseous layer above the Earth's surface is the **atmosphere**. Finally, you, the gulls, the beach grasses, and all other forms of life in the sea, on land, and in the air are parts of the **biosphere,** the realm of organisms.

You can readily observe that the atmosphere is in motion because clouds waft across the sky and wind blows against your face. Animals, and to a lesser extent, plants also move. Flowing streams, crashing waves, and falling rain are all familiar examples of motion in the hydrosphere. Although it is less apparent, the geosphere is also moving and dynamic. Vast masses of subterranean rock flow vertically and horizontally within the planet's interior, continents drift, mountains rise and then erode into sediment. Throughout this book we will study many of these phenomena to learn what energy forces set matter in motion and how the motion affects the world we live on. Figure 1.10 shows schematically all the possible interactions among the spheres. This figure will be repeated throughout the book with important arrows highlighted to emphasize interactions discussed in the accompanying text.

Figure 1.3 shows that the geosphere is by far the largest of the four spheres. The Earth's radius is about 6400 kilometers, $1\frac{1}{2}$ times the distance from New York to Los Angeles. Despite this great size, nearly all of our direct contact with the Earth occurs at or very near its surface. The deepest well penetrates only about 12 kilometers, $\frac{1}{533}$ of the total distance to the center. The oceans make up most of the hydrosphere, and the central ocean floor is about 5 kilometers deep. Most of the Earth's atmosphere lies within 30 kilometers of the surface, and the biosphere is a thin shell about 15 kilometers thick.

The Geosphere

Our Solar System coalesced from a frigid cloud of dust and gas that was rotating slowly in space. The Sun was formed as gravity pulled material toward the swirling center. At the same time, rotational forces spun material in the outer cloud into a thin disk. When the turbulence of the initial accretion subsided, small grains stuck together to form fist-sized masses. These planetary seeds then accreted to form rocky clumps, which grew to form larger planetesimals, 100 to 1000 kilometers in diameter. Finally, the planetesimals collected to form the planets. This process was completed about 4.6 billion years ago.

As the Earth coalesced, the rocky chunks and planetesimals were accelerated by gravity so that they slammed together at high speeds. Particles heat up when they collide, so the early Earth warmed as it formed. Later, asteroids, comets, and more

The Earth and Its Four Spheres

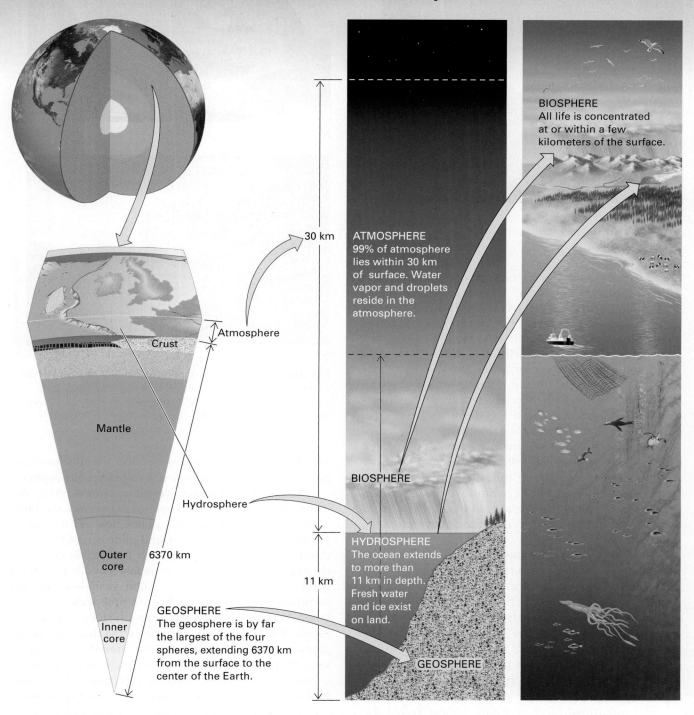

Figure 1.3   Most of the Earth is solid rock surrounded by the hydrosphere, the biosphere, and the atmosphere.

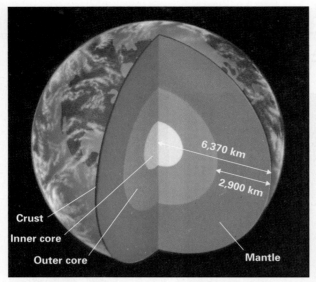

Figure 1.4 The geosphere is divided into three major layers: the crust, mantle, and core.

A

B

Figure 1.5 The Earth's crust is made up of different kinds of rock. (A) The granite of Baffin Island is gray, hard, and strong. (B) The sandstone and limestone of the Utah desert are red, crumbly, and show horizontal layering.

planetesimals crashed into the surface, generating additional heat. At the same time, radioactive decay heated the Earth's interior. As a result of all three of these processes, our planet became so hot that all or most of it melted soon after it formed.

Within the molten Earth, the denser materials gravitated toward the center, while the less dense materials floated toward the top, creating a layered structure. Today, the geosphere consists of three major layers: a dense, metallic **core,** a less dense rocky mantle, and an even less dense surface **crust** (Figure 1.4).

The core is composed mainly of iron and nickel, heated to 6000°C, about as hot as the surface of the Sun. At this extreme temperature, the outer core is molten to form a vast subterranean sea of liquid metal. However, at the center, the intense pressure of the Earth's weight overwhelms the temperature effect and compresses the inner core into a solid.

The **mantle** surrounds the core and lies beneath the crust. The physical characteristics of the mantle vary with depth. Near the surface, the outermost mantle is cool because the Earth's interior heat has escaped into space. This cool rock is relatively strong and hard. In contrast, the layer below the surface is so hot that the rock is weak, soft, plastic, and flows slowly—like cold honey. Even deeper in the Earth, pressure overwhelms temperature and the mantle rock becomes strong again.

The outermost layer is a thin veneer called the crust. Below a layer of soil and beneath the ocean water, the crust is composed almost entirely of solid rock. Even a casual observer sees that rocks of the crust are different from one another: Some are soft, others hard, and they come in many colors (Figure 1.5). Thus crust

and the uppermost portion of the mantle are cool, hard, and strong. This region is called the **lithosphere.**

According to a theory developed in the 1960s, the lithosphere is broken into several segments called **tectonic plates.** These tectonic plates float on the weak, plastic mantle rock beneath, and glide across the Earth (Figure 1.6). For example, North America is currently drifting toward China about as fast as your fingernail grows. In a few hundred million years—almost incomprehensibly long on a human time scale, but brief when compared with planetary history—Asia and North America may collide, crumpling the edges of the continents and building a giant mountain range. In later chapters we will learn how plate tectonic theory explains earthquakes, volcanic eruptions, the formation of mountain ranges, and many other phenomena.

The Hydrosphere

The hydrosphere includes all of the Earth's water, which circulates among oceans, continents, glaciers, and the atmosphere. Oceans cover 71 percent of the

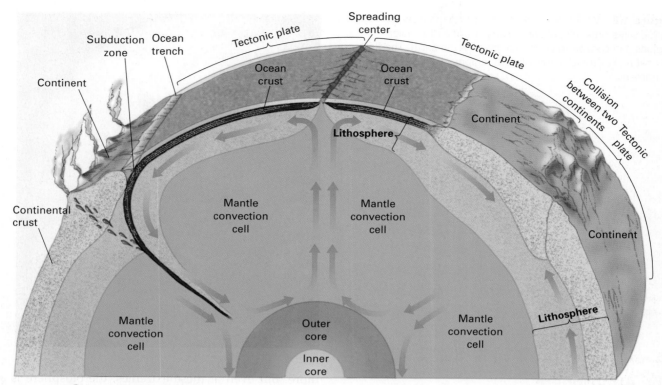

Earth Science ⊛ Now™ **ACTIVE FIGURE 1.6** The lithosphere is composed of the crust and the uppermost mantle. It is a 100-kilometer-thick layer of strong rock that floats on the underlying plastic mantle. The lithosphere is broken into seven major segments, called tectonic plates, that glide horizontally over the plastic mantle at rates of a few centimeters per year. In the drawing, the thickness of the mantle and the lithosphere are exaggerated to show detail.

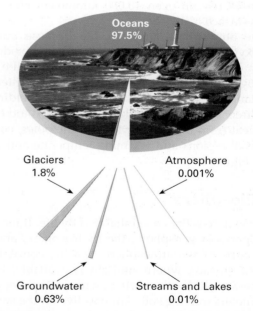

Figure 1.7 The oceans contain most of the Earth's surface water. Most fresh water is frozen into glaciers. Most available fresh water is stored underground as ground water.

Interactive Question: How would a doubling of the amount of water in the atmosphere affect the oceans? How would it affect weather and climate?

Earth and contain 97.5 percent of its water. Ocean currents transport heat across vast distances, altering global climate.

About 1.8 percent of the Earth's water is frozen in glaciers. Although glaciers cover about 10 percent of the Earth's land surface today, they covered much greater portions of the globe as recently as 18,000 years ago.

Only about 0.64 percent of the Earth's total water exists on the continents as a liquid. While this is a small amount from a global perspective, fresh water is essential to life on Earth. Lakes, rivers, and clear, sparkling streams are the most visible reservoirs of continental water, but they constitute only 0.01 percent of the total. In contrast, **ground water**, which saturates rock and soil of the upper few kilometers of the geosphere, is much more abundant and accounts for 0.63 percent of the Earth's water. A minuscule amount, 0.001 percent, exists in the atmosphere, but this water is so mobile that it profoundly affects both the weather and climate of our planet (Figure 1.7).

Figure 1.8 Winds often drive clouds into great swirls. At the same time, global winds carry warm air to cooler regions and cool air to equatorial parts of the Earth. The flow of heat makes the climates of both regions more favorable to humans.

Courtesy NASA

The Atmosphere

The atmosphere is a mixture of gases, mostly nitrogen and oxygen, with smaller amounts of argon, carbon dioxide, and other gases. It is held to the Earth by gravity and thins rapidly with altitude. Ninety-nine percent is concentrated in the first 30 kilometers, but a few traces remain even 10,000 kilometers above the Earth's surface.

The atmosphere supports life because animals need oxygen, and plants need both carbon dioxide and oxygen. In addition, the atmosphere supports life indirectly by regulating climate. Air acts both as a filter and as a blanket, retaining heat at night and shielding us from direct solar radiation during the day. Wind transports heat from the equator toward the poles, cooling equatorial regions and warming temperate and polar zones (Figure 1.8).

The Biosphere

The biosphere is the zone inhabited by life. It includes the uppermost geosphere, the hydrosphere, and the lower parts of the atmosphere. Sea life concentrates near the surface, where sunlight is available. Plants also grow on the Earth's surface, with roots penetrating a few meters into the soil. Animals live on the surface, fly a kilometer or two above it, or burrow a few meters underground. Large populations of bacteria live in rock to depths of as much as four kilometers, some organisms live on the ocean floor, and a few windblown microorganisms drift at heights of 10 kilometers or

more. But even at these extremes, the biosphere is a very thin layer at the Earth's surface.

Plants and animals are clearly affected by the Earth's environment. Organisms breathe air, require water, and thrive in a relatively narrow temperature range. Terrestrial organisms ultimately depend on soil, which is part of the geosphere. Although it is not as obvious, plants and animals also alter and form the environment that they live in. For example, living organisms contributed to the evolution of the modern atmosphere. We will discuss these interactions throughout the book.

Earth Science ⊛ Now™

CLICK Earth Science Interactive to work through an activity on the Earth's layers and plate locations through Plate Tectonics.

1.3 Earth Systems

A **system** is any assemblage or combination of interacting components. For example, the human body is a system composed of stomach, bones, nerves, and many other organs. Each organ is discrete, yet all the organs interact to produce a living human. Blood nurtures the stomach; the stomach helps provide energy to maintain the blood.

The Earth is also composed of components: geosphere, hydrosphere, atmosphere, and biosphere.

Just as organs in the human body are interrelated, these seemingly separate systems of the Earth are all part of an integrated whole. To understand any component of the Earth, we first study its physical and chemical properties and the energy sources that drive it. Then we look at interactions with all the other components of the planet. For example, if we were studying volcanic eruptions, we would examine the chemical properties of molten rock, determine when and where the rock melts, and study how and why such melting occurs. Once we understand the mechanism of a single volcanic eruption, we may take a broader scope and observe that lava spewing to the surface may build a mountain and alter nearby drainage systems. Hot lava kills living organisms in its path. Gas and dust rise into the atmosphere, reflecting sunlight and cooling the Earth. Changes in temperature and evaporation rates alter rainfall patterns. Thus a single event, powered by heat originating hundreds or even thousands of kilometers beneath the surface, can initiate change throughout the planet.

In the laboratory, scientists often create closed systems, where no energy or matter enters or leaves. Yet, few natural systems are closed. Our body is an open system because we ingest food and oxygen and excrete wastes and carbon dioxide. Very little matter enters or leaves the Earth, but it is an open system because it receives energy in the form of sunlight and dissipates heat energy out into space.

Systems are driven by the flow of energy and matter, but energy and matter behave in fundamentally different ways: Once used, energy becomes less useful; however, matter can be reused in the same way over and over again.

Energy and the Laws of Thermodynamics

A gallon of gasoline has a specific amount of potential energy. If you burn the gasoline in the engine of a car, the potential energy is first converted to heat; then some of that heat is converted to work and the remainder is released through the tailpipe as heat. The laws of thermodynamics describe the flow of energy through a car or any other system.

The **first law of thermodynamics** states that *energy is always conserved.* If we continue to use the example of a car engine, when fuel is burned, some energy is converted to heat; if you drive the car up a hill, some may be stored in what is called potential energy of position—but we can account for every last joule. (A joule is the standard unit of energy.) Energy is never lost or gained.

The **second law of thermodynamics** states that *a closed system always shifts toward disorder, or homogeneity.*

Thus, if you place a drop of dark blue ink in a glass of water, the drop will disperse until the water becomes homogeneously light blue. The original order—ink in one region and clear water throughout the remainder of the glass—spontaneously morphs into disorder—ink and water all mixed together. In a similar manner, if you place a hot rock into a cold glass of water, the rock will cool and the water will warm up until both reach the same temperature. No one has ever observed any other behavior. **Entropy** is a measure of the disorder, or homogeneity in a system. One statement of the second law is that *the entropy of a closed system always increases.*

Starting with this basic premise, scientists have shown that whenever heat is converted to work, some of the energy is always degraded so that it becomes less useful to perform work. No one can ever devise a way to efficiently trap all of the energy in the hot exhaust from a car to power the car again. In other words, no heat engine is 100 percent efficient. Plants trap sunlight, animals eat plants, plants and animals die and decompose to form petroleum, petroleum burns in the engine of a car, and finally the energy is dissipated as heat. If we want to drive the car farther, we need to find another gallon of gasoline.

The Earth's surface systems—the atmosphere, hydrosphere, and biosphere—are ultimately powered by the Sun. Wind is powered by uneven solar heating of the atmosphere, ocean waves are driven by the wind, currents move in response to wind or temperature differences, and so on. Luckily for us, the Earth receives a continuous influx of solar energy, and will continue to receive this energy for another 5 billion years or so.

In contrast, the Earth's interior is powered by the decay of radioactive elements and by residual heat from the primordial coalescence of the planet. We will discuss these sources further in later chapters.

However, matter, unlike energy, can be recycled. Imagine that you mine iron ore, smelt the ore to make metal, and use the metal to manufacture a car. When the car is old and worn out, you can melt it back down and make a new car. The process could be repeated over and over, indefinitely.

Several material cycles are fundamental to our study of Earth systems. These include the rock cycle (Chapter 3), the hydrological cycle (or water cycle) (Chapter 11), the carbon cycle (Chapter 17), and the nitrogen cycle (Chapter 17). During the course of these cycles, matter is always conserved—however, matter continuously and commonly changes form.

For example, solid water (ice) melts to form liquid, and if more heat is added, liquid vaporizes to a gas. Reverse processes occur when heat is removed. Thus, in the hydrological cycle, water evaporates from the ocean, is transported as vapor or small droplets in the atmosphere, falls to Earth as rain or snow, and eventually flows back to the oceans. Chemical reactions also change the physical properties of matter. Common table salt is a solid, crystalline mineral. If you drop a crystal of salt in water, it dissolves, thus altering the properties of both the salt and the water. Or, as another example, carbon dioxide gas reacts with other matter to form solid rock, limestone—and limestone reacts to form carbon dioxide gas and other products.

Because matter exists in so many different chemical and physical forms, most materials occur in all four of Earth's major spheres: geosphere, hydrosphere, atmosphere, and biosphere. This is illustrated by the following examples. On Earth, water is chemically bound into clays and other minerals, as a component of the geosphere. It is the primary constituent of the hydrosphere. It exists in the atmosphere as vapor and clouds. Water is an essential part of all living organisms. The mineral salt provides another example of a material found in the four spheres: Thick layers of salt occur as sedimentary rocks, large quantities of salt are dissolved in the oceans, salt aerosols are suspended in the atmosphere, and salt is an essential component of life. Thus, all the spheres are interconnected.

Material cycles illustrate the exchange of matter among the four spheres. Because matter exists in so many different forms, these cycles are also interconnected. Recall from the earlier discussion about planetary environments that carbon exists in many forms. It occurs as dioxide gas in the atmosphere, it dissolves in seawater, and it combines with calcium and oxygen to form a type of rock called limestone (Figure 1.9). The formation of limestone from carbon dioxide is part of the rock cycle, because limestone is a rock. But at the same time, the exact same process—the formation of limestone from carbon dioxide—is part of the carbon cycle because both limestone and carbon dioxide are composed of carbon. It is no contradiction that two cycles intersect. In our study of Earth systems, we categorize the four separate spheres and numerous material cycles independently, but, we also recognize that Earth materials and processes are all part of one integrated system (Figure 1.10).

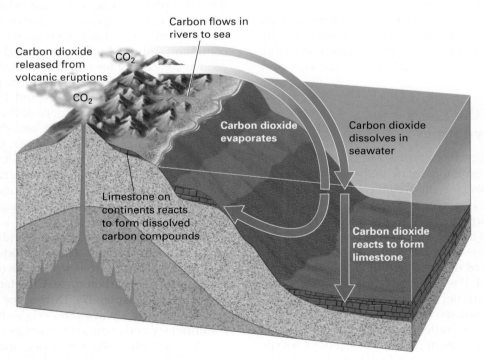

Figure 1.9 All of Earth's cycles and spheres are interconnected. For example, the formation and decomposition of limestone is part of the rock cycle because limestone is a rock. The same process is also part of the carbon cycle because limestone is composed partly of carbon.

Figure 1.10 All of Earth's cycles and spheres are interconnected.

1.4 Time in Earth Science

James Hutton was a gentleman farmer who lived in Scotland in the late 1700s. Although trained as a physician, he never practiced medicine and, instead, turned to geology. Hutton observed that a certain type of rock, called **sandstone,** is composed of sand grains cemented together (Figure 1.11). He also noted that rocks slowly decompose into sand, and that streams carry sand into the lowlands. He inferred that sandstone is composed of sand grains that originated by the erosion of ancient cliffs and mountains.

Hutton tried to deduce how much time was required to form a thick bed of sandstone. He studied sand grains slowly breaking away from rock outcrops. He watched sand bouncing down stream beds. Finally he traveled to beaches and river deltas where sand was accumulating. By estimating the time needed for thick

layers of sand to accumulate on beaches, Hutton concluded that sandstone must be much older than human history. Hutton, overwhelmed by the magnitude of geological time, wrote:

> On us who saw these phenomena for the first time, the impression will not easily be forgotten. . . .We felt ourselves necessarily carried back to the time . . . when the sandstone before us was only beginning to be deposited, in the shape of sand and mud, from the waters of an ancient ocean. . . .The mind seemed to grow giddy by looking so far into the abyss of time . . .
>
> We find no vestige of a beginning, no prospect of an end.

Hutton had no way to measure the magnitude of geologic time. However, modern geologists have learned that certain radioactive materials in rocks act as clocks to record the passage of time. Using these clocks and other clues embedded in the Earth's crust, the moon, and in meteorites fallen from space, ge-

Figure 1.11 Hutton observed that a sandstone outcrop, like this cliff rising above the Escalante River, Utah, is composed of tiny round sand grains cemented together.

ologists estimate that the Earth formed 4.6 billion years ago.

The primordial planet was vastly different from our modern world. There was no crust as we know it today, no oceans, and the diffuse atmosphere was vastly different from the modern one. There were no living organisms.

No one knows exactly when the first living organisms evolved, but we know that life existed at least as early as 3.8 billion years ago, 800 million years after the planet formed. For the following 3.3 billion years, life evolved slowly, and although some multicellular organisms developed, most of the biosphere consisted of single-celled organisms. Organisms rapidly became more complex, abundant, and varied about 544 million years ago. The dinosaurs flourished between 225 million and 65 million years ago.

Homo sapiens and our direct ancestors have been on Earth for 5 to 7 million years, only about 0.1 percent of the planet's history. In his book *Basin and Range,* John McPhee offers us a metaphor for the magnitude of geologic time. If the history of the Earth were represented by the old English measure of a yard—the distance from the king's nose to the end of his outstretched hand—all of human history could be erased by a single stroke of a file on his middle fingernail. Figure 1.12 summarizes Earth history in graphical form.

Geologists routinely talk about events that occurred millions or even billions of years ago. If you live on the East Coast of North America, you may be familiar with the Appalachian mountains, which started rising from a coastal plain nearly half a billion years ago. If you live in Seattle, the land you are standing on was an island in the Pacific between 80 and 100 million years ago, when dinosaurs walked the Earth.

There are two significant consequences of the vast span of geologic time:

1. Events that occur slowly become significant. If a continent moves a few centimeters a year, the movement makes no noticeable alteration of Earth systems over decades or centuries. But over hundreds of millions of years, the effects are significant.

2. Improbable events occur regularly. The chances are great that a large meteorite won't crash into Earth tomorrow, or next year, or during the next century. But during the past 500 million years, several catastrophic impacts have occurred and they will probably occur sometime in the future.

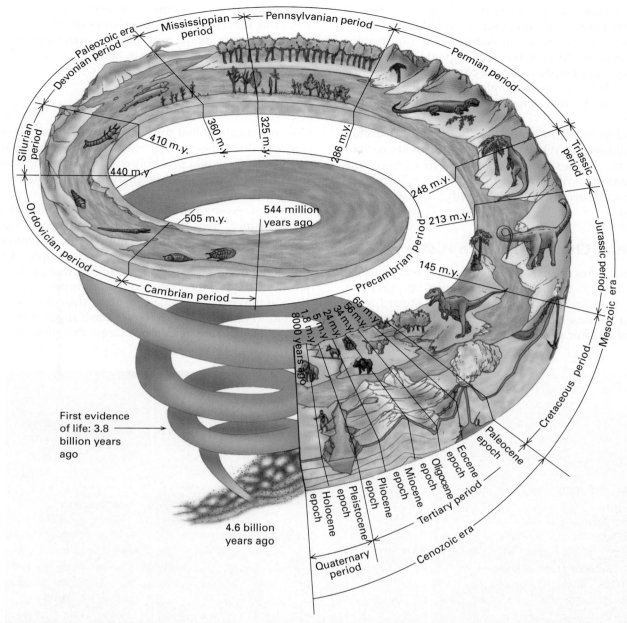

Figure 1.12 The geologic time scale is shown as a spiral to indicate the great length of time before multicellular organisms became abundant, about 544 million years ago.

1.5 Rates of Change in Earth History

Recall that James Hutton deduced that sandstone forms when rocks slowly decompose to sand, the sand is transported to lowland regions, and the grains cement together. This process occurs step by step—over many years. Hutton's conclusions led him to formulate a principle now known as **gradualism** or **uniformitarianism.** The principle states that geologic change oc-

curs over long periods of time, by a sequence of almost imperceptible events. Hutton surmised that geologic processes operating today also operated in the past. Thus scientists can explain events that occurred in the past by observing changes occurring today. Sometimes this idea is summarized in the statement, "The present is the key to the past."

However, not all geologic change is gradual. William Whewell, another early geologist, argued that geologic change was sometimes rapid. He wrote that the geologic past may have "consisted of epochs of paroxysmal and catastrophic action, interposed between periods of comparative tranquility." Earthquakes and volcanoes are examples of catastrophic events but, in addition, Whewell argued that occasionally huge catastrophes alter the course of Earth history. He couldn't give an example because they happen so infrequently that none had occurred within human history.

Today, geologists know that both Hutton's uniformitarianism and Whewell's **catastrophism** are correct. Over the great expanses of geologic time, slow, uniform processes alter the Earth. In addition, infrequent catastrophic events radically modify the path of slow change.

Gradual Change in Earth History

Tectonic plates creep slowly across the Earth's surface. Since the first steam engine was built 200 years ago, North America has migrated 8 meters westward, a distance a sprinter can run in 1 second. Thus, the movement of tectonic plates is too slow to be observed without sensitive instruments. However, over geologic time, this movement alters the shapes of ocean basins, forms lofty mountains and plateaus, generates earthquakes and volcanic eruptions, and affects our planet in many other ways.

Catastrophic Change in Earth History

Chances are small that the river flowing through your city will flood this spring, but if you lived to be 100 years old, you would probably see a catastrophic flood. In fact, destructive floods occur every year, somewhere on the planet.

When geologists study the 4.6 billion years of Earth history, they find abundant evidence of catastrophic events that are highly improbable in a human lifetime or even in human history. For example, clues preserved in rock and sediment indicate that giant meteorites have smashed into our planet, vaporizing portions of the crust and spreading dense dust clouds over the sky (Figure 1.13). Geologists have suggested that some meteorite impacts (much larger than that shown

Meteor Crater National Monument

Figure 1.13 Fifty thousand years ago, a meteorite crashed into the northern Arizona desert, creating Meteor Crater. Catastrophic events have helped shape Earth history.

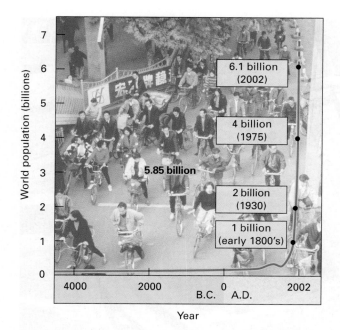

Figure 1.14 The human population has increased rapidly since the 1700s. For most of human history, there were fewer than one-half billion people on Earth. In mid-year 2002, 6.1 billion people inhabited our planet. *Source:* Data from the Population Reference Bureau

Interactive Question: Approximately how many years did it take for the human population to double from 2 billion to 4 billion? If that doubling rate were to continue, how many people would live on Earth in the year 2500? 3000?

in Figure 1.13) have almost instantaneously driven millions of species into extinction. As another example, when the continental glaciers receded at the end of the last Ice Age, huge floods were orders of magnitude larger than any floods in historic times. In addition, periodically throughout Earth history, catastrophic volcanic eruptions changed conditions for life across the globe.

Threshold and Feedback Effects

Imagine that some process gradually warmed the atmosphere. Imagine further that the summer temperature of coastal Greenland glaciers was −1.0°C. If gradual change warmed the atmosphere by 0.2°C, the glaciers would not be affected appreciably because ice melts at 0°C and the summer temperature would remain below freezing, −0.8°C. But now imagine that gradual warming brought summer temperature to −0.2°C. At this point, the system is at a threshold. Another small increment of change would raise the temperature to the melting point of ice. As soon as ice starts to melt, large changes occur rapidly: Glaciers recede and global sea level rises. A **threshold effect** occurs when the environment initially changes slowly (or not at all) in response to a small perturbation, but after the threshold is crossed, an additional small perturbation causes rapid and dramatic change.

A **feedback mechanism** occurs when a small initial perturbation affects another component of the Earth systems, which amplifies the original effect, which perturbs the system even more, which leads to an even greater effect, and so on. (Picture a falling

stack of dominos.) The evolution of the Venusian climate is a perfect example of a feedback mechanism: Solar energy evaporated surface water. The water vapor trapped more heat in the atmosphere. The temperature rose. Without surface water, carbon dioxide remained in the atmosphere. Carbon dioxide trapped even more heat. The temperature rose further. And so on.

Threshold and feedback mechanisms remind us that Earth systems often change in ways that are difficult to predict. These complexities provide the challenge and fascination of Earth Science.

1.6 Humans and Earth Systems

Ten thousand years ago, a mere eye-blink in Earth history, human population was low and technology was limited. Sparsely scattered bands hunted and gathered for their food, built simple dwellings, and warmed themselves with small hearth fires. Human impact was not appreciably different from that of many other species on the planet. But today there are 6.1 billion people on Earth (Figure 1.14). Farms, pasture lands and cities cover 40 percent of the land area of the planet (Figure 1.15). We divert half of all the fresh water on the continents and control 45 percent of the total net terrestrial biological productivity. As the land and its waters have been domesticated, other animal and plant species have perished. The species extinction rate today is 1000 times more rapid than it was before the Industrial Revolution. In fact, species extinction hasn't

Figure 1.15 This cloverleaf near Denver, Colorado, is but one example of the global conversion of natural ecosystems into developed landscapes.

been this rapid since a giant meteorite smashed into the Earth's surface 65 million years ago, leading to the demise of the dinosaurs and many other species.

Emissions from our fires, factories, and transportation machines have raised the atmospheric carbon dioxide concentration to its highest level in 420,000 years. In turn, the increased carbon dioxide level has raised the Earth's average surface temperature by almost 1°Celsius.

Roughly 20 percent of the human population lives in wealthy industrialized nations where food, shelter, clean drinking water, efficient sewage disposal, and advanced medical attention are all readily available. At the same time as those in the industrialized, developed nations enjoy opulent sustenance and infrastructure, in the impoverished regions of the world, 1.5 billion people survive on less than one dollar per day. One eighth to one half of the human population on this planet is malnourished and 14 million infants or young children starve to death every year. If you lived in a family in the Himalayan region of northern India, where you spent hours every day gathering scant firewood or cow dung for fuel, where meals consisted of an endless repetition of barley gruel and peas, where

you brought your sheep and goats into the house during the winter so you could all huddle together for warmth, then your view of the planet would be different from what it is now (Figure 1.16).

Regardless of whether we are rich or poor, our survival is interconnected with the flow of energy and materials within Earth systems. We affect the Earth, and at the same time the Earth affects us; it is the most intimate and permanent of marriages.

Predictions for the future are, by their very nature, uncertain. Over 200 years ago, in 1798, the Reverend Thomas Malthus argued that human population was growing exponentially while food production was increasing much more slowly. As a result, humankind was facing famine, "misery and vice." But technological advancements led to an exponential increase in food production, keeping pace—more or less—with population growth. Today, the rate of population growth is slowing, so optimists predict that we may soon reach a halcyon age when people have enough to eat and global ecosystems stabilize.

But many scientists are not so sanguine about our future. These people argue that human population is likely to reach 10 billion and that there are ultimate

Hypothesis, Theory, and Law

On an afternoon field trip, you may find several different types of rocks or watch a river flow by. But you can never see the rocks or river as they existed in the past or as they will exist in the future. Yet a geologist might explain how the rocks formed millions or even a few billion years ago and might predict how the river valley will change with time.

Scientists not only study events that they have never observed and never will observe, but they also study objects that can never be seen, touched, or felt. In this book we describe the center of the Earth 6400 kilometers beneath our feet and distant galaxies billions of light-years away, even though no one has ever visited these places and no one ever will.

Much of science is built on inferences about events and objects outside the realm of direct experience. An inference is a conclusion based on available information, thought, and reason. How certain are we that a conclusion of this type is correct?

Scientists develop an understanding of the natural world according to a set of guidelines known as the **scientific method,** which involves three basic steps: (1) observation, (2) forming a preliminary conclusion or hypothesis, and (3) testing the hypothesis and developing a theory.

Observation

All modern science is based on observation. Recall that James Hutton observed that ocean currents and rivers transported and deposited sand. He observed that the sand accumulates slowly, layer by layer. Then he saw cliffs of layered sandstone hundreds of meters high. Observations of this kind are the starting point of science.

Forming a Hypothesis

A scientist tries to organize observations to recognize patterns. Hutton noted that the sand layers deposited along the coast look just like the layers of sand in the sandstone cliffs. Starting with these observed facts, he then concluded that the thick layers of sandstone had been deposited in an ancient ocean or river delta. He further inferred that, because layers of sand are deposited slowly, the thick layers of sandstone must have accumulated over a long time. Finally, he took one more step of logic to hypothesize that the Earth is old.

A **hypothesis** is a tentative explanation built on strong supporting evidence. Once a scientist or group of scientists proposes a hypothesis, others test it by comparison with additional observations and experiments. If the hypothesis explains some of the facts but not all of them, it must be altered, or if it cannot be changed satisfactorily, it must be discarded and a new hypothesis developed.

Testing the Hypothesis and Forming a Theory

If a hypothesis explains new observations as they accumulate and is not substantively contradicted, it becomes accepted by more and more people. As the tentative nature of a hypothesis is gradually dispelled, it is elevated to a **theory.** Theories differ widely in form and content, but all obey four fundamental criteria:

1. A theory must be based on a series of confirmed observations or experimental results.
2. A theory must explain all relevant observations or experimental results.
3. A theory must not contradict any relevant observations or other scientific principles.
4. A theory must be internally consistent. Thus, it must be built in a logical manner so that the conclusions do not contradict any of the original premises.

For example, the theory of plate tectonics states that the outer layer of the Earth is broken into a number of plates that move horizontally relative to one another. As you will see in Chapter 6, this theory is supported by many observations and seems to have no major inconsistencies.

Many theories cannot be absolutely proven. For example, even though scientists are just about certain that their image of atomic structure is correct, no one has or ever will watch an individual electron travel in its orbit. Therefore, our interpretation of atomic structure is called atomic theory.

In some instances, observations are so universal that there is no doubt of their verity. A **law** is a statement of how events always occur under given conditions. It is considered to be factual and correct. For example, the law of gravity states that all objects are attracted to one another in direct proportion to their masses. We cannot conceive of any contradiction to this principle, and none has been observed. Hence, the principle is called a law. Modern science is in such constant flux and our Universe is so complex, that very few laws are formulated any more.

FOCUS QUESTION:

Obtain a copy of a news article in a weekly news magazine. Underline the facts with one color pencil and the authors' opinions with another. Did the authors follow the rules for the scientific method outlined here to reach their conclusion?

Figure 1.16 People in the Himalayas scratch a meager living out of thin soil. This photo was taken in Ladakh, northern India.

Courtesy of Graham R. Thompson /Jonathan Turk

limits to Earth resources and productivity. John Holdren, professor at the John F. Kennedy School of Government, argues that the problem is "not that we are running out of energy, food, or water but that we are running out of environment—that is, running out of the capacity of air, water, soil and biota to absorb, without intolerable consequences for human well-being, the effects of resource extraction, transportation, transformation, and use."[1] Professor Holdren and many other like-minded scientists are studying the effects of burgeoning human population and resource consumption. Will we have enough energy to drive the fossil fuel intensive farming needed to feed 10 billion people? But beyond the question of food, many scientists are concerned that we are pushing Earth systems close to thresholds where feedback mechanisms will spiral catastrophically out of control. Will a small additional increase in carbon dioxide concentration trigger a rapid and cataclysmic climate change? If we continue to log our tropical rain forests and fragment existing ecosystems, could we trigger dramatic changes in local weather that destroys the remaining forests, which in turn alters global rainfall patterns?

These are extremely complex questions. This book will not provide definite answers—because there are none—but it will provide a background so that you can understand important issues concerning our stewardship of the planet.

[1] John P. Holdren, "Energy: Asking the Wrong Question." *Scientific American* (January 2002): 65.

Summary

On Venus, a runaway greenhouse effect produced torridly hot temperatures; on Mars a reverse greenhouse effect plunged the planet into a deep freeze, while temperate conditions have prevailed on Earth.

Earth consists of four spheres: The **geosphere** is composed of a dense, hot, central **core**, surrounded by a large **mantle** that comprises 80 percent of the Earth's volume, with a thin, rigid **crust**. The crust and mantle are composed of rock while the core is composed of iron and nickel. The **hydrosphere** is mostly ocean water. Most of the Earth's fresh water is locked in glaciers. Most of the liquid fresh water lies in ground water reservoirs; streams, lakes, and rivers account for only 0.01 percent of the planet's water. The **atmosphere** is a mixture of gases, mostly nitrogen and oxygen. The Earth's atmosphere supports life and regulates climate. The **biosphere** is the thin zone inhabited by life.

A **system** is composed of interrelated, interacting components. Energy cannot be recycled, but matter is recycled continuously. The **first law of thermodynamics** states that energy is always conserved. The **second law of thermodynamics** states that energy is always degraded so that it becomes less useful to perform work. In order to understand a system, we must study the exchange of energy and matter both within the system and with the outside surroundings.

The Earth is about 4.6 billion years old; life formed at least 3.8 billion years ago; abundant multicellular life evolved about 544 million years ago, and hominids have been on this planet for a mere 5 to 7 million years.

The principle of **gradualism** or **uniformitarianism** states that geologic change occurs over a long period of time by a sequence of almost imperceptible events. In contrast, **catastrophism** postulates that geologic change occurs mainly during infrequent catastrophic events. In many instances, **threshold** and **feedback** effects modify simple gradualistic or catastrophic processes.

Due to our sheer numbers and technological prowess, humans have become a significant engine of change in Earth systems.

Key Terms

geosphere 4	tectonic plates 6	sandstone 11	hypothesis 17
hydrosphere 4	ground water 7	gradualism 13	theory 17
atmosphere 4	system 8	uniformitarianism 13	law 17
biosphere 4	first law of	catastrophism 14	
core 6	thermodynamics 9	threshold effect 15	
crust 6	second law of	feedback	
mantle 6	thermodynamics 9	mechanism 15	
lithosphere 6	entropy 9	scientific method 17	

For Review

1. Explain how water vapor and carbon dioxide influenced the evolution of the climate and atmosphere on Venus, Earth, and Mars.
2. List and briefly describe each of the Earth's four spheres.
3. List the three major layers of the Earth. Which is/are composed of rock, which is/are metallic? Which is the largest; which is the thinnest?
4. List six types of reservoirs that collectively contain most of the Earth's water.
5. What is ground water? Where in the hydrosphere is it located?
6. What two gases compose most of the Earth's atmosphere?
7. How thick is the Earth's atmosphere?
8. Briefly discuss the size and extent of the biosphere.
9. Define a system and explain why a systems approach is useful in Earth science.
10. Briefly explain the statement: "Matter can be recycled, but energy cannot."

11. Summarize the first and second laws of thermo-dynamics.
12. How old is the Earth? When did life first evolve? How long have humans and their direct ancestors been on this planet?
13. Compare and contrast uniformitarianism and catastrophism. Give an example of each type of geologic change.
14. Briefly explain threshold and feedback effects.
15. Briefly outline the magnitude of human impact on the planet.

For Discussion

1. What cautionary warnings can you deduce from your knowledge of the evolution of climate and atmospheric composition on Venus, Earth, and Mars?
2. Only 0.64 percent of Earth's water is fresh and liquid—the rest is salty seawater or is frozen in glaciers. What are the environmental implications of such a small proportion of fresh water?
3. List five ways that organisms, including humans, change the Earth. What kinds of Earth processes are unaffected by humans and other organisms?
4. Twelve generic types of interactions are possible among the four spheres. These are:
   (a) Changes in the solid Earth perturb the hydrosphere.
   (b) Changes in the hydrosphere perturb the solid Earth.
   (c) Changes in the solid Earth perturb the atmosphere.
   (d) Changes in the atmosphere perturb the solid Earth.
   (e) Changes in the solid Earth perturb the biosphere
   (f) Changes in the biosphere perturb the solid Earth.
   (g) Changes in the hydrosphere perturb the atmosphere.
   (h) Changes in the atmosphere perturb the hydrosphere.
   (i) Changes in the hydrosphere perturb the biosphere.
   (j) Changes in the biosphere perturb the hydrosphere.
   (k) Changes in the atmosphere perturb the biosphere.
   (l) Changes in the biosphere perturb the atmosphere.
   Write an example to illustrate each possibility.
5. A windmill produces energy from the wind, which is free. Is this a contradiction of the second law of thermodynamics? Explain.
6. Give an example of a threshold or feedback effect in science, politics, human relationships, or any field you can think of.

Earth Science ⊛ Now™

Assess your understanding of this chapter's topics with additional quizzing and comprehensive interactivities at **http://earthscience.brookscole.com/earthsci3e** as well as current and up-to-date weblinks, additional readings, and InfoTrac College Edition exercises.

Chapter 5

Geologic Resources

Charles E. Rotkin /CORBIS

The GEM of Egypt was a gigantic power shovel used by the Hanna Mining Company for earth moving in Ohio in the 1960s and 1970s. It weighed 7000 tons and could scoop up 200 tons in a single bite of its 130-cubic-yard bucket.

Since human-like creatures emerged 5 to 7 million years ago, human use of geologic resources has become increasingly sophisticated. Early hominids used sticks and rocks as simple weapons and tools. Later prehistoric people used flint and obsidian to make more effective weapons and tools, and used natural pigments to create elegant art on cave walls (Figure 5.1). About 8000 B.C., people learned to shape and fire clay to make pottery. Archaeologists have found copper ornaments in Turkey dating from 6500 B.C.; 1500 years later, Mesopotamian farmers used copper farm implements. Today, geologic resources provide the silicon chip that operates your computer, the titanium valves in a space probe, and the gasoline that powers your car.

We use two different types of geologic resources: **mineral resources** and **energy resources.** Mineral resources include all useful rocks and minerals. Energy resources supply us with heat, light, work, and communication.

Figure 5.1 A cave painting created between the fifth and second millenium B.C., showing a bison. Altamira Cave, Santillana de Mar, Spain.

Figure 5.2 In the early 1900s, miners extracted gold, copper, and other metal ores from underground mines such as this one 600 meters below the surface in Butte, Montana.

Earth Science ⊕ Now™

This icon, appearing throughout the book, indicates an opportunity to explore interactive tutorials, animations, or practice problems available on the Earth ScienceNow Web site at **http://earthscience.brookscole.com/earthsci3e**

5.1 Mineral Resources

Mineral resources include both metal **ore** and **nonmetallic mineral resources.** Ore is rock sufficiently enriched in one or more minerals to be mined profitably (Figure 5.2). Geologists usually use the term ore to refer to metallic mineral deposits, and the term is commonly accompanied by the name of the metal—for example, "iron ore" or "silver ore."

A nonmetallic resource is any useful rock or mineral that is not a metal, such as salt, building stone, sand, and gravel. When we think about "striking it rich" from mining, we usually think of gold. However, more money has been made mining sand and gravel than gold. For example, in the United States in the year 2000, sand and gravel produced $5.8 billion in revenue, but gold produced only $3.0 billion. Sand and gravel are mined from stream and glacial deposits, sand dunes, and beaches. In turn, these materials are mixed with portland cement to make concrete. Portland cement is made by heating a mixture of crushed limestone and clay. Reinforced with steel, concrete is used to build roads, bridges, and buildings. Thus reinforced concrete is one of the basic building materials of the modern world. In addition, many buildings are faced with stone—usually granite or limestone, although marble, slate, sandstone, and other rocks used for building are also mined from quarries cut into bedrock (Figure 5.3).

Figure 5.3 A Chinese quarryman splits a large granite block with a sledge hammer. After he splits the rock, the circular saws in the background cut it into thin slabs for floors and walls.

Courtesy of Graham R. Thompson/Jonathan Turk

TABLE 5.1 Some Important Elements and Their Uses

Mineral	Type	Some Uses
Aluminum (Al)	Metal	Structural materials (airplanes, automobiles), packaging (beverage cans), fireworks
Borax ($Na_2B_4O_7$)	Nonmetal	Diverse manufacturing uses—glass, enamel, artificial gems, soaps, antiseptics
Chromium (Cr)	Metal	Chrome plate, pigments, steel alloys (tools, jet engines, bearings)
Cobalt (Co)	Metal	Pigments, alloys (jet engines, tool bits), medicine, varnishes
Copper (Cu)	Metal	Alloy ingredient in gold jewelry, silverware, brass, and bronze; electrical wiring, pipes, cooking utensils
Gold (Au)	Metal	Jewelry, money, dentistry, alloys, specialty electronics
Gravel	Nonmetal	Concrete (buildings, roads)
Gypsum ($CaSO_4-2H_2O$)	Nonmetal	Plaster of Paris, wallboard, soil treatments
Iron (Fe)	Metal	Basic ingredient of steel (buildings, machinery)
Lead (Pb)	Metal	Pipes, solder, battery electrodes, pigments
Magnesium (Mg)	Metal	Alloys (aircraft), firecrackers, bombs, flashbulbs
Manganese (Mn)	Metal	Steel, alloys (steamship propellers, gears), batteries, chemicals
Mercury (Hg)	Liquid metal	Thermometers, barometers, dental inlays, electric switches, street lamps, medicine
Molybdenum (Mo)	Metal	Steel alloys, lamp filaments, boiler plates, rifle barrels
Nickel (Ni)	Metal	Money, alloys, metal plating
Phosphorus (P)	Nonmetal	Medicine, fertilizers, detergents
Platinum (Pt)	Metal	Jewelry, delicate instruments, electrical equipment, cancer chemotherapy, industrial catalyst
Potassium (K)*	Nonmetal	Salts used in fertilizers, soaps, glass, photography, medicine, explosives, matches, gunpowder
Common salt (NaCl)	Nonmetal	Food additive
Sand (largely SiO_2)	Nonmetal	Glass, concrete (buildings, roads)
Silicon (Si)	Nonmetal	Electronics, solar cells, ceramics, silicones
Silver (Ag)	Metal	Jewelry, silverware, photography, alloys
Sulfur (S)	Nonmetal	Insecticides, rubber tires, paint, matches, papermaking, photography, rayon, medicine, explosives
Tin (Sn)	Metal	Cans and containers, alloys, solder, utensils
Titanium (Ti)	Metal	Paints; manufacture of aircraft, satellites, and chemical equipment
Tungsten (W)	Metal	High-temperature applications, lightbulb filaments, dentistry
Zinc (Zn)	Metal	Brass, metal coatings, electrodes in batteries, medicine (zinc salts)

*Potassium, which is very reactive chemically, is never found free in nature; it is always combined with other elements.

Table 5.1 lists important metals and other elements obtained from mineral resources. About 40 metals are commercially important. Some, such as iron, lead, copper, aluminum, silver, and gold, are familiar. Others, such as vanadium, titanium, and tellurium, are less well known but vital to industry.

All mineral resources are nonrenewable: We use them up at a much faster rate than natural processes create them. Even though mineral resources are limited, many can be recycled and used again.

5.2 Ore and Ore Deposits

If you pick up any rock and send it to a laboratory for analysis, the report will probably show that the rock contains measurable amounts of iron, gold, silver, aluminum, and other valuable metals. However, the concentrations of these metals are so low in most rocks that the extraction cost would be much greater than the income gained by selling the metals. In certain locations, however, geologic processes have enriched metals many times above their normal concentrations. Table 5.2 shows that the concentration of a metal in ore may exceed its average abundance in ordinary rock by a factor of more than 100,000.

One of the primary objectives of many geologists is to find new ore deposits. Successful exploration requires an understanding of the processes that concentrate metals to form ore. For example, platinum concentrates in certain types of igneous rocks. Therefore, if you were exploring for platinum, you would focus on those rocks rather than on sandstone or limestone. The following sections describe some of the more common ore-forming processes.

Magmatic Processes

Magmatic processes form mineral deposits as liquid magma solidifies to form an igneous rock. These processes create metal ores as well as some gems and valuable sulfur deposits.

Some large bodies of igneous rock, particularly those of mafic (basaltic) composition, solidify in layers. Each layer contains different minerals, and is of a different chemical composition than is found in adjacent layers. Some of the layers may contain rich ore deposits. The layering can develop by at least two processes.

1. Recall from Chapter 3 that cooling magma does not solidify all at once. Instead, higher-temperature minerals crystallize first, and lower-temperature minerals form later as the temperature drops. Most minerals are denser than magma. Consequently, early-formed crystals may sink to the bottom of a magma chamber in a process called **crystal settling** (Figure 5.4). In some instances, ore minerals crystallize with other early-formed minerals and accumulate in layers near the bottom of a pluton.
2. Some large bodies of mafic magma crystallize from the bottom upward. Thus, early-formed ore minerals become concentrated near the base of the pluton.

The largest ore deposits found in mafic layered plutons are the rich chromium and platinum reserves of South Africa's Bushveld intrusion. The pluton is about 375 by 300 kilometers in area—roughly the size

TABLE 5.2	Comparison of Concentrations of Specific Elements in Earth's Crust with Concentrations Needed to Operate a Commercial Mine		
Element	Natural Concentration in Crust (% by Weight)	Concentration Required to Operate a Commercial Mine (% by Weight)	Enrichment Factor
Aluminum	8	24–32	3–4
Iron	5.8	40	6–7
Copper	0.0058	0.46–0.58	80–100
Nickel	0.0072	1.08	150
Zinc	0.0082	2.46	300
Uranium	0.00016	0.19	1,200
Lead	0.00010	0.2	2,000
Gold	0.0000002	0.0008	4,000
Mercury	0.000002	0.2	100,000

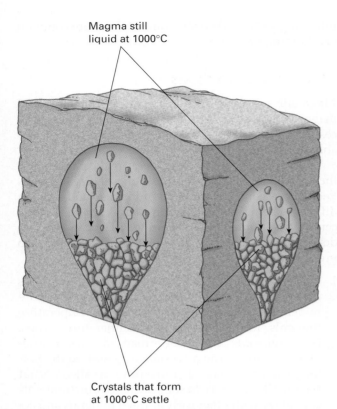

Magma still
liquid at 1000°C

Crystals that form
at 1000°C settle

Figure 5.4 Early formed crystals settle and concentrate near the bottom of a magma chamber. The crystals are magnified for clarity. In actuality the crystals may be a few millimeters in diameter, whereas, the magma chamber may be a kilometer in width.

of the state of Maine—and about 7 kilometers thick. The Bushveld deposits contain more than 20 billion tons of chromium and more than 10 billion grams of platinum, the greatest reserves in any known deposit on Earth. The world's largest known nickel deposit occurs in a layered mafic pluton at Sudbury, Ontario, and rich platinum ores are mined from layered plutons in southern Montana and Norilsk, Russia.

Hydrothermal Processes

Hydrothermal processes are probably responsible for the formation of more ore deposits, and a larger total quantity of ore, than all other processes combined. To form a hydrothermal ore deposit, hot water (hence the roots *hydro* for water and *thermal* for hot) dissolves metals from rock or magma. The metal-bearing solutions then seep through cracks or through permeable rock until they precipitate to form an ore deposit.

Hydrothermal water comes from three sources:

1. Granitic magma contains more dissolved water than solid granite rock. Thus, the magma gives off hydrothermal water as it solidifies. For this reason, hydrothermal ore deposits are commonly associated with granite and similar igneous rocks.

2. Ground water can seep into the crust where it is heated and forms a hydrothermal solution. This is particularly true in volcanic areas where hot rock or magma heat ground water at shallow depths. For this reason, hydrothermal ore deposits are also common in volcanic regions.

3. In the oceans, hot, young basalt near the Mid-Oceanic Ridge heats seawater as it seeps into cracks in the sea floor.

Although water by itself is capable of dissolving minerals, most hydrothermal waters also contain dissolved salts, which greatly increase their ability to dissolve minerals. Therefore, hot, salty, hydrothermal water is a very powerful solvent, capable of dissolving and transporting metals.

Table 5.2 shows that tiny amounts of all metals are found in average rocks of the Earth's crust. For example, gold makes up 0.0000002 percent of the crust, while copper makes up 0.0058 percent and lead 0.0001 percent. Although the metals are present in very low concentrations in country rock, hydrothermal solutions percolate through vast volumes of rock, dissolving and accumulating the metals. The solutions then deposit the metals when they encounter changes in temperature, pressure, or chemical environment (Figure 5.5). In this way, hydrothermal solutions scavenge metals from large volumes of normal crustal rocks, and then deposit them locally to form ore.

A **hydrothermal vein** deposit forms when dissolved metals precipitate in a fracture in rock. Ore veins range from less than a millimeter to several meters in width. A single vein can yield several million dollars worth of gold or silver. The same hydrothermal solutions may also soak into pores in country rock near the vein to create a large but much less concentrated **disseminated ore** deposit. Because they commonly form from the same solutions, rich ore veins and disseminated deposits are often found together. The history of many mining districts is one in which early miners dug shafts and tunnels to follow the rich veins. After the veins were exhausted, later miners used huge power shovels to extract low-grade ore from disseminated deposits surrounding the veins.

Disseminated copper deposits, with ore veins, are abundant along the entire western margin of North and South America (Figure 5.6). They are most commonly associated with large granitic plutons. Both the plutons and the copper ore formed as a result of subduction that occurred as tectonic plates carrying North and South America migrated westward to converge with oceanic plates. Other metals, including lead, zinc, molybdenum, gold, and silver, are found with the copper ore. Examples of such deposits occur at Butte,

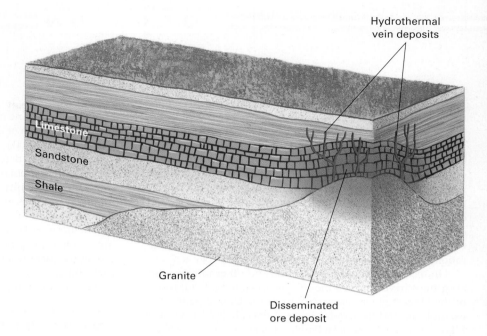

Figure 5.5 Hot water deposits metallic minerals in veins that fill fractures in bedrock. It also deposits low-grade disseminated metal ore in large volumes of rock surrounding the veins.

Montana; Bingham, Utah; Morenci, Arizona; and Ely, Nevada.

In volcanically active regions of the sea floor, near the Mid-Oceanic Ridge and submarine volcanoes, seawater circulates through the hot, fractured oceanic crust. The hot seawater dissolves metals from the rocks and then, as it rises through the upper layers of oceanic crust, cools and precipitates the metals to form **submarine hydrothermal ore** deposits.

The metal-bearing solutions can be seen today as jets of black water, called **black smokers,** spouting from fractures in the mid-oceanic ridge (Figure 5.7). The black color is caused by precipitation of fine-grained metal sulfide minerals as the solutions cool upon contact with seawater. The precipitating metals accumulate as chimney-like structures near the hot water vent.

Ore deposits rich in copper, lead, zinc, gold, silver, and other metals have formed in submarine volcanic environments throughout time. For example, on land an ore deposit containing 2.5 percent zinc is rich enough to mine commercially; but some undersea zinc deposits contain 55 percent zinc. The cost of operating machinery beneath the sea is so great that these deposits cannot be mined profitably. However, in some places tectonic forces have lifted submarine ore deposits to the Earth's surface. The ancient Romans mined copper, lead, and zinc ores of this type in the Apennine Mountains of Italy. This geologic wealth contributed to the political and military ascendancy of Rome.

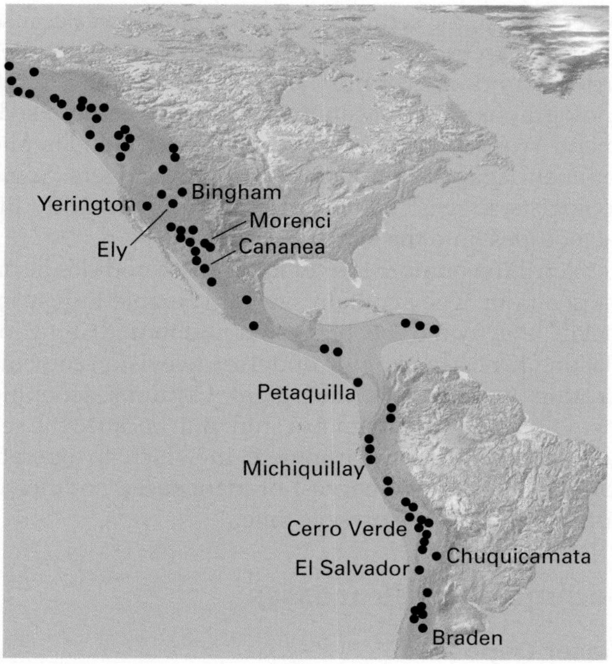

Manganese Nodules

About 25 to 50 percent of the Pacific Ocean floor is covered with golf ball to bowling ball sized **manganese nodules** (Figure 5.8). A typical nodule contains 20 to 30 percent manganese, 6 percent iron, about 1 percent each of copper and nickel, and lesser amounts of other metals. (Much of the remaining 60 to 70 percent con-

Figure 5.6 Rich deposits of copper and other metals exist throughout the Cordillera of North, Central, and South America. These deposits formed along modern or ancient tectonic plate boundaries. Dots indicate mines.

The 1872 Mining Law

The 1872 Mining Law governs the mining of metal ore on public land in the United States. In the mid-1800s, when pioneers were exploring the western frontier, the intent of the law was to encourage the exploration and development of America's natural resources and to foster economic growth. The law states that any individual or corporation can obtain mineral rights to metal ore on public land. The miner need only prove that he or she can make a profit by mining the deposit and complete a small amount of development work on the claim each year. The miner pays no royalties or other fees to the government or public for the ore extracted. In some cases, corporations or citizens can buy land for as little as $5 per acre.

In recent years, conservationists and other public interest groups have attacked the 1872 law, claiming that it is one of the biggest giveaway programs in the United States. For example, in 1994 the federal government sold 2000 acres near Elko, Nevada, to American Barrick Resources, Inc., for $9765. Geologists estimate that the property contains $10 billion worth of gold, although profits will be much less because of mining expenses. In another instance, a mining company bought 160 acres near Keystone, Colorado. They operated a mine on a portion of the land and sold the rest for ski condominiums for $11,000 per acre.

In response, defenders of the 1872 law argue that mineral exploration entails a great deal of risk and expense because the probability of finding new ore is low. In addition, mining companies must invest large sums of money to locate and develop an ore deposit before any profit is earned. The potential rewards, as guaranteed by the 1872 law, must be great to make exploration attractive to investors. Defenders also argue that the law has worked well for more than a century and has produced one of the world's most productive and efficient mining industries.

FOCUS   QUESTION

How does the public benefit from mining of resources on public land?

---

sists of oxygen and other anions chemically bonded to the metals.) The metals are probably added to seawater by volcanic activity at the Mid-Oceanic Ridge, perhaps by the black smokers. Chemical reactions between seawater and sea-floor sediment precipitate the dissolved metals to form the nodules.

Figure 5.7 A black smoker spouts from the East Pacific rise. Seawater becomes hot as it circulates through the hot basalt near a spreading center or submarine volcano. The hot water dissolves sulfur, iron, zinc, copper, and other ions from the basalt. The ions then precipitate as "smoke," consisting of tiny metallic mineral grains, when the hot solution meets cold ocean water. The hot, nutrient-rich water sustains thriving plant and animal communities.

Dudley Foster, Woods Hole Oceanographic Institution

The nodules grow by about 10 layers of atoms per year, which amounts to 3 millimeters per million years. Curiously, they are found only on the surface of, but never within, the sediment on the ocean floor. Because sediment accumulates much faster than the nodules grow, why doesn't it bury the nodules as they form? Photographs show that animals churn up sea-floor sediment. Worms burrow into it, and other animals pile sediment against the nodules to build shelters. Some geologists suggest that these activities constantly lift the nodules onto the surface.

A trillion or more tons of manganese nodules lie on the sea floor. They contain several valuable industrial metals that could be harvested without drilling or blasting. One can imagine undersea television cameras locating the nodules, and giant vacuums scooping them up and lifting them to a ship. But, because the sea floor is a difficult environment in which to operate complex machinery, harvest of manganese nodules is not profitable at the present time.

Sedimentary Processes

Placer Deposits

Gold is denser than any other mineral. Therefore, if you swirl a mixture of water, gold dust, and sand in a gold pan, the gold falls to the bottom first (Figure 5.9). Differential settling also occurs in nature.

Figure 5.8 Manganese nodules cover many parts of the sea floor in both the Pacific and Atlantic Oceans. These lie at a depth of 5500 meters in the northeastern Atlantic.

Figure 5.9 Jeffery Embrey panning for gold near his cabin in Park City, Montana, in 1898.

Many streams carry silt, sand, and gravel with an occasional small grain of gold. The gold settles first when the current slows down. Over years, currents agitate the sediment and the dense gold works its way into cracks and crevices in the stream bed. Thus grains of gold concentrate in gravel and bedrock cracks in the stream bed, forming a **placer** deposit (Figure 5.10). Most of the prospectors who rushed to California in the Gold Rush of 1849 searched for placer deposits.

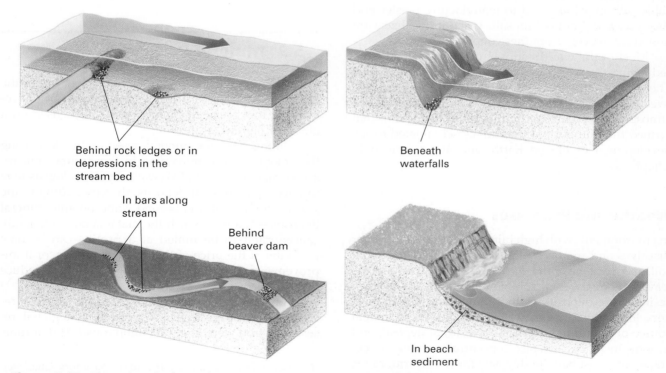

Behind rock ledges or in depressions in the stream bed

Beneath waterfalls

In bars along stream

Behind beaver dam

In beach sediment

Figure 5.10 Placer deposits form where water currents slow down and deposit high-density minerals.

Precipitates

Ground water dissolves minerals as it seeps through soil and bedrock. In most environments, ground water eventually flows into streams and then to the sea. Some of the dissolved ions, such as sodium and chloride, make seawater salty. In deserts, however, playa lakes develop with no outlet to the ocean. Water flows into the lakes but can escape only by evaporation. As the water evaporates, the dissolved salts concentrate until they precipitate to form **evaporite** deposits.

You can perform a simple demonstration of evaporation and precipitation. Fill a bowl with warm water and add a few teaspoons of table salt. The salt dissolves and you see only a clear liquid. Set the bowl aside for a few days until the water evaporates. The salt precipitates and encrusts the sides and bottom of the bowl.

Evaporite deposits formed in desert lakes include table salt, borax, sodium sulfate, and sodium carbonate. These salts are used in the production of paper, soap, and medicines, and for the tanning of leather.

Several times during the past 500 million years, shallow seas covered large regions of North America and all other continents. At times, those seas were so poorly connected to the open oceans that water did not circulate freely between them and the oceans. Consequently, evaporation concentrated the dissolved salts until they precipitated as marine evaporites. Periodically, storms flushed new seawater from the open ocean into the shallow seas, providing a new supply of salt. Thick marine evaporite beds, formed in this way, underlie nearly 30 percent of North America. Table salt, gypsum (used to manufacture plaster and sheetrock), and potassium salts (used in fertilizer) are mined extensively from these deposits.

Most of the world's supply of iron is mined from sedimentary rocks called **banded iron formations**. These iron-rich rocks precipitated from the seas between 2.6 and 1.9 billion years ago, as a result of rising atmospheric oxygen concentrations. The processes that formed these important ores are closely related to the development of life on Earth, and are described in Chapter 17.

Weathering Processes

In environments with high rainfall, the abundant water dissolves and removes most of the soluble ions from soil and rock near the Earth's surface. This process leaves the relatively insoluble ions in the soil to form **residual ore** deposits. Both aluminum and iron have very low solubilities in water. **Bauxite**, the principal source of aluminum, forms as a residual deposit, and in some instances iron also concentrates enough to become ore. Most bauxite deposits form in warm, rainy, tropical, or subtropical environments where chemical

Figure 5.11 Bauxite forms by intense weathering of aluminum-rich rocks.

weathering occurs rapidly. Thus bauxite ores are common in Jamaica, Cuba, Guinea, Australia, and parts of the southeastern United States (Figure 5.11). Some bauxite deposits are found today in regions with dry, cool climates. Most of them, however, formed when the regions had a warm, wet climate, and they reflect climatic change since their origin.

5.3 Mineral Reserves

Mineral reserves are the known supply of ore in the ground. The term can refer to the amount of ore remaining in a particular mine, or it can be used on a global or national scale.

Mining depletes mineral reserves by decreasing the amount of ore remaining in the ground; but reserves may increase in two ways. First, geologists may discover new mineral deposits, thereby adding to the known amount of ore. Second, subeconomic mineral deposits—those in which the metal is not sufficiently concentrated to be mined at a profit—can become profitable if the price of that metal increases, or if improvements in mining or refining technology reduce extraction costs.

Consider an example of the changing nature of reserves. In 1966 geologists estimated that global reserves of iron were about 5 billion tons.[1] At that time,

[1] B. Mason, *Principles of Geochemistry*, 3rd ed. (New York: John Wiley, 1966), Appendix III.

world consumption of iron was about 280 million tons per year. Assuming that consumption continued at the 1966 rate, the global iron reserves identified in 1966 would have been exhausted in 18 years, and we would have run out of iron ore in 1984. But iron ore is still plentiful and cheap today because new and inexpensive methods of processing lower-grade iron ore were developed. Thus, large deposits that were subeconomic in 1966, and therefore not counted as reserves, are now ore.

The Geopolitics of Metal Resources

The Earth's mineral resources are unevenly distributed, and no single nation is self-sufficient in all minerals. For example, almost two thirds of the world's molybdenum reserves, and more than one third of the lead reserves, are located in the United States. More than half of the aluminum reserves are found in Australia and Guinea. The United States uses 40 percent of all aluminum produced in the world, yet it has no large bauxite deposits. Zambia and the Democratic Republic of Congo supply half of the world's cobalt, although neither nation uses the metal for its own industry.

Five nations—the United States, Russia, South Africa, Canada, and Australia—supply most of the mineral resources used by modern societies. Many other nations have few mineral resources. For example, Japan has almost no metal or fuel reserves; despite its modern economy and high productivity, it relies entirely on imports for metals and fuel.

Developed nations consume most of the Earth's mineral resources. Four nations—the United States, Japan, Germany, and Russia—consume about 75 percent of the most intensively used metals, although they account for only 14 percent of world population.

Currently, the United States depends on 25 other countries for more than half of its mineral resources. Some must be imported because we have no reserves of our own. We do have reserves of others, but we consume them more rapidly than we can mine them, or we can buy them more cheaply than we can mine them.

Figure 5.12 Machinery extracts coal from an underground coal mine.

Figure 5.13 The Bingham Canyon, Utah, open-pit copper mine is the largest human-created hole on Earth. It is 4 kilometers in diameter and 0.8 kilometer deep.

5.4 Mines and Mining

Miners extract both ore and coal (described in the following section) from underground mines and surface mines. A large **underground mine** may consist of tens of kilometers of interconnected passages that commonly follow ore veins or coal seams (Figure 5.12). The lowest levels may be several kilometers deep. In contrast, a **surface mine** is a hole excavated into the Earth's surface. The largest human-created hole is the open-pit copper mine at Bingham Canyon, Utah. It is 4 kilometers in diameter and 0.8 kilometers deep. The mine produced 270,000 tons of copper in 2001 and smaller amounts of gold, silver, and molybdenum (Figure 5.13). Most modern coal mining is done by large power shovels that extract coal from huge surface mines (Figure 5.14).

In the United States, the Surface Mining Control and Reclamation Act requires that mining companies restore mined land so that it can be used for the same purposes for which it was used before mining began. In addition, a tax is levied to reclaim land that was mined

Figure 5.14 A huge power shovel dwarfs a person standing inside the Navajo Strip Mine in New Mexico.

Figure 5.15 This house tilted and broke in half as it sank into an abandoned underground coal mine.

and destroyed before the law was enacted. Enforcement and compliance of environmental laws waxes and wanes with the political climate in Washington. Yet environmental awareness has increased dramatically over the past generation and, overall, mining operations are less polluting today than they were when your parents were in their teens. One of the big challenges for the future is to clean up old mines that were operated under lax or nonexistent environmental regulations of the past. In the United States, more than 6000 unrestored coal and metal surface mines cover an area of about 90,000 square kilometers, slightly smaller than the state of Virginia. This figure does not include abandoned sand and gravel mines and rock quarries, which probably account for an even larger area.

Although underground mines do not directly disturb the land surface, some abandoned mines collapse, and occasionally buildings have fallen into the holes (Figure 5.15). Over 800,000 hectares (2 million acres) of land in central Appalachia have settled into underground coal mine shafts.

Mining of both metal ores and coal also creates huge piles of waste rock, rock that must be removed to get at the ore or coal. If the waste piles are not treated properly, rain rapidly erodes the loose rock, and leaches toxic elements such as arsenic, sulfur, and heavy metals from the piles, choking the streams with sediment and contaminating both stream and ground water. These environmental effects are discussed in Chapter 12.

5.5 Energy Resources: Fossil Fuels

Petroleum, coal, and natural gas are called **fossil fuels** because they formed from the remains of plants and animals. Fossil fuels are not only nonrenewable but also unrecyclable. When a lump of coal or a liter of oil is burned, the energy dissipates into the air and is, for all practical purposes, lost. Thus our fossil fuel supply inexorably diminishes.

Coal

Coal is a combustible rock composed mainly of carbon. Humans began using coal before they used petroleum and natural gas because coal is easily mined and can be burned without refining.

Coal-fired electric generating plants burn about 60 percent of the coal consumed in the United States. The remainder is used to make steel or to produce steam in factories. Although it is easily mined and abundant in many parts of the world, coal emits air pollutants that can be removed only with expensive control devices.

Large quantities of coal formed worldwide during the Carboniferous period, between 360 and 286 million years ago, and later in Cretaceous and Paleocene times, when warm, humid swamps covered broad areas of low-lying land. Coal is probably forming today in some places, such as in the Ganges River Delta in India, but the process is much slower than the rate at which we are consuming coal reserves. As shown in Figure 5.16, widespread availability of this fuel is projected at least until the year 2200.

When plants die in forests and grasslands, or-

Figure 5.16 Past and predicted global coal supplies based on two different estimates of reserves. Shaded area shows coal already consumed.

A Litter falls to floor of stagnant swamp

B Debris accumulates, barrier forms, decay is incomplete

C Sediment accumulates, organic matter is converted to peat

D Peat is lithified to coal

Figure 5.17 Peat and coal form as sediment buries organic litter in a swamp.

ganisms consume some of the litter, and chemical reactions with oxygen and water decompose the remainder. As a result, little organic matter accumulates except in the topsoil. In some warm swamps, however, plants grow and die so rapidly that newly fallen vegetation quickly buries older plant remains. The new layers prevent atmospheric oxygen from penetrating into the deeper layers, and decomposition stops before it is complete, leaving brown, partially decayed plant matter called **peat**. Commonly, peat is then buried by mud deposited in the swamp.

Plant matter is composed mainly of carbon, hydrogen, and oxygen and contains large amounts of water. During burial, rising pressure expels the water

and chemical reactions release most of the hydrogen and oxygen. As a result, the proportion of carbon increases until coal forms (Figure 5.17). The grade of coal, and the heat that can be recovered by burning coal, varies considerably depending on the carbon content (Table 5.3).

Petroleum

The first commercial oil well was drilled in the United States in 1859, ushering in a new energy age. Crude oil, as it is pumped from the ground, is a gooey, viscous, dark liquid made up of thousands of different chemical compounds. It is then refined to produce propane,

TABLE 5.3 Classification of Coal by Grade, Heat Value, and Carbon Content

Type	Color	Water (%)	Other Volatiles and Non-combustible Compounds (%)	Carbon (%)	Heat Value (BTU/lb)
Peat	Brown	75	10	15	3,000–5,000
Lignite	Dark Brown	45	20	35	7,000
Bituminous (soft coal)	Black	5–15	20–30	55–75	12,000
Anthracite (hard coal)	Black	4	1	95	14,000

Figure 5.18 An oil refinery converts crude oil into useful products such as gasoline.

Courtesy of Graham R. Thompson / Jonathan Turk

gasoline, heating oil, and other fuels (Figure 5.18). Many petroleum products are used to manufacture plastics, nylon, and other useful materials.

Formation of Petroleum

Streams carry organic matter from decaying land plants and animals to the sea and to some large lakes, and deposit it with mud in shallow coastal waters. Marine plants and animals die and settle to the sea floor, adding more organic matter to the mud. Over millions of years, younger sediment buries this organic-rich mud to depths of a few kilometers, where rising temperature and pressure convert the mud to shale. At the same time, the elevated temperature and pressure convert the organic matter to liquid **petroleum** that is dispersed throughout the rock (Figure 5.19). The activity of bacteria may enhance the process. Typically, petroleum forms in the temperature range from 50 to 100°C.

The shale or other sedimentary rock in which oil originally forms is called the **source rock**. Oil dispersed in shale cannot be pumped from an oil well because shale is relatively impermeable; that is, liquids do not flow through it rapidly. But under favorable condi-tions, petroleum migrates slowly to a nearby layer of permeable rock—usually sandstone or limestone—where it can flow readily. Because petroleum is less dense than water or rock, it then rises through the permeable rock until it is trapped within the rock or escapes onto the Earth's surface.

Many **oil traps** form where a layer of impermeable rock such as shale prevents the petroleum from rising further. Oil or gas then accumulates in a petroleum **reservoir**. Folds and faults create several types of oil traps (Figure 5.20). In some regions, large, lightbulb-shaped bodies of salt have flowed upward through solid rocks to form salt domes. The rising salt folded the surrounding rock to form an oil trap (Fig. 5.20D). The salt originated as a sedimentary bed of marine evaporite, and it rose because salt is less dense than the surrounding rocks. An oil reservoir is not an underground pool or lake of oil. It consists of oil-saturated permeable rock that is like an oil-soaked sponge.

Geologic activity can destroy an oil reservoir as well as create one. A fault may fracture the reservoir rock, or tectonic forces may uplift the reservoir and expose it to erosion. In either case, the petroleum escapes once the trap is destroyed. Sixty percent of all oil wells are found in relatively young rocks that formed during the Cenozoic era. Undoubtedly, much petroleum that had formed in older Mesozoic and Paleozoic rocks escaped long ago and decomposed at the Earth's surface.

Petroleum Extraction, Transport, and Refining

To extract petroleum, an oil company drills a well into a reservoir. After the hole has been bored, the expensive drill rig is removed and replaced by a pumper that slowly extracts the petroleum. Fifty years ago, many reservoirs lay near the surface and oil was easily pumped from shallow wells. But these reserves have been exploited, and modern oil wells are often a few kilometers or more deep.

In the past, oil wells were drilled vertically into the reservoir. Oil then flowed through the reservoir to the

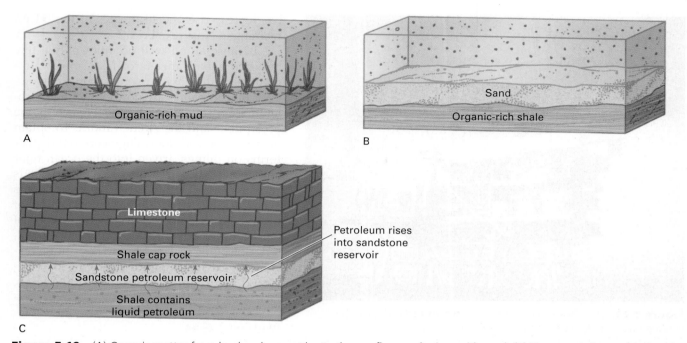

Figure 5.19 (A) Organic matter from land and sea settles to the sea floor and mixes with mud. (B) Younger sediment buries this organic-rich mud. Rising temperature and pressure convert the mud to shale, and the organic matter to petroleum. (C) The petroleum is trapped in the reservoir by an impermeable cap rock.

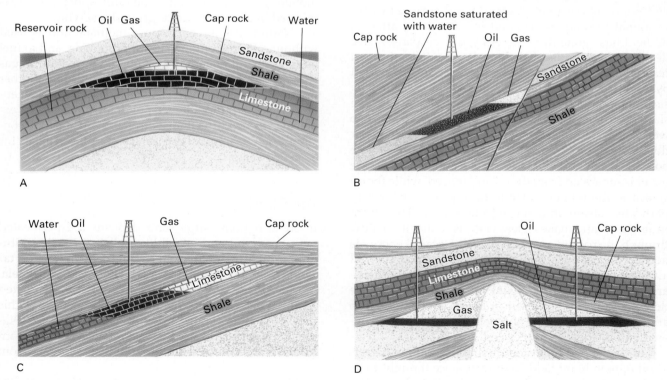

Figure 5.20 Four different types of oil traps. (A) Petroleum rises into permeable limestone capped by impermeable shale in a structural dome. (B) A trap forms where a fault has moved impermeable shale against permeable sandstone. (C) Horizontally bedded shale traps oil in tilted limestone. (D) Sedimentary salt rises and deforms overlying strata to create a trap.

has increased earlier estimates of the oil remaining in North America.[2]

Because an oil well occupies only a few hundred square meters of land, most cause relatively little environmental damage. However, oil companies are now extracting petroleum from fragile environments such as the ocean floor and the Arctic tundra. To obtain oil from the sea floor, engineers build platforms on pilings driven into the ocean floor and mount drill rigs on these steel islands (Figure 5.21). Despite great care, accidents occur during the drilling and extraction of oil. When accidents occur at sea, millions of barrels of oil can spread throughout the waters, poisoning marine life and disrupting marine ecosystems. Significant oil spills have occurred in virtually all offshore drilling areas.

Figure 5.21 An offshore oil drilling platform extracts oil from the continental shelf beneath a shallow sea.

Sun Oil

well, where pumps raised it to the surface. The amount of oil that reached the well was limited by the permeability of the reservoir rock and by the viscosity of the oil.

On the average, more than half of the oil in a reservoir is too viscous to be pumped to the surface by conventional techniques. This oil is left behind after an oil field has "gone dry." Recently, oil companies have developed methods of drilling horizontally through reservoirs, allowing access to vast amounts of oil left by earlier wells. Additional oil can be extracted by **secondary and tertiary recovery** techniques. In one simple secondary process, water is pumped into one well, called the "injection well." The pressurized water floods the reservoir, driving oil to nearby wells, where both the water and oil are extracted. At the surface, the water is separated from the oil and reused, while the oil is sent to the refinery. One tertiary process forces superheated steam into the injection well. The steam heats the oil and makes it less viscous so that it can flow through the rock to an adjacent well. Because energy is needed to heat the steam, this type of extraction is not always cost effective or energy efficient. Another tertiary process pumps detergent into the reservoir. The detergent dissolves the remaining oil and carries it to an adjacent well, where the petroleum is then recovered and the detergent recycled.

In the United States, more than 300 billion barrels of oil remain in oil fields that were once thought to be depleted. As the technology for extracting this oil has become available, the United States Geological Survey

Natural Gas

Natural gas forms in source rock or an oil reservoir when crude oil is heated above 100°C during burial. (Natural gas is methane, CH_4, an organic molecule consisting of a single carbon atom bonded to 4 hydrogen atoms.) Consequently, many oil fields contain a mixture of oil, with natural gas floating above the heavier liquid petroleum. In other instances, the lighter, more mobile gas escaped into the atmosphere, or was trapped in a separate underground reservoir.

Natural gas is nearly pure methane and is used without refining for home heating, cooking, and to fuel large electrical generating plants. Because natural gas contains few impurities, it releases no sulfur and other pollutants when it burns. This fuel has a higher net energy yield, produces fewer pollutants, and is less expensive to produce than petroleum. At current consumption rates, global natural gas supplies will last for 80 to 200 years.

Tar Sands

In some regions, large sand deposits are permeated with heavy oil and an oil-like substance called **bitumen**, which are too thick to be pumped. The richest **tar sands** exist in Alberta (Canada), Utah, and Venezuela.

In Alberta alone, tar sands contain an estimated 1 trillion barrels of petroleum. About 10 percent of this fuel is shallow enough to be surface mined (Figure 5.22). Tar sands are dug up and heated with steam to make the bitumen fluid enough to separate from

[2] R. C. Burruss, "Petroleum Reserves in North America," *Geotimes* (July 1995):14.

Figure 5.22 Heavy equipment mines tar sands, which are abundant in Alberta, Canada.

the sand. The bitumen is then treated chemically and heated to convert it to crude oil. At present, several companies mine tar sands profitably, producing 11 percent of Canada's petroleum. Deeper deposits, comprising the remaining 90 percent of the reserve, can be extracted using subsurface techniques similar to those discussed for secondary and tertiary recovery.

Oil Shale

Some shales and other sedimentary rocks contain a waxy, solid organic substance called **kerogen**. Kerogen is organic material that has not yet converted to oil. Kerogen-bearing rock is called **oil shale**. If oil shale is mined and heated in the presence of water, the kerogen converts to petroleum. In the United States, oil shales contain the energy equivalent of 2 to 5 trillion barrels of petroleum, enough to fuel the nation for 300 to 700 years at the 2001 consumption rate (Figure 5.23). However, many oil shales are of such low grade that more energy is required to mine and convert the kerogen to petroleum than is generated by burning the oil. Consequently, these low-grade shales will probably never be used for fuel. Oil from higher-grade oil shales in the United States can supply this country for nearly 70 years. Oil shale deposits in most other nations are not as rich, so oil shale is less promising as a global energy source.

Water consumption is a serious problem in oil shale development. Approximately two

barrels of water are needed to produce each barrel of oil from shale. Oil shale occurs most abundantly in the semiarid western United States. In this region, scarce water is also needed for agriculture, domestic use, and industry.

When oil prices rose to $45 per barrel in 1981, major oil companies built experimental oil shale recovery plants. However, when prices plummeted a few years later, most of this activity came to a halt. Today, no large-scale oil shale mining is taking place in the United States.

5.6 Energy Resources: Nuclear Fuels and Reactors

Nuclear fuels are radioactive isotopes used to generate electricity in nuclear reactors. Uranium is the most commonly used nuclear fuel. These energy resources, like mineral resources, are nonrenewable, although uranium, the most commonly used nuclear fuel, is abundant.

A modern nuclear power plant uses nuclear **fission** to produce heat and generate electricity. One isotope of uranium, U-235, is the major fuel. When a U-235

Figure 5.23 Secondary recovery, tar sands, and oil shale increase our petroleum reserves significantly

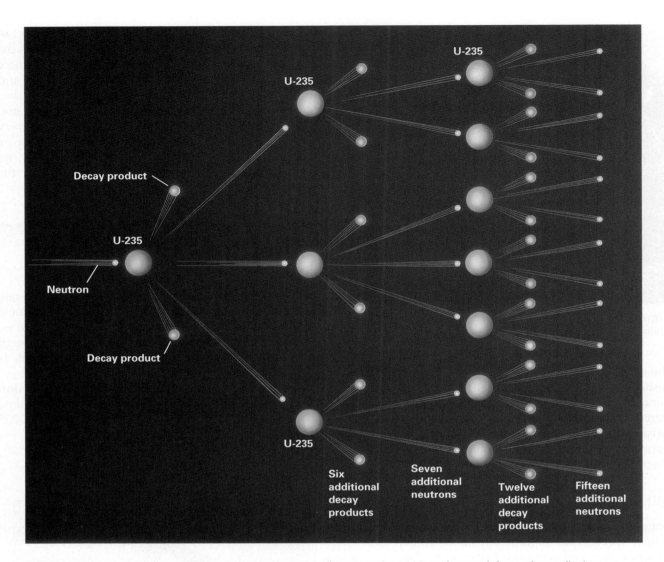

Figure 5.24 In a branching chain reaction, a neutron strikes a uranium-235 nucleus and the nucleus splits into two roughly equal fragments and emits two or three neutrons. These neutrons can then initiate additional reactions, which produce more neutrons. A branching chain reaction accelerates rapidly through a sample of concentrated uranium-235.

Labels in figure: Decay product · U-235 · Neutron · Decay product · U-235 · U-235 · U-235 · Six additional decay products · Seven additional neutrons · Twelve additional decay products · Fifteen additional neutrons

nucleus is bombarded with a neutron, it breaks apart (*fission* means "splitting"). The initial reaction releases two or three neutrons. Each of these neutrons can trigger the fission of additional nuclei; hence, this type of nuclear reaction is called a **branching chain reaction** (Figure 5.24). Because this fission is initiated by neutron bombardment, it is not a spontaneous process and is different from natural radioactivity.

To fuel a nuclear reactor, uranium concentrated with U-235 is compressed into small pellets. Each pellet could easily fit into your hand but contains the energy equivalent of 1 ton of coal. A column of pellets is encased in a 2-meter-long pipe, called a **fuel rod** (Figure 5.25). A typical nuclear power plant contains about 50,000 fuel rods bundled into assemblies of 200 rods

each. **Control rods** made of neutron-absorbing alloys are spaced among the fuel rods. The control rods fine-tune the reactor. If the reaction speeds up because too many neutrons are striking other uranium atoms, then the power plant operator lowers the control rods to absorb more neutrons and slow down the reaction. If fission slows down because too many neutrons are absorbed, the operator raises the control rods. If an accident occurs and all internal power systems fail, the control rods fall into the reactor core and quench the fission.

The reactor core produces tremendous amounts of heat. A fluid, usually water, is pumped through the reactor core to cool it. The cooling water (which is now radioactive from exposure to the core) is then passed

A

B

Courtesy Westinghouse Electric Corp., Commercial Nuclear Fuel Division

Figure 5.25 (A) Fuel pellets contain enriched uranium-235. Each pellet contains the energy equivalent of 1 ton of coal. (B) Fuel pellets are encased into narrow rods that are bundled together and lowered into the reactor core.

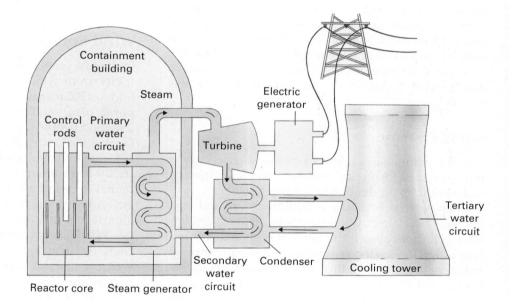

Figure 5.26 In a nuclear power plant, fission energy creates heat, which is used to produce steam. The steam drives a turbine, which generates electricity.

through a radiator, where it heats another source of water to produce steam. The steam drives a turbine, which in turn generates electricity (Figure 5.26).

Every step in the mining, processing, and use of nuclear fuel produces radioactive wastes. The mine waste discarded during mining is radioactive. Enrichment of the ore produces additional radioactive waste. When a U-235 nucleus undergoes fission in a reactor, it splits into two useless radioactive nuclei that must be discarded. Finally, after several months in a reactor, the U-235 concentration in the fuel rods drops until the fuel pellets are no longer useful. In some countries, these pellets are reprocessed to recover U-235, but in the United States this process is not economical and the pellets are discarded as radioactive waste. In Chapter

12 we discuss problems and solutions for storing radioactive wastes.

In recent years, construction of new reactors in the United States has become so costly that electricity generated by nuclear power is more expensive than that generated by coal-fired power plants. Public concern about accidents and radioactive waste disposal has become acute. The demand for electricity has risen less than expected during the past two decades. As a result, growth of the nuclear power industry has halted. After 1974, many planned nuclear power plants were canceled; and after 1981, no new orders were placed for nuclear power plants in the United States.

In the early 1970s, many energy experts predicted that nuclear energy would proliferate and dominate the generation of electric energy. Some experts even suggested that electricity would become "too cheap to meter." These predictions have not been realized. In contrast, *Forbes* business magazine called the United States nuclear power program "the largest managerial disaster in U.S. business history, involving $1 trillion in wasted investment and $10 billion in direct losses to stockholders."

5.7 Energy Resources: Alternative Energy

Unlike fossil and nuclear fuels, alternative energy resources are renewable; natural processes replenish them as we use them. These resources include solar; wind; geothermal; hydroelectric; wood and other biomass fuels; and ocean waves and currents. Although the amount of energy produced today by alternative sources is small compared to that provided by fossil and nuclear fuels, alternative resources have the potential to supply all of our energy needs. Except for biomass fuels, alternative energy sources emit no carbon dioxide and therefore do not contribute to global warming.

Solar Energy

Current technologies allow us to use solar energy in three ways: passive solar heating, active solar heating, and electricity production by solar cells.

A passive solar house is built to absorb and store the Sun's heat directly. In active solar heating systems, solar collectors absorb the Sun's energy and use it to heat water. Pumps then circulate the hot water through radiators to heat a building, or the inhabitants use the hot water directly for washing and bathing.

A **solar cell** produces electricity directly from sunlight. A modern solar cell is a semiconductor. Sunlight energizes electrons in the semiconductor so that they travel through the crystal, producing an electric current (Figure 5.27). Some scientists have suggested that solar cells have the potential to supply between 50 and 100 percent of all electricity used in the United States.

At present, the cost of purchasing and operating solar cells to supply electricity to a home is approximately five times greater than purchasing the same amount of electricity from a local power company over a 25-year period. Consequently, most domestic solar cell systems are sold to homeowners living in remote places that are not served by commercial power companies. Although solar cells cannot compete with other commercial systems at present, their potential for producing cheap, pollution-free energy is so great that a

Figure 5.27 This bank of solar cells generates electricity for the visitor center at Natural Bridges National Monument, Utah.

few research breakthroughs that lower their cost could alter the way the world produces its electricity.

Wind Energy

In the five years from 1997 to 2002, production of electricity from wind in the United States increased 2.5 fold to 4200 megawatts, as much as that of four nuclear power plants and enough to power a city of more than 2 million people (Figure 5.28). The largest single wind farm in the United States is located on Hawaii's island of Oahu. Other gigantic wind farms now generate electricity in southern California. A huge, untapped potential for wind generation exists in several midwestern and western states, where winds blow strongly and almost continuously.

Wind energy production is growing rapidly because construction of wind generators is cheaper than building new fossil fuel-fired power plants. Wind energy is also clean and virtually limitless. Most people feel that the environmental side effects of wind farms (noise, unsightliness, or interference with bird migration patterns) are acceptable alternatives to the pollution involved in mining and burning coal to produce the same amount of electricity.

Geothermal Energy

Energy extracted from the Earth's internal heat is called "geothermal energy." Natural hot ground water can be pumped to the surface to generate electricity, or it can be used directly to heat homes and other buildings. Alternatively, cool surface water can be pumped deep into the ground to be heated by subterranean rock, and then circulated to the surface for use. The United States is the largest producer of geothermal electricity in the world, with a production capacity of 2500 megawatts,

Figure 5.28 Wind turbines generate electricity at Cowley Ridge, Alberta, Canada.

an amount equivalent to the power output of 2.5 large nuclear reactors.

Hydroelectric Energy

If a river is dammed, the energy of water dropping downward through the dam can be harnessed to turn turbines that produce electricity. Hydroelectric generators supply between 15 and 20 percent of the world's electricity. They provide about 3.5 percent of all energy consumed in the United States, but about 15 percent of our electricity.

The United States is unlikely to increase its production of hydroelectric energy. Large dams are expensive to build, and few suitable sites remain. Environmentalists commonly oppose dam construction because the resulting reservoirs flood large areas—destroying wildlife habitat, agricultural land, towns, and migratory fish populations. For example, the dams on the Columbia River and its tributaries are largely responsible for the demise of salmon populations in the Pacific Northwest. Undammed wild rivers and their canyons are often prized for their aesthetic and recreational value.

Biomass Energy

Biomass (plant) fuels currently produce about 3 quads (quadrillion BTU) of energy, about half that generated by nuclear power plants. Wood is the most productive of all biofuels, followed by controlled garbage inciner-

ation and alcohol fuels. Wood-burning stoves produce so much smoke and particulate pollution that their use is banned in some cities and restricted in others. Recently, wood stoves have been designed that are 65 percent efficient and produce only 10 percent as much pollution as older wood stoves. But these updated stoves are expensive, and wood will probably be a significant energy source in rural areas only.

Some biofuel experts suggest that trees grow too slowly and, instead, rapidly growing crops such as sugar cane, corn, or sunflowers should be grown for the energy content in their sugars, oils, or starches. In this case, the plant products are fermented to make ethanol. Ethanol burns more cleanly in automobile engines than conventional gasoline and is used as an additive to reduce urban air pollution. However, more energy from fossil fuels is required to grow the plants and distill the ethanol than is obtained from burning the ethanol. Thus production and use of ethanol as a fuel involves an overall energy loss. In addition, the large-scale cultivation of ethanol-producing crops would require large amounts of agricultural land, putting energy production in direct competition with food production.

Energy from the Seas

Twice a day, seawater flows into a bay or estuary with the rising tide, and twice a day it rushes outward. The energy of these currents can be harnessed by a tidal dam and turbine. However, tidal dams are costly and create environmental problems. Tidal bays are commonly productive estuaries where fish breed, and they are also popular places for recreation. If these areas are dammed, some of the natural qualities and resources are lost.

Waves strike every coastline in the world, and their energy can be harnessed with a wave generator. In one type, water from an incoming wave rises in a concrete chamber, where it forces air through a narrow valve. The air spins a rotor that drives an electrical generator. At present, wave generators are too expensive to be practical in most places.

Limitations to Renewable Energy Resources

Solar cells, wind turbines, and hydroelectric dams, as well as geothermal, tidal, and wave systems harness nature's energy to produce electricity. Solar heaters and geothermal and biomass resources are used to heat

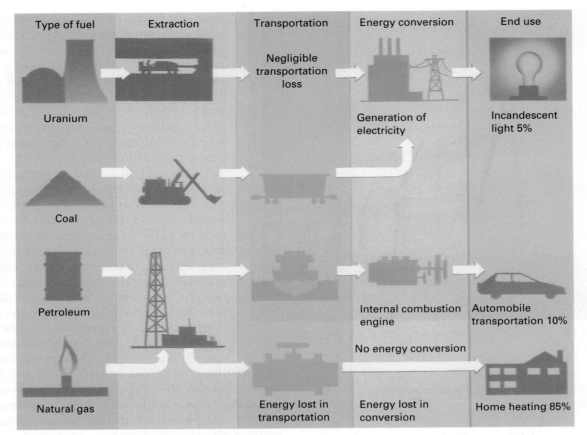

Type of fuel	Extraction	Transportation	Energy conversion	End use

Figure 5.29 The end-use efficiencies of common energy-consuming systems. Only 15 percent of the energy generated in the United States performs useful tasks; 85 percent is wasted. Half of the waste is unavoidable but half could be avoided with improved technology and conservation.

Interactive Question: Use the data in this figure to list ways in which you could conserve energy this week. Order the list from most effective (greatest energy savings) to least effective.

water or buildings. But none of these resources can be utilized directly to power mobile transportation systems such as cars and trucks.* There are several methods available to convert these energy sources for use in transportation.

Perhaps the easiest way to use electricity to transport people is the old-fashioned electric train. Electric streetcars, commuter trains, and subways have been used for decades. If we would build more electric mass transit systems, and if people would use them, then we could shift away from our dependence on the internal combustion engine and on petroleum. Eventually, the required electricity consumption could, at least in theory, be supplied by renewable energy sources.

Another solution is the electric car. Battery-only and gasoline-battery hybrid cars are discussed in the subsection, Transportation, which follows.

---

* Electricity can be used to charge a battery which powers a car. This option is discussed further in the text.

Energy planners also talk about the possibility of a **hydrogen economy**. In such a system, electricity can be used to dissociate water into hydrogen and oxygen. The hydrogen can power a fuel cell that drives an electric motor in an automobile. When the hydrogen dissociates in the fuel cell, it reacts to form water again. There is no pollution. At the present time, with abundant inexpensive petroleum, there is no economic incentive to develop large-scale production of hydrogen from water. However, the hydrogen car is being developed as a solution to air pollution and to greenhouse gas emissions.

Conservation as an Alternative Energy Resource

The single quickest and most effective way to decrease energy consumption and to prolong the availability of cheap fossil fuels, is to conserve energy (Figure 5.29). Energy conservation practices have already produced dramatic results in the United States, where fuel consumption has decreased steadily from 1.5 barrels of petroleum per $1,000 of GDP (gross domestic product) in 1978 to 0.8 in 2000. However, total fuel consumption continues to rise, and there is much room for continued improvement. Some energy experts have suggested that as much as half of the energy consumed by industrialized nations could be conserved by changing to more efficient equipment and human habits.

Energy use in the United States falls into three categories: buildings, industry, and transportation. Two kinds of conservation strategies can be applied in each of those categories. Technical solutions involve switching to more efficient implements. Social solutions involve decisions to use existing energy systems more efficiently.

Technical Solutions

Buildings

Residential and commercial buildings consume about 36 percent of all the energy produced in the United States. Most of that energy is used for heating, air conditioning, and lighting. A super-insulated home or commercial building costs about 5 percent more to construct than a conventional one, but the energy savings can compensate for the extra cost within about 5 years. After that time, the super-insulated construction saves both energy and money. About 25 percent of the electricity generated in the United States is used for lighting. A fluorescent bulb uses one fourth of the energy consumed by a comparable incandescent bulb. Although fluorescent bulbs cost about $15 each, they last 10 times longer than incandescent bulbs and yield an energy savings equivalent to three times their cost. Switching to more efficient light sources would conserve the electricity generated by about 120 large generating plants and would save $30 billion in fuel and maintenance expenses every year.

Industry

Industry consumes another 36 percent of the energy used in the United States. In general, industry quickly adapts conservation practices if they are cost effective. Industry in the United States reduced its energy consumption by about 70 percent per unit of production between 1973 and 1983. Since 1983, industrial efficiency has been relatively static. As a result, industry still wastes great amounts of energy.

For example, about 70 percent of the electricity consumed by industry—half of all electricity produced in the United States—drives electric motors. Most motors are inefficient because they run only at full speed and are slowed by brakes to operate at the proper speeds to perform their tasks. This approach is like driving your car with the gas pedal pressed to the floor and controlling your speed with the brakes. Replacing older electric motors with variable speed motors would save an amount of electricity equal to that generated by 150 large power plants, but such replacement has been slow.

Transportation

About 28 percent of all energy and two thirds of all the oil consumed in the United States are used to transport people and goods. Americans own one third of all automobiles in the world and drive as much as the rest of the world's population combined. Ten percent of all oil consumed in the world is used by Americans on their way to and from work, about two thirds of them driving alone. The efficiency of auto and truck engines is about 10 percent. Thus, much energy can be saved by changing to more efficient cars and trucks.

Over the past few decades, automobile manufacturers have offered increasingly efficient mass production automobiles. In 1996, General Motors introduced a production electric car. But consumers weren't interested and after leasing only 800 vehicles, GM abandoned the project. Today, Toyota and Honda sell hybrid gasoline-electric cars that achieve 45 to 50 miles per gallon. These cars have both an internal-combustion engine and a battery-operated electric motor. Instead of conventional braking when the driver wishes to slow down, the kinetic energy of the car is converted to electrical energy, which is stored in a battery and used during acceleration. Using these and other energy-efficient vehicles, American motorists could easily realize a 50 percent (or greater) increase in average automobile fuel economy, which would save 3 million barrels of oil a day, about one third of the current oil imports.

Social Solutions

Social solutions involve altering human behavior to conserve energy. Energy conserving actions can be applied in buildings, in industry, and in transportation. Some result in inconvenience to individuals. For example, if you choose to carpool rather than drive your own car, you save fuel but inconvenience yourself by coordinating your schedule with your carpool companions. Our national fondness for large sport utility vehicles and pickup trucks, which have poor fuel economy, has resulted in a decline in average fuel efficiency of all American cars and light trucks from 25.9 mpg in 1985 to 23.8 mpg in 1999. As explained above, high-mileage cars are on the market, but they will only make an impact if people make the social decision to use them. People argue that this social decision comes at a cost because light vehicles make the driver and passengers more vulnerable in case of an accident.

At home and in the workplace, lowering the thermostat in winter and wearing a sweater, and using less air conditioning in summer, might reduce the comfort margin but can save considerable energy. Many social solutions, however, are cost-free in terms of inconvenience. When practiced by everyone, simply turning off the lights, the television set, and other appliances when you leave the room will conserve large amounts of energy.

5.8 Energy for the Twenty-First Century

In the year 2000, fossil fuels supplied 86 percent of all energy used in the United States; oil alone accounted for 39 percent, natural gas for 24 percent, and coal for 23 percent (Figure 5.30). Thus, oil is our major source of energy. In addition, oil is the only portable energy resource currently in popular use, and thus is the main energy resource for transportation in the United States. At current rates of consumption, we have more than 200 years of domestic coal reserves, and at least several decades of natural gas reserves. Oil, however is another story.

In 1956, M. King Hubbert was a geologist working at the Shell research lab in Houston, Texas. Hubbert compared U.S. domestic oil reserves with current and predicted rates of oil consumption. He then forecast that U.S. oil production would peak in the early 1970s, and would, thereafter, decline continuously. He predicted that Americans would have to make up an ever-increasing difference between domestic oil supply and consumption by relying on larger and larger imports, or they would have to turn to other energy resources. Other experts and economists laughed at his prediction, but in 1971 the U.S. domestic oil production reached its maximum and it has been slowly declining since then.

In 2000, the United States ranked eighth in global oil production. (Saudia Arabia was first.) But due to the fact that U.S. petroleum consumption was higher than it was in 1970 and production was lower, the United States imported slightly more than half of its petroleum. (Figure 5.31). Because of this high dependence on foreign oil, the U.S. energy future is intimately linked with the global one. In November 2002, the U.S. Energy Information Agency predicted that the nation will need to import two thirds of its oil by 2025.

In 1971, Hubbert predicted that global oil production would peak between 1995 and 2000, and that the world supply of oil will be 90 percent depleted between 2020 and 2030. Twice in the 1970s, the major oil-producing nations reduced oil production and raised the price, causing economic disruptions. In 1990, Iraq invaded Kuwait and threw global petroleum markets into turmoil. Within a week, the price of petroleum skyrocketed from below $20 per barrel to $40 per barrel; it then fell again after the brief Gulf War. As we are writing this edition of *Earth Science and the Environment,* the Middle East is again in turmoil and American troops have taken over Iraq. Yet, despite these fluctuations and disruptions, oil is readily available and relatively inexpensive at the end of 2003.

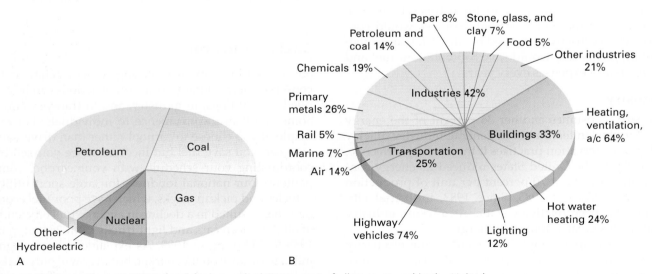

Figure 5.30 In the year 2000, fossil fuels supplied 86 percent of all energy used in the United States; oil alone accounted for 39 percent, natural gas for 24 percent, and coal for 23 percent.
Source: Energy Information Administration/Annual Energy Review 2000.

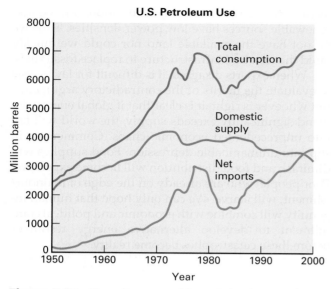

Figure 5.31 Our reliance on oil imports has increased steadily since 1971 as Hubbert predicted. *Source:* Energy Information Administration/Annual Energy Review 2000

In 2002 Kenneth Deffeyes, an oil geologist and professor at Princeton University, used Hubbert's methods to recalculate petroleum supply and demand. As a result, he predicted a global peak in oil production before 2010[3]. He argued that even new exploration and recovery technologies could not forestall declining worldwide oil production and increasing consumption in the very near future. Some economists and geologists suggest that the fluctuations in gasoline prices seen in recent years are the first wave of disruptions resulting from declining global oil reserves, and that much greater disturbances will occur imminently.

In rebuttal to this article, many energy experts argue that just as Hubbert was wrong about global oil production peaking between 1995 and 2000, Deffeyes is wrong for the same reason: His estimates of reserves are too low and there is more oil than he estimated. However, these arguments simply alter the estimate of *when* global oil supplies will fall below global demand. No one seriously suggests that the Earth has an unlimited supply and that the current energy economy will persist indefinitely.

So what will happen when global oil production drops below demand? First of all, petroleum will not just "run out" one day, with all the wells suddenly going dry. As supply dwindles and demand increases, the price of fuel will rise. People will not be able to afford as much fuel as they would like, so social and technical conservation strategies, which were previ-

[3] Kenneth Deffeyes, *Hubbert's Peak: The Impending World Oil Shortage* (Princeton, NJ: Princeton University Press, 2002).

ously rejected, will be implemented. As a result, demand will decrease. But if this decrease is not sufficient, petroleum prices will continue to rise. Secondary and tertiary reserves and oil shale development will then become profitable. Tar sands that were buried so deeply that they were unprofitable will become economical. In World War II, when allies cut Germany's oil imports, Nazi chemists synthesized petroleum from coal. In the future, when the global price of petroleum becomes high enough, such synthesis will become profitable throughout the world. But all of these measures are simply a new face on an old monkey: fossil fuels as the overwhelming component of global energy production (Figure 5.32).

What is the potential to drastically alter the global energy production from a predominantly fossil-fuel economy to an economy of renewable energy resources? In 2001, the United Nations Intergovernmen-

Figure 5.32 Geologic resources have been one of the foundations of human development from the Stone Age to the Space Age. No one can accurately predict how society will adapt when global energy demand significantly exceeds supply. However, we can be virtually certain that the future will not mimic the past.

tal Panel on Climate Change (IPCC) concluded that significant reduction of fossil fuel use is possible with renewable "technologies that exist in operation or pilot-plant stage today . . . without any drastic technological breakthroughs."[4] In other words, they suggested that if we vigorously develop all the renewable energy resources listed in Section 5.7, the global economic system could absorb a drastic decline in petroleum production without massive disruptions. A year later, eighteen prominent energy experts published a rebuttal in *Science,* proposing the exact opposite conclusion. Using almost the same phrases, with the simple addition of the word, "not" they argued that, "Energy resources that can produce 100 to 300 percent of present world power consumption without fossil fuels and greenhouse emissions do not exist operationally or as pilot plants."[5] Their basic counter argu-ment is that global energy consumption is huge and renewable sources have low power densities. Thus we do not have the available land nor could we quickly build the required infrastructure to replace fossil fuels.

When experts disagree, it is difficult for lay people to evaluate the merits of the contradictory arguments. But whoever is right, it is clear that if global energy demand significantly exceeds supply, the world will fall into unprecedented economic chaos. Commerce will slip into unimaginable depression. Food supplies will diminish and food distribution will become expensive. Poor people, who are already on the edge of malnourishment, will starve. We can only hope that human ingenuity will combine with economic and political commitment to develop alternative energy resources before these catastrophes become reality.

[4] B. Metz et al., eds., *Climate Change 2001: Mitigation* (New York: Cambridge University Press, 2001) 8.

[5] Martin Hoffert et al., *Science* 298 (November 1, 2002).

Summary

Geologic resources fall into two major categories. (1) Useful rocks and minerals are called **mineral resources;** they include both **nonmetallic mineral resources** and metals. All mineral resources are nonrenewable. (2) **Energy resources** include fossil fuels, **nuclear fuels,** and alternative energy resources.

Ore is rock or other Earth material that can be mined profitably. **Mineral reserves** are the estimated supply of ore in the ground. Four types of geologic processes concentrate elements to form ore: (1) **Magmatic processes** form ore as magma solidifies. (2) **Hydrothermal processes** transport and precipitate metals from hot water. (3) Sedimentary processes form **placer** deposits, **evaporite** deposits, and **banded iron formations.** (4) Weathering removes easily dissolved elements from rocks and minerals, leaving behind **residual ore** deposits such as **bauxite.** Metal ores and coal are extracted from **underground mines** and **surface mines.**

Fossil fuels include **coal,** oil, and **natural gas.** Plant matter decays to form **peat.** Peat converts to coal when it is buried and subjected to elevated temperature and pressure. **Petroleum** forms from the remains of organisms that settle to the ocean floor or lake bed and are incorporated into **source rock.** The organic matter converts to liquid oil when it is buried and heated. The petroleum then migrates to a **reservoir,** where it is retained by an **oil trap.** Additional supplies of petroleum can be extracted by **secondary and tertiary recovery** from old wells and from tar sands and oil shale.

Nuclear power is expensive, and questions about the safety and disposal of nuclear wastes have diminished its future in the United States. Inexpensive uranium ore will be available for a century or more. Alternative energy resources currently supply a small fraction of our energy needs but have the potential to provide abundant renewable energy.

Earth Systems Interactions

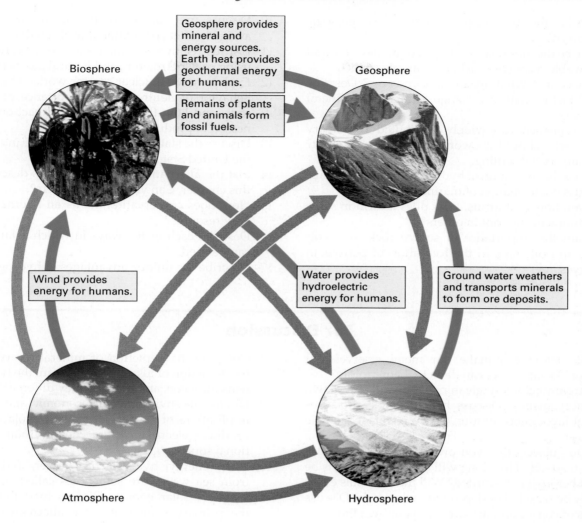

Biosphere

Geosphere provides mineral and energy sources. Earth heat provides geothermal energy for humans.

Remains of plants and animals form fossil fuels.

Geosphere

Wind provides energy for humans.

Water provides hydroelectric energy for humans.

Ground water weathers and transports minerals to form ore deposits.

Atmosphere

Hydrosphere

Key Terms

mineral resources   95
energy resources   95
ore   95
nonmetallic mineral
    resources   95
magmatic processes   97
crystal settling   97
hydrothermal processes
    98
hydrothermal vein   98
disseminated ore   98
submarine hydrothermal
    ore   99

black smoker   99
manganese nodule   99
placer   101
evaporite   102
banded iron formation
    102
residual ore   102
bauxite   102
mineral reserve   102
underground mine   103
surface mine   103
fossil fuel   104
coal   104

peat   105
petroleum   106
source rock   106
oil trap   106
reservoir   106
secondary and tertiary
    recovery (of oil)   108
natural gas   108
bitumen   108
tar sands   108
kerogen   109
oil shale   109
nuclear fuels   109

fission   109
branching chain reaction
    110
fuel rod   110
control rod   110
solar cell   112
hydrogen economy   114

For Review

1. Describe the two major categories of geologic resources.
2. Describe the differences between nonrenewable and renewable resources. List one example of each.
3. What is ore? What are mineral reserves? Describe three factors that can change estimates of mineral reserves.
4. If most elements are widely distributed in ordinary rocks, why should we worry about running short?
5. Explain crystal settling.
6. Discuss the formation of hydrothermal ore deposits.
7. Discuss the formation of marine evaporites.
8. Explain how coal forms. Why does it form in some environments but not in others?
9. Explain the importance of source rock, reservoir rock, and oil traps in the formation of petroleum reserves.
10. Discuss two sources of petroleum that will be available after conventional wells go dry.
11. List the relative advantages and disadvantages of using coal, petroleum, and natural gas as fuels.
12. Explain how a nuclear reactor works. Discuss the behavior of neutrons, the importance of control rods, and how the heat from the reaction is harnessed to produce useful energy.
13. Discuss the status of the nuclear power industry in the United States.
14. List the alternative energy resources described in this chapter. Can you think of others?
15. How does conservation act as an alternative energy resource?
16. Describe each of the ways in which solar energy can be used.
17. Describe the unique advantages of hydrogen fuel.

For Discussion

1. What factors can make our metal reserves last longer? What factors can deplete them rapidly?
2. It is common for a single mine to contain ores of two or more metals. Discuss how geologic processes might favor concentration of two metals in a single deposit.
3. List ten objects that you own. What resources are they made of? How long will each of the objects be used before it is discarded? Will the materials eventually be recycled or deposited in the trash? Discuss ways of conserving resources in your own life.
4. If you were searching for petroleum, would you search primarily in sedimentary rock, metamorphic rock, or igneous rock? Explain.
5. If you were a space traveler abandoned on an unknown planet in a distant solar system, what clues would you look for if you were searching for fossil fuels?
6. Is an impermeable cap rock necessary to preserve coal deposits? Why or why not?
7. Discuss problems in predicting the future availability of fossil fuel reserves. What is the value of the predictions?
8. Compare the depletion of mineral reserves with the depletion of fossil fuels. How are the two problems the same, and how are they different?
9. Discuss the environmental, economic, and political implications of the development of a solar cell that produces electricity more cheaply than conventional sources.
10. Wind energy, hydroelectric power, and energy from sea waves are sometimes called secondary forms of solar energy. Discuss how the Sun is the primary source of those alternative energy resources.

Earth Science ⊛ Now™

Assess your understanding of this chapter's topics with additional quizzing and comprehensive interactivities at **http:// earthscience.brookscole.com/earthsci3e** as well as current and up-to-date weblinks, additional readings, and InfoTrac College Edition exercises.

The Atmosphere

A storm over the South Rim of Grand Canyon.

Sitton/ImageState/PictureQuest

Chapter 17

The Atmosphere

Courtesy of Graham R. Thompson/Jonathan Turk

The midnight sun rises above the Arctic National Wildlife Refuge, Alaska.

If you decided to climb Mount Everest, you might start walking in the Nepali lowlands, then hike through mountain foothills where hearty farmers cultivate barley and peas in the thin mountain soil. When you reach an elevation around 4,000 meters, your breathing would be labored and even simple activities might seem difficult. Yet, the local people, acclimatized to living at high altitudes, would be scurrying up steep trails to tend their terraced fields. Near Everest base camp, at about 5,000 meters, there is half as much oxygen in the air as there is at sea level. Most climbers stop at base camp for a week to acclimatize. Above this point, even the strongest climbers struggle for breath in the frigid air as they ascend the glaciers and snowfields of Everest's lower flanks. At 7,000 meters, a lungful of air contains only 44 percent of the oxygen at sea level and the nighttime temperature frequently plunges to $-20°$ or even to $-30°C$. Above this level, you enter the "death zone," where people cannot survive for long periods of time and where even the fittest athletes may perish.

Every multicellular organism needs oxygen to survive. If the oxygen abundance in the atmosphere were to drop below 44 percent of its current value, life on Earth as we know it would perish. If oxygen is essential to life, would we be better off if we had an even greater supply? The answer is yes, to a limit. Even at sea level, athletes can enhance their performance by breathing a small amount of bottled oxygen. But, paradoxically, too much oxygen is poisonous. If you breathe air containing greater than 55 percent more oxygen than is found at sea level, your body metabolism is so rapid that essential molecules and enzymes decompose. In addition, fires burn more rapidly with increased oxygen concentration. If the oxygen level in the atmosphere were to rise significantly, fires would burn uncontrollably across the planet, altering ecosystems as we know them.

Temperatures in the Solar System range from the frigid, $-270°C$ void of interplanetary space to the torrid 15 million $°C$ plasma in the Sun's core. Yet, life thrives within a precariously narrow temperature range, from about $0°$ to $40°C$. Although many organisms, including people, can survive for long periods in arctic cold, almost all photosynthesis occurs at above-freezing temperatures. While other organisms live in boiling hot springs or hot deep-sea vents, they are the exceptions, not the rule.

The Earth is the near-perfect size and distance from a stable and medium-temperature star to permit such conditions. But in addition, atmospheric composition and temperature are not determined solely by planetary size and distance from the Sun. Our planet's environment is finely regulated by Earth systems interactions. In this, and subsequent chapters, we will study those interactions. During this study, we will ask whether humans could disrupt the Earth's climate and diminish conditions for life.

Earth Science ⊕ Now™

This icon, appearing throughout the book, indicates an opportunity to explore interactive tutorials, animations, or practice problems available on the Earth ScienceNow Web site at **http://earthscience.brookscole.com/earthsci3e**

17.1 Earth's Early Atmospheres

The First Atmospheres: 4.6 to 4.0 Billion Years Ago

Our Solar System formed from a cold, diffuse cloud of interstellar gas and dust. About of 99.8 percent of this cloud was composed of the two lightest elements, hydrogen and helium. Consequently, when the Earth formed, its primordial atmosphere was composed almost entirely of these two light elements. But, because the Earth is relatively close to the Sun and its gravitational force is relatively weak, its primordial hydrogen and helium atmosphere rapidly boiled off into space and escaped.

In Chapter 15, we learned that most of the volatile compounds that form the Earth's hydrosphere, atmo-

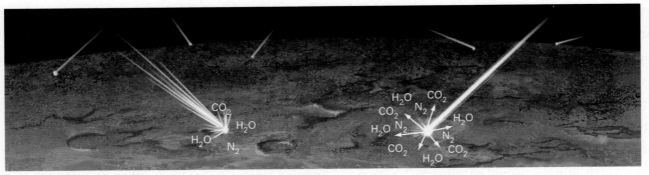

Figure 17.1 Comets, meteoroids, and asteroids imported the Earth's volatiles from outer parts of the Solar System.

sphere, and biosphere originated from outer parts of the Solar System. Recall that, in its infancy, the Solar System was crowded with bits of rock, comets, ice chunks, and other debris left over from the initial coalescence of the planets. These bolides crashed into the planet in a near continuous rain that lasted almost 800 million years. Carbonate compounds and carbon-rich rocks reacted under the heat and pressure of impact to form carbon dioxide (Figure 17.1). Ice quickly melted into water. Ammonia, common in the icy tail of comets, reacted to form nitrogen. Scientists hypothesize that by about 4 billion years ago, the Earth's atmosphere consisted of 80 percent carbon dioxide, 10 percent water vapor, 10 percent nitrogen, and trace amounts of other gases.

As shown in Figure 17.2, this atmosphere is radically different from the modern one. Note that today, life-giving oxygen comprises 21 percent of the atmosphere, whereas the 4-billion-year-old atmosphere contained almost no oxygen. Another major difference is that carbon dioxide is a trace gas today, but it was the most abundant gas 4 billion years ago. Recall that carbon dioxide is a greenhouse gas that warms the atmosphere and the Earth's surface. Since 1957, the carbon dioxide concentration has risen from .031 percent to .035 percent, coinciding with greenhouse warming of about 0.5 degree Celsius. Yet, 4 billion years ago, the carbon dioxide concentration was approximately 80 percent, more than 2,000 times its present level! Why didn't the planet heat up to torrid temperature extremes and vaporize the early oceans? The Sun's output was about 25 percent weaker 4 billion years ago than it is today. According to calculations, the combination of a weak Sun and a dense greenhouse atmosphere produced surface temperatures of 80 to 90°C, close to the boiling point of wa-

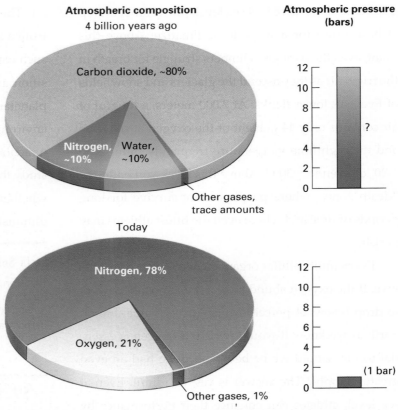

Figure 17.2 Four billion years ago, atmospheric composition and pressure were radically different from today's conditions. Table 17.1 (on page 414) lists the other gases of the modern atmosphere.

ter. Under modern atmospheric pressure, the oceans would quickly vaporize at 80 to 90°C. But the primordial atmospheric pressure was so high that it acted like a giant pressure cooker, reducing vaporization and maintaining liquid oceans.

Thus the Earth's primary and secondary atmospheres formed mainly from gases that accreted from outer space. But, later, as bombardment from outer space slowed down, interactions among living organisms, moving tectonic plates, seawater, and air altered the chemistry and composition of the atmosphere.

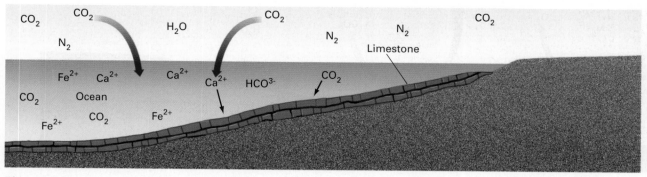

Figure 17.3 Much of the early atmospheric carbon dioxide dissolved in seawater where it reacted with other compounds to form limestone. As a result, the atmosphere lost much of its carbon dioxide.

When Life Began: 4.0 to 2.6 Billion Years Ago

During Hadean times, water collected on the Earth's surface; oceans formed and rain fell. Later, continents rose out of the depths, exposing rock to the air. As the oceans and continents evolved, reactions among the atmosphere, hydrosphere, and geosphere led to a radical reduction in the atmospheric carbon dioxide concentration (Figure 17.3). Three processes were responsible for this decline:

1. Large quantities of carbon dioxide dissolved in ocean water.
2. Dissolved carbon dioxide reacted with other elements in seawater to form limestone. As the dissolved carbon dioxide precipitated into rock, additional atmospheric carbon dioxide dissolved in the water, continually lowering its concentration in the atmosphere.
3. Weathering of limestone and silicate rocks removed even more carbon dioxide from the atmosphere to form ions that dissolve in sea water.

Fortuitously, at the same time that the carbon dioxide concentration declined, the Sun heated up sufficiently to stabilize the Earth's temperature in a range that was compatible for the evolution of life.

17.2 Life, Iron, and the Evolution of the Modern Atmosphere

The first living organisms formed by accretion of complex abiotic (nonliving) organic molecules. But these complex organic molecules are oxidized and destroyed in an oxygen-rich environment. (This oxidation is analogous to slow burning.) If large amounts of oxygen were present in the Earth's early atmosphere, the abiotic precursors to living organisms could not have formed.

By studying the minerals in a rock, a geochemist can determine whether it formed in an oxygen-rich or an oxygen-poor environment. Recent studies of the Earth's oldest rocks indicate that the atmospheric oxygen concentration was extremely low prior to 3.5 billion years ago. Thus, the molecules necessary for the emergence of living organisms were preserved in the primordial atmosphere.

Although life could not have emerged in an oxygen-rich environment, complex multicellular life requires an oxygen-rich atmosphere to survive. How did oxygen become abundant in our atmosphere?

The world's earliest organisms fed on amino acids and other complex organic molecules that formed by abiotic processes. Later, organisms subsisted, in part, by eating each other. But these food chains were limited because there were only a few organisms on Earth. A crucial step in evolution occurred when primitive bacteria evolved the ability to harness the energy in sunlight and produce organic tissue. This process, known as **photosynthesis,** is the foundation for virtually all modern life. During photosynthesis, organisms convert carbon dioxide and water to organic sugars. They release oxygen as a byproduct (Figure 17.4). In 1972, an English chemist named James Lovelock hypothesized that the oxygen produced by primitive organisms gradually accumulated to create the modern atmosphere. When the oxygen concentration reached a critical level to sustain efficient metabolism in late Precambrian time, multicellular organisms evolved and the biosphere as we know it was born. Lovelock was so overwhelmed by the intimate connection between living and nonliving components of the Earth's systems that he likened our planet to a living creature, which he called *Gaia* (Greek for Earth).

In the 30 years since Lovelock published his Gaia hypothesis, other scientists have proposed additional abiotic mechanisms for the introduction of oxygen into the Precambrian atmosphere. For example, some scientists have shown that the strong ultraviolet sunlight of the Precambrian could have dissociated water into hydrogen and oxygen. The hydrogen then boiled off into space and the oxygen remained.

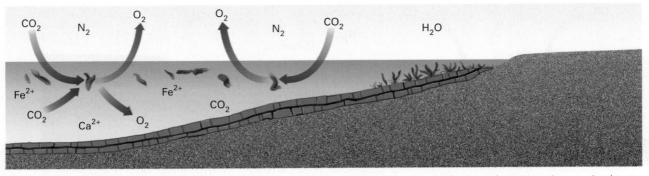

Figure 17.4 Later, the oxygen content of the atmosphere gradually increased as Archean and Proterozoic aquatic plants released oxygen.

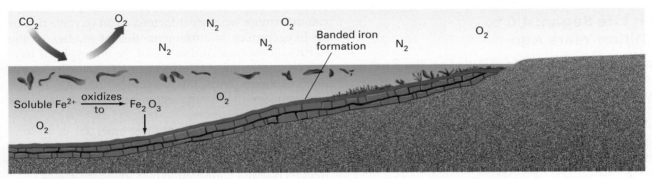

Figure 17.5 The oxygen concentration in the atmosphere and sea water reached a threshold at which the oxygen combined with dissolved iron to form iron minerals. The iron minerals precipitated to the sea floor to form the first layer of a banded iron formation.

Origin of Iron Ore and the Evolution of Earth's Atmosphere

Oxygen dissolves in water. As a result, when the oxygen content of the atmosphere rose, some of this oxygen dissolved in sea water. In an oxygen-poor environment, iron also dissolves in water. However, when oxygen is abundant, it reacts with dissolved iron and causes the iron to precipitate rapidly. Thus, if air contains little or no oxygen, there is also little oxygen in sea water, and large amounts of iron dissolve in the seas. If the oxygen concentration of the atmosphere and the ocean rises to a threshold level, iron precipitates rapidly, forming a layer of iron oxide minerals on the sea floor. Thus, when enough oxygen had accumulated in sea water to react with the dissolved iron, vast quantities of iron minerals precipitated onto the sea floor, producing layers of iron-rich minerals (Figure 17.5).

Iron, the main ingredient in steel, is the world's most commonly used metal. About 1 billion tons of iron are mined every year, 90 percent from **banded iron formations,** the sedimentary layers of iron-rich minerals sandwiched between beds of clay and other silicate minerals. The alternating layers are a few centimeters thick and give the rocks their banded appearance (Figure 17.6). A single iron formation of this type may be hundreds of meters thick and cover

Figure 17.6 In this banded iron formation from Michigan, the red bands are iron oxide minerals and the dark layers are chert (silica).

Barbara Gerlach / Visuals Unlimited

Figure 17.7 The Mesabi Range in northern Minnesota is a banded iron formation that is one of the chief iron-producing regions in the world.

tens of square kilometers (Figure 17.7). Most of the Earth's banded iron deposits formed from 2.6 to 1.9 billion years ago, although a few are older and some are younger.

The alternating layers of iron minerals and other minerals may have developed because, for a long time, the oxygen level in the seas hovered near the threshold at which soluble iron converts to the insoluble variety. When the dissolved oxygen concentration increased, the oxygen reacted with the dissolved iron to precipitate iron oxide minerals on the sea floor. But the formation of those minerals extracted oxygen as well as iron from the sea water, and lowered its oxygen concentration below the threshold. Then, dissolved iron accumulated again in the seas while the oxygen was slowly replenished. During that time, clay and other minerals washed from the continents and accumulated on the sea floor as they do today, forming the thin layers of silicate minerals that lie between the iron-rich layers. When the oxygen concentration rose above the threshold again, another layer of iron minerals formed.

Banded iron formations contain thousands of alternating layers of iron minerals and silicates. The great thickness of the iron formations, coupled with the fact that they continued to form from 2.6 to 1.9 billion years

ago, suggests that these reactions must have kept the levels of dissolved oxygen close to the threshold for 700 million years. Oxygen levels in both sea water and the atmosphere rose above the threshold only after nearly all of the dissolved iron had been removed from sea water by precipitation of iron minerals. Thus the iron-rich rocks that support our industrial society were formed by interactions among early photosynthetic organisms, sunlight, air, and the oceans.

Evolution of the Modern Atmosphere

After precipitation of the banded iron formations ceased about 1.9 billion years ago, slowly increasing photosynthesis and additional photo-dissociation continued to add molecular oxygen to the atmosphere. One more critical step was required before multicellular organisms could evolve. The Sun emits energy largely in the form of high-energy ultraviolet light. These rays are energetic enough to break complex molecules apart and kill evolving multicellular organisms. But high-altitude oxygen absorbs ultraviolet radiation in a process that forms ozone (see Section 17.7). Thus oxygen, largely produced by the earliest photosynthetic organisms, was not only necessary for life, it also protected life by filtering out harmful solar rays.

Multicellular plants and animals emerged in late Precambrian time, between 1 billion and 543 million years ago. As the numbers and diversity of organisms rose, increasing photosynthetic activity added even more oxygen to the atmosphere. The Earth's atmosphere reached its present oxygen level of 21 percent about 450 million years ago. Fires burn rapidly if oxygen is abundant; if its concentration were to increase even by a few percent, fires would burn uncontrollably across the planet. If atmospheric oxygen levels were to decrease appreciably, most modern plants and animals would not survive. If the carbon dioxide concentration were to increase by a small amount, atmospheric temperature would rise as a result of greenhouse warming.

The compatibility of Earth's atmosphere with its organisms is not a lucky accident. Organisms did not simply adapt to an existing atmosphere; they partially created it by photosynthesis and respiration. Thus not only is our delicate oxygen–carbon dioxide balance biologically maintained, but living organisms were partly responsible for creating the environment that they need to proliferate. Most probably, if all life on Earth were to cease, the atmosphere would revert to an oxygen-poor composition and become poisonous to modern plants and animals.

The Earth's atmosphere not only sustains us, it insulates the Earth's surface and winds distribute the Sun's heat around the globe, so the surface is neither too hot nor too cold for life. Clouds form from water vapor in the atmosphere and rain falls from clouds. In addition, the atmosphere filters out much of the Sun's ultraviolet radiation, which can destroy living tissue and cause cancer. The atmosphere carries sound; without air we would live in silence. Without an atmo-sphere, airplanes and birds could not fly, wind would not transport pollen and seeds, the sky would be black rather than blue, and no reds, purples, and pinks would color the sunset.

17.3 The Modern Atmosphere

The modern atmosphere is mostly gas with small quantities of water droplets and dust. The gaseous composition of dry air is roughly 78 percent nitrogen, 21 percent oxygen, and 1 percent other gases (Figure 17.2B and Table 17.1). Nitrogen, the most abundant gas, does not react readily with other substances. Oxygen, on the other hand, reacts chemically as fires burn, iron rusts, and plants and animals respire. Notice that carbon dioxide, which formed 80 percent of the secondary Hadean atmosphere, is a trace gas with a concentration of only .035 percent. Carbon dioxide and the greenhouse effect are discussed further in Chapter 21.

In addition to the gases listed in Table 17.1, air contains water vapor, water droplets, and dust. The types and quantities of these components vary with both location and altitude. In a hot, steamy jungle, air may contain 5 percent water vapor by weight, whereas in a desert or cold polar region, only a small fraction of a percent may be present.

If you sit in a house on a sunny day, you may see a sunbeam passing through a window. The visible beam is light reflected from tiny specks of suspended dust. Clay, salt, pollen, bacteria, and viruses, bits of cloth, hair, and skin are all components of dust. People travel to the seaside to enjoy the "salt air." Visitors to the Great Smoky Mountains in Tennessee view the bluish,

TABLE 17.1 Gaseous Composition of Natural Dry Air*

Gas	Concentration (%)
Nitrogen, N_2	78.09
Oxygen, O_2	20.94
Inert gases, mostly argon, with much smaller concentrations of neon, helium, krypton, and xenon	0.93
Carbon dioxide, CO_2	0.03
Methane, CH_4, a natural part of the carbon cycle	0.0001
Hydrogen, H_2	0.00005
Oxides of nitrogen, mostly N_2O and NO_2, both produced by solar radiation and by lightning	0.00005
Carbon monoxide, CO, from oxidation of methane and other natural sources	0.00003
Ozone, O_3, produced by solar radiation and by lightning	Trace

*Natural dry air is defined as air without water or industrial pollutants. Carbon dioxide, methane, oxides of nitrogen, carbon dioxide, and ozone are all components of natural air, but they are also industrial pollutants. Therefore, the concentrations of these gases may vary, especially in urban areas. Pollution and its consequences are discussed in Chapter 19.

hazy air formed by sunlight reflecting from pollen and other dust particles.

Within the past century, humans have altered the chemical composition of the atmosphere in many different ways. We have increased the carbon dioxide concentration by burning fuels and igniting wildfires. Factories release chemicals into the air—some are benign, others are poisonous. Smoke and soot change the clarity of the atmosphere. These changes are discussed in Section 17.6.

17.4 Atmospheric Pressure

The molecules in a gas zoom about in a random manner. For example, at 20°C, an average oxygen molecule is traveling at 425 meters/second (950 miles per hour). In the absence of gravity, temperature differences, or other perturbations, a gas will fill a space homogeneously. Thus, if you floated a cylinder of gas in space, the gas would disperse until there was an equal density of molecules and an equal pressure throughout the cylinder. But gases that surround the Earth are perturbed by many influences, which ultimately create the complex and turbulent atmosphere that helps shape the world we live in.

Within our atmosphere, gas molecules zoom about, as in the imaginary cylinder, but in addition, gravity pulls them downward. As a result of this downward force, more molecules concentrate near the surface of the Earth than at higher elevations. Therefore, the atmosphere is denser at sea level than it is at higher elevations—and the pressure is higher. Density and pressure then decrease exponentially with elevation (Figure 17.8). As explained in the introduction, at an elevation of about 5000 meters, the atmosphere contains about half as much oxygen as it does at sea level. If you ascended in a balloon to 16000 meters (16 kilometers) above sea level, you would be above 90 percent of the atmosphere and would need an oxygen mask to survive. At an elevation of 100 kilometers, pressure is only 0.00003 that of sea level, approaching the vacuum of outer space. There is no absolute upper boundary to the atmosphere.

Atmospheric pressure is measured with a **barometer** and is often called **barometric pressure.** A simple but accurate barometer is constructed from a glass tube that is sealed at one end. The tube is evacuated and the open end is placed in a dish of a liquid such as mercury. The mercury rises in the tube because atmospheric pressure depresses the level of mercury in the dish but there is no air in the tube (Figure 17.9). At sea level mercury rises approximately 76 centimeters, or 760 millimeters (about 30 inches), into an evacuated tube.

Meteorologists express pressure in inches or millimeters of mercury, referring to the height of a column of mercury in a barometer. They also express pressure in bars and millibars. A **bar** is approximately equal to sea level atmospheric pressure. A millibar is $\frac{1}{1000}$ of a bar.

A mercury barometer is a cumbersome device nearly a meter tall, and mercury vapor is poisonous. A safer and more portable instrument for measuring pressure, called an aneroid barometer, consists of a partially evacuated metal chamber connected to a pointer. When atmospheric pressure increases, it compresses the chamber and the pointer moves in one direction. When pressure decreases, the chamber expands, directing the pointer the other way (Figure 17.10).

Changing weather can also affect barometric pressure. On a stormy day at sea level, pressure may be 980 millibars (28.94 inches), although it has been known to drop to 900 millibars (26.58 inches) or less during a hurricane. In contrast, during a period of clear, dry weather, a typical high pressure reading may be 1025 millibars (30.27 inches). These changes are discussed in Chapter 19.

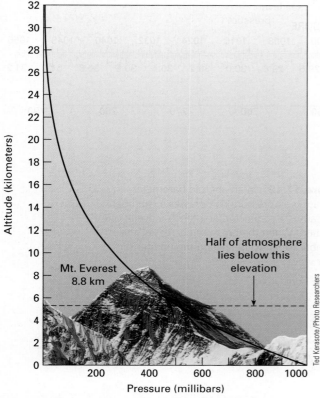

Half of atmosphere lies below this elevation

Mt. Everest 8.8 km

Ted Kerasote/Photo Researchers

Figure 17.8 Atmospheric pressure decreases with altitude. One half of the atmosphere lies below an altitude of 5600 meters.

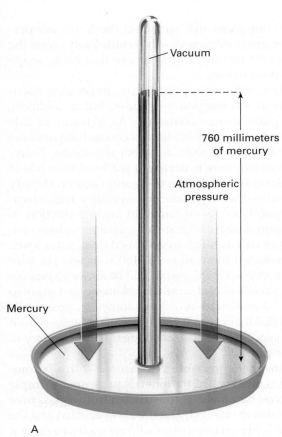

Vacuum

760 millimeters
of mercury

Atmospheric
pressure

Mercury

A

Figure 17.9 (A) Atmospheric pressure forces mercury upward in an evacuated glass tube. The height of the mercury in the tube is a measure of air pressure. (B) Three common scales for reporting atmospheric pressure and the conversion among them.

Interactive Question: Express 750 mm in inches and millibars.

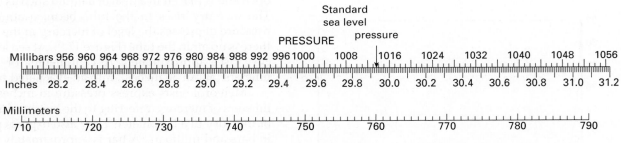

B

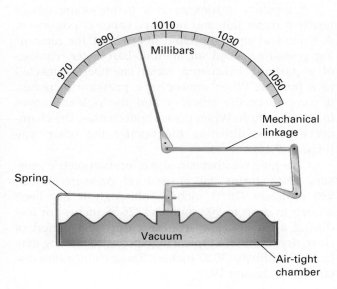

Figure 17.10 In an aneroid barometer, increasing air pressure compresses a chamber and causes a connected pointer to move in one direction. When the pressure decreases, the chamber expands, deflecting the pointer the other way.

17.5 Atmospheric Temperature

The temperature of the atmosphere changes with altitude (Figure 17.11). The layer of air closest to the Earth, the layer we live in, is the **troposphere.** Virtually all of the water vapor and clouds exist in this layer, and almost all weather occurs here. The Earth's surface absorbs solar energy, and thus the surface of the planet is warm. But, as explained above, continents and oceans also radiate heat, and some of this energy is absorbed in the troposphere. At higher elevations in the troposphere, the atmosphere is thinner and absorbs less energy; in addition, lower parts of the troposphere have absorbed much of the heat radiating from the Earth's surface. Consequently, temperature decreases at higher levels in the troposphere. Thus, mountaintops are generally colder than valley floors, and pilots flying at high altitudes must heat their cabins.

The top of the troposphere is the **tropopause,** which lies at an altitude of about 17 kilometers at the equator, although it is lower at the poles. At the tropopause the steady decline in temperature with altitude ceases abruptly. Cold air from the upper troposphere is too dense to rise above the tropopause. As a result, little mixing occurs between the troposphere and the layer above it, called the **stratosphere.**

In the stratosphere, temperature remains constant to 35 kilometers and then increases with altitude until, at about 50 kilometers, it is as warm as that at the Earth's surface. This reversal in the temperature profile occurs because the troposphere and stratosphere are heated by different mechanisms. As already explained, the troposphere is heated primarily from below, by the Earth. The stratosphere, on the other hand, is heated primarily from above, by solar radiation.

Oxygen molecules (O_2) in the stratosphere absorb energetic ultraviolet rays from the Sun. The radiant energy breaks the oxygen molecules apart, releasing free oxygen atoms. The oxygen atoms then recombine to form ozone (O_3). Ozone absorbs ultraviolet energy more efficiently than oxygen does, warming the upper stratosphere. Ultraviolet radiation is energetic enough to affect organisms. Small quantities give us a suntan, but large doses cause skin cancer and cataracts of the eye, inhibit the growth of many plants, and otherwise harm living tissue. The ozone in the upper atmosphere protects life on Earth by absorbing much of this high-energy radiation before it reaches Earth's surface.

Ozone concentration declines in the upper portion of the stratosphere, and therefore at about 55 kilometers above the Earth, temperature once more begins to decline rapidly with elevation. This boundary between rising and falling temperature is the **stratopause,** the ceiling of the stratosphere. The second zone of declining temperature is the **mesosphere.** Little radiation is absorbed in the mesosphere, and the thin air is extremely cold. Starting at about 80 kilometers above the Earth, the temperature again remains constant and then rises rapidly in the **thermosphere.** Here the atmosphere absorbs high-energy X-rays and ultraviolet radiation from the Sun. High-energy reactions strip electrons from atoms and molecules to produce ions. The temperature in the upper portion of the thermosphere is just below freezing, not extremely cold by surface standards.

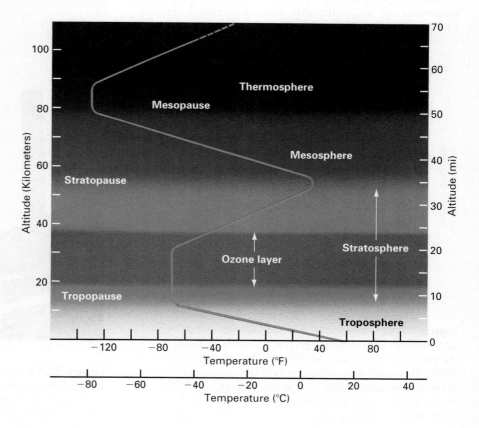

Figure 17.11 Atmospheric temperature varies with altitude. The atmospheric layers are zones in which different factors control the temperature.

Interactive Question: If you were ascending from Earth in a rocket, what layer would you be in at 5 km, 20 km, and 80 km? What would the outside temperature be at each of these elevations?

17.6 Air Pollution

Ever since the first cave dwellers huddled around a smoky fire, people have introduced impurities into the air. The total quantity of these impurities is minuscule compared with the great mass of our atmosphere and with the monumental changes that occurred during the evolution of the planet. Yet air pollution remains a significant health, ecological, and climatological problem for modern industrial society.

In 1948, Donora was an industrial town of about 14,000 located 50 kilometers south of Pittsburgh, Pennsylvania. One large factory in town manufactured structural steel and wire and another produced zinc and sulfuric acid. During the last week of October 1948, dense fog settled over the town. But it was no ordinary fog; the moisture contained pollutants from the two factories. After four days, visibility became so poor that people could not see well enough to drive, even at noon with their headlights on. Gradually at first, and then in increasing numbers, residents sought medical attention for nausea, shortness of breath, and constrictions in the throat and chest. Within a week, 20 people had died and about half of the town was seriously ill.

Other incidents similar to that in Donora occurred worldwide. In response to the growing problem, the United States enacted the Clean Air Act in 1963. As a result of the Clean Air Act and its amendments, total emissions of air pollutants have decreased (Figure 17.12) and air quality across the country has improved

A

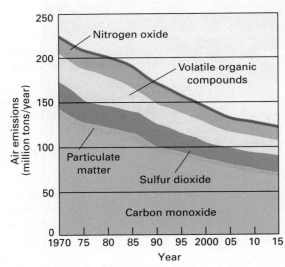

Figure 17.12 Emission of five air pollutants in the United States beginning in 1970 with projections to the year 2015. The Clean Air Act was first enacted in 1963. (This graph does not show local concentrations in heavily congested areas such as Los Angeles.)
Source: EPA documents and *Chemical and Engineering News,* May 12, 1997, page 26.

B

Figure 17.13 (A) Before the Clean Air Act, most factory smokestacks had no pollution control devices. (B) Pollution controls installed after the Clean Air Act reduced emissions by large proportions.

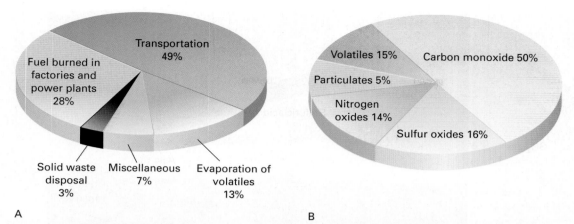

Figure 17.14 (A) Sources of air pollution in the United States. (B) Types of air pollutants in the United States. (Although carbon dioxide is a greenhouse gas, it is not listed as a pollutant because it is not toxic.)
Source: EPA

(Figure 17.13). Donora-type incidents have not been repeated. Smog has decreased, and rain has become less acidic. Yet some people believe that we have not gone far enough and that air pollution regulations should be strengthened further.

Sources and types of air pollution are listed in Figure 17.14 and discussed in the following section.

Gases Released When Fossil Fuels Are Burned

Coal is largely carbon, which, when burned completely, produces carbon dioxide. Petroleum is a mixture of hydrocarbons, compounds composed of carbon and hydrogen. When hydrocarbons burn completely, they produce carbon dioxide and water. Neither is poisonous, but both are greenhouse gases. If fuels were composed purely of compounds of carbon and hydrogen, and if they always burned completely, air pollution from burning of fossil fuels would pose little direct threat to our health. However, fossil fuels contain impurities, and combustion is usually incomplete. As a result, other products form.

Products of incomplete combustion include hydrocarbons such as benzene and methane. Benzene is a carcinogen (a compound that causes cancer), and methane is another greenhouse gas. Incomplete combustion of fossil fuels releases many other pollutants including carbon monoxide, CO, which is colorless and odorless, yet very toxic.

Additional problems arise because coal and petroleum contain impurities that generate other kinds of pollution when they are burned. Small amounts of sulfur are present in coal and, to a lesser extent, in petroleum. When these fuels burn, the sulfur forms oxides, mainly sulfur dioxide, SO_2, and sulfur trioxide, SO_3. High sulfur dioxide concentrations have been associated with major air pollution disasters of the type

that occurred in Donora. Today the primary global source of sulfur dioxide pollution is coal-fired electric generators.

Nitrogen, like sulfur, is common in living tissue and therefore is found in all fossil fuels. This nitrogen, together with a small amount of atmospheric nitrogen, reacts when coal or petroleum is burned. The products are mostly nitrogen oxide, NO, and nitrogen dioxide, NO_2. Nitrogen dioxide is a reddish-brown gas with a strong odor. It therefore contributes to the "browning" and odor of some polluted urban atmospheres. Automobile exhaust is the primary source of nitrogen oxide pollution.

Acid Rain

As explained above, sulfur and nitrogen oxides are released when coal and petroleum burn. These oxides are also released when metal ores are refined. In moist air, sulfur dioxide reacts to produce sulfuric acid and nitrogen oxides react to form nitric and nitrous acid. All of these are strong acids. Atmospheric acids dissolve in water droplets and fall as **acid precipitation,** also called **acid rain** (Figure 17.15).

Acidity is expressed on the **pH scale.** A solution with a pH of 7 is neutral, neither acidic nor basic. On a pH scale, numbers lower than 7 represent acidic solutions, and numbers higher than 7 represent basic ones. For example, soapy water is basic and has a pH of about 10, whereas vinegar is an acid with a pH of 2.4.

Rain reacts with carbon dioxide in the atmosphere to produce a weak acid. As a result, natural rainfall has a pH of about 5.7. However, in the "bad old days" before the Clean Air Act was properly enforced, rain was much more acidic. A fog in southern California in 1986 reached a pH of 1.7, which approaches the acidity of toilet bowl cleaners.

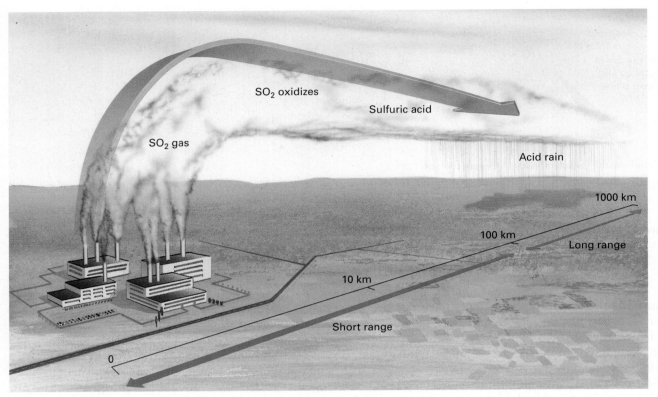

Figure 17.15 Acid rain develops from the addition of sulfur compounds to the atmosphere by industrial smokestacks.

Consequences of Acid Rain

Sulfur and nitrogen oxides impair lung function, aggravating diseases such as asthma and emphysema. They also affect the heart and liver and have been shown to increase vulnerability to viral infections such as influenza.

Acid rain corrodes metal and rock. Limestone and marble are especially susceptible because they dissolve rapidly in mild acid. In the United States the cost of deterioration of buildings and materials from acid precipitation is estimated at several billion dollars per year (Figure 17.16).

Acid rain also affects plants. In 1982, about 8 percent of the trees in West Germany were unhealthy. A year later, 34 percent of the trees were affected, and by 1995 more than half of the trees in Germany's western forests were sick or dying. Experiments indicate that acid precipitation, combined with the effects of other air pollutants, killed the trees. Air pollution has caused the loss of about $10 billion worth of timber in Germany alone. But the loss goes beyond the value of the wood. Forests regulate water, protect the soil, furnish essential habitat for many animals and plants, and provide prime recreation for people. Tree death is not as rampant in the United States, but the U.S. Forest Service has reported that pines in the Southeast grew 20 to 30 percent more slowly between 1972 and 1982 than they did between 1961 and 1971, when rain was less acidic.

Smog and Ozone in the Troposphere

Imagine that your great-grandfather had entered the exciting new business of making moving pictures. Old-time photographic film was "slow" and required lots of sunlight, so he would hardly have moved to the polluted and overcast industrial northeast. Southern California, with its warm, sunny climate and little need for coal, was preferable. Thus, a district of Los Angeles called Hollywood became the center of the movie industry. Its population boomed, and after World War II automobiles became about as numerous as people. Then the quality of the air deteriorated in a strange way. People noted four different kinds of changes:

(1) A brownish haze called *smog* settled over the city (Figure 17.17); (2) people felt irritation in their eyes and throats; (3) vegetable crops became damaged; and (4) the sidewalls of rubber tires developed cracks.

In the 1950s, air pollution experts worked mostly in the industrialized cities of the East Coast and the Midwest. When they were called to diagnose the problem in southern California, they looked for the sources of air pollution they knew well, especially sulfur dioxide. But the smog was nothing like the pollution they were familiar with. These researchers eventually

Figure 17.16 Acid rain has destroyed this 1817 marble tombstone in England.

Interactive Question: In the United States, many large coal-fired electric generating facilities are located in the desert in the Southwest. Argue for or against the statement: Because there is little rain in the desert, sulfur dioxides emitted by these generators are less likely to react to form acid precipitation. Therefore the air pollutants are less likely to cause harm.

Figure 17.17 A brownish haze of smog settles over Los Angeles. Note that the smog is thick beneath a distinct line caused by an atmospheric inversion. Above the inversion level the air is much cleaner.

learned that incompletely burned gasoline in automobile exhaust reacts with nitrogen oxides and atmospheric oxygen in the presence of sunlight to form ozone, O_3. The ozone then reacts further with automobile exhaust to form smog (Figure 17.18).

Earlier in this chapter, we read about the harmful effects of excessive ozone in the air over cities such as Los Angeles. In this chapter we will learn that ozone in the stratosphere absorbs ultraviolet radiation and protects life on Earth. Is ozone a pollutant to be eliminated, or a beneficial component of the atmosphere that we want to preserve? The answer is that it is both, depending on *where* it is found. Ozone in the troposphere reacts with automobile exhaust to produce smog and therefore it is a pollutant. Ozone in the stratosphere is beneficial and the destruction of the ozone layer creates serious problems.

Ozone irritates the respiratory system, causing loss of lung function and aggravating asthma in susceptible individuals. Ozone also increases susceptibility to heart disease and is a suspected carcinogen. High ozone concentrations slow the growth of plants, which is a particularly serious problem in the rich agricultural areas of California.

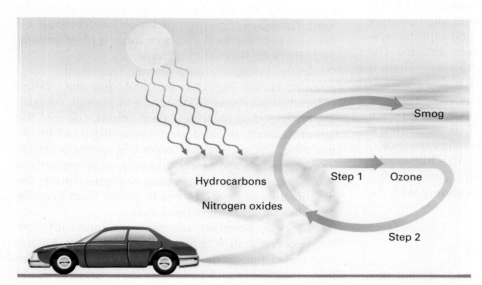

Figure 17.18 Smog forms in a sequential process. *Step 1:* Automobile exhaust reacts with air in the presence of sunlight to form ozone. *Step 2:* Ozone reacts with automobile exhaust to form smog.

Toxic Volatiles

A volatile compound is one that evaporates readily and therefore easily escapes into the atmosphere. Whenever chemicals are manufactured or petroleum is refined, some volatile byproducts escape into the atmosphere. When metals are extracted from ores, gases such as sulfur dioxide are released. When pesticides are sprayed onto fields and orchards, some of the spray is carried off by wind. When you paint your house, the volatile parts of the paint evaporate into the air. As a result of all these processes, tens of thousands of different volatile compounds are present in polluted air: Some are harmless, others are poisonous, and many have not been studied. Consider the case of dioxin.

Very little dioxin is intentionally manufactured. It is not an ingredient in any herbicide, pesticide, or other industrial formulation. You cannot buy dioxin at your local hardware store or pharmacy. Dioxin forms as an unwanted byproduct in the production of certain chemicals and when specific chemicals are burned. For example, In the United States today, garbage incineration is the most common source of dioxin. When a compound containing chlorine, such as the plastic polyvinyl chloride, is burned, some of the chlorine reacts with organic compounds to form dioxin. The dioxin then goes up the smokestack of the incinerator, diffuses into the air, and eventually falls to Earth. Cattle eat grass lightly dusted with dioxin, and store the dioxin in their fat. Humans ingest the compound mostly in meat and dairy products. The EPA estimates that the average U.S. citizen ingests about 0.0000000001 grams (100 picograms) of dioxin in food every day. Although this is a minuscule amount, the EPA has argued that dioxin is the most toxic known chemical and that even these low background levels may cause adverse effects such as cancer, disruption of regulatory hormones, reproductive and immune system disorders, and birth defects. Others disagree. The Chemical Manufacturers Association wrote, "There is no direct evidence to show that any of the effects of dioxins occur in humans in everyday levels."

No one knows whether very small doses of potent poisons are harmful. Environmentalists argue that it better to be "safe than sorry," and therefore we should reduce ambient concentrations of volatiles like dioxin. Others counter that because the harmful effects are unproven, we should not burden our economy with the costs of control.

Particulates and Aerosols

A **particle** or **particulate** is any small piece of solid matter, such as dust or soot. An **aerosol** is any small particle that is larger than a molecule and suspended in air. These three terms are used interchangeably to discuss air pollution. Many natural processes release aerosols. Windblown silt, pollen, volcanic ash, salt spray from the oceans, and smoke and soot from wildfires are all aerosols. Industrial emissions add to these natural sources.

Smoke and soot are carcinogenic aerosols formed whenever fuels are burned. Coal always contains clay and other noncombustible minerals that accumulated when the coal formed in the muddy bottoms of ancient swamps. When the coal burns, some of these minerals escape from the chimney as **fly ash,** which settles as gritty dust. When metals are mined, the drilling, blasting, and digging raise dust, and this, too, adds to the total load of aerosols.

In 1988, EPA epidemiologists noted that whenever atmospheric aerosol levels rose above a critical level in Steubenville, Ohio, the number of fatalities from all causes—car accidents to heart attacks—rose. After several studies substantiated the Steubenville report, the EPA proposed additional reductions of the ambient aerosol levels in the United States. Opponents argued that it is unfair to target all aerosols because the term covers a wide range of substances from a benign grain of salt to a deadly mist of toxic volatiles. The EPA is scheduled to release a comprehensive aerosol report in 2005.

17.7 Depletion of the Ozone Layer

Solar energy breaks oxygen molecules (O_2) apart in the stratosphere, releasing free oxygen atoms (O). The free oxygen atoms combine with oxygen molecules to form ozone (O_3). Ozone absorbs high-energy ultraviolet light. This absorption protects life on Earth because ultraviolet light causes skin cancer, inhibits plant growth, and otherwise harms living tissue.

In the 1970s, scientists learned that organic compounds containing chlorine and fluorine, called **chlorofluorocarbons (CFCs),** or compounds containing bromine and chlorine, called **halons**, rise into the upper atmosphere and destroy ozone (Figure 17.19). At that time, CFCs were used as cooling agents in almost all refrigerators and air conditioners, as propellants in some aerosol cans, as cleaning solvents during the manufacture of weapons, and in plastic foam in coffee cups and some building insulation.

In 1985, scientists observed an unusually low ozone concentration in the stratosphere over Antarctica, called the **ozone hole.** The ozone concentration over Antarctica continued to decline between 1985 and 1993, until it was 65 percent below normal over 23 million square kilometers, an area almost the size of North America. Research groups also reported significant in-

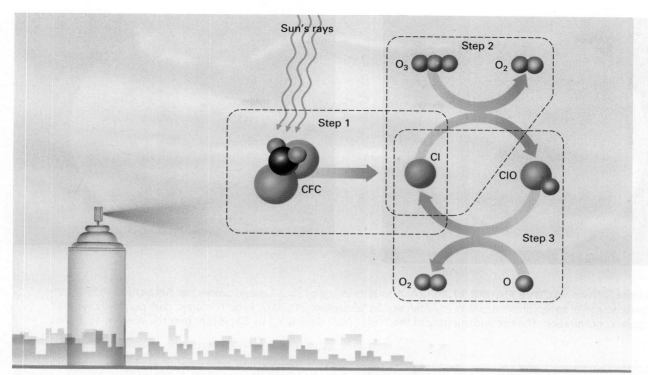

Figure 17.19 CFCs destroy the ozone layer in a three-step reaction. *Step 1:* CFCs rise into the stratosphere. Ultraviolet radiation breaks the CFC molecules apart, releasing chlorine atoms. *Step 2:* Chlorine atoms react with ozone, O_3, to destroy the ozone molecule and release oxygen, O_2. The extra oxygen atom combines with chlorine to produce ClO. *Step 3:* The ClO sheds its oxygen to produce another free chlorine atom. Thus, chlorine is not used up in the reaction, and one chlorine atom reacts over and over again to destroy many ozone molecules.

creases in ultraviolet radiation from the Sun at ground level in the region. In addition, scientists recorded ozone depletion in the Northern Hemisphere. In March 1995, ozone concentration above the United States was 15 to 20 percent lower than during March 1979.

Data on global ozone depletion persuaded the industrial nations of the world to limit the use of CFCs and other ozone-destroying compounds. In a series of international agreements signed between 1978 and 1992, many nations of the world agreed to reduce or curtail production of compounds that destroy atmospheric ozone. Most industrialized countries stopped production of CFCs on January 1, 1996.

The international bans have had positive results. The concentration of ozone-destroying chemicals peaked in the troposphere (lower atmosphere) in 1994 and has been declining ever since. As a result, fewer CFCs and halons have been drifting into the stratosphere. The CFCs and halons that are already in the stratosphere break down slowly but scientists think that the concentration of ozone-destroying chemicals in the stratosphere has peaked and is beginning to decline. In September, 2002, the ozone hole had declined to 60 percent of its average size over the previous 6 years. Although this data indicates that the ozone hole is diminishing, scientists warn that the result may be anomalous due to meteorological conditions (Figure 17.20).

Earth Science ⊕ Now™

CLICK Earth Science Interactive to work through an activity on Ozone Hole Through Weather and Climate

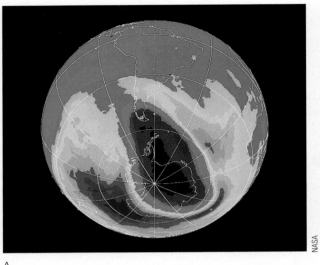

A

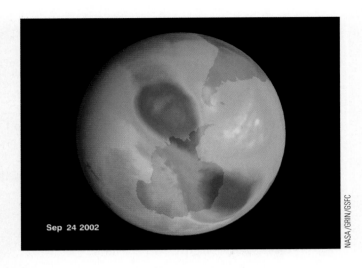

Sep 24 2002

B

NASA

NASA/GRIN/GSFC

Earth Science⊛Now™   **ACTIVE FIGURE 17.20**   (A) A satellite image of stratospheric ozone over Antarctica in 1994. (B) A satellite image of stratospheric ozone over Antarctica on September 24, 2002. In both images, dark purple shows the lowest ozone concentration. The size and intensity of the "hole" have diminished by 60 percent over the intervening 8 years.

Summary

The Earth's primary atmosphere was predominantly hydrogen and helium. After these light elements boiled off into space, bolides carried gases to create a secondary atmosphere, which was composed predominantly of carbon dioxide, with lesser amounts of water and nitrogen, and trace gases. By 4 billion years ago, the carbon dioxide concentration was beginning to decline and volcanic eruptions injected gases into the atmosphere.

Photosynthesis and photo-dissociation of water generated oxygen. As the oxygen concentration increased, it reacted with dissolved iron in sea water to form **banded iron formations.** Oxygen concentration rose to its present level after nearly all the dissolved iron had been removed by precipitation.

Today, dry air is roughly 78 percent nitrogen (N_2), 21 percent oxygen (O_2), and 1 percent other gases. Air also contains water vapor, dust, liquid droplets, and pollutants. Atmospheric pressure is the weight of the atmosphere per unit area. Pressure varies with weather and decreases with altitude.

Atmospheric temperature decreases with altitude in the **troposphere.** The temperature rises in the **stratosphere** because ozone absorbs solar radiation. The temperature decreases again in the **mesosphere,** and then in the uppermost layer, the **thermosphere,** temperature increases as high-energy radiation is absorbed.

The increasing ill-effects of air pollution prior to and just after Word War II convinced people to pass air pollution control legislation.

Incomplete combustion of coal and petroleum produces carcinogenic hydrocarbons such as benzene as well as carbon monoxide and methane, which is a greenhouse gas. Impurities in these fuels burn to produce oxides of nitrogen and sulfur.

Nitrogen and sulfur oxides react in the atmosphere to produce **acid precipitation,** which damages health, weathers materials, and reduces growth of crops and forests. Incompletely burned fuels in automobile exhaust react with nitrogen oxides in the presence of sunlight and atmospheric oxygen to form ozone. Ozone then reacts further with automobile exhaust to form **smog.** Sunlight provides the energy to convert automobile exhaust to smog.

Dioxin is an example of a compound that is produced inadvertently during chemical manufacture and when certain materials are burned. Some scientists argue that even tiny amounts of dioxin and other toxic volatiles may be harmful to human health, but others disagree.

Scientific studies show that industrial aerosols are harmful to health, but aerosols are so varied that it is difficult to know which ones are most harmful.

Chlorofluorocarbons and halons, compounds containing chlorine and bromine, in the stratosphere deplete the ozone that filters out harmful UV radiation and protects the Earth. Ozone-destroying chemicals have been regulated by international treaty and their concentration in the troposphere is diminishing.

Earth Systems Interactions

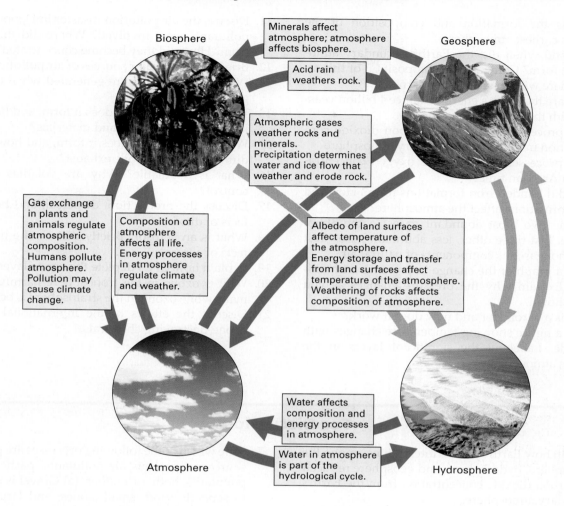

Biosphere

Minerals affect atmosphere; atmosphere affects biosphere.

Acid rain weathers rock.

Geosphere

Atmospheric gases weather rocks and minerals. Precipitation determines water and ice flow that weather and erode rock.

Gas exchange in plants and animals regulate atmospheric composition. Humans pollute atmosphere. Pollution may cause climate change.

Composition of atmosphere affects all life. Energy processes in atmosphere regulate climate and weather.

Albedo of land surfaces affect temperature of the atmosphere. Energy storage and transfer from land surfaces affect temperature of the atmosphere. Weathering of rocks affects composition of atmosphere.

Water affects composition and energy processes in atmosphere.

Water in atmosphere is part of the hydrological cycle.

Atmosphere

Hydrosphere

Key Terms

For Review

1. Discuss the formation and composition of the Earth's earliest atmosphere.
2. How and when did the Earth's secondary atmosphere form? Compare the composition of this atmosphere with that of the modern one.
3. Compare the Earth's energy balance 4 billion years ago with the energy balance today.
4. What processes reduced the carbon dioxide concentration in the Earth's secondary atmosphere?
5. What processes increased the oxygen concentration in Archean times?
6. How did banded iron formations form? How did their formations affect the atmosphere?
7. List the two most abundant gases in the atmosphere. List three other, less abundant gases. List three nongaseous components of natural air.
8. Draw a graph of the change in pressure with altitude. Explain why the pressure changes as you have shown.
9. What is a barometer and how does it work?
10. Draw a figure showing temperature changes with altitude. Label all the significant layers in the Earth's atmosphere.
11. Discuss the air pollution disaster in Donora. What pollutants were involved? Where did they come from? How did they become concentrated?
12. Briefly list the major sources of air pollution.
13. What air pollutants are generated when coal and gasoline burn?
14. What is acid rain, how does it form, and how does it affect people, crops, and materials?
15. What is smog, how does it form, and how does it differ from automobile exhaust?
16. What is a volatile? Why are volatiles hard to control?
17. Discuss the production, dispersal, and health effects of dioxin.
18. What is an aerosol? Briefly discuss the health effects of aerosols.
19. Explain how CFCs deplete the ozone layer.
20. Why is ozone in the troposphere harmful to humans while ozone in the stratosphere is beneficial?
21. Discuss the effects of the international ban on ozone-destroying chemicals.

For Discussion

1. Explain how Earth systems interactions among the atmosphere, hydrosphere, and geosphere reduced the carbon dioxide concentration from the Earth's secondary atmosphere.
2. Explain how Earth systems interactions among the atmosphere, hydrosphere, and geosphere led to the formation of the banded iron formations.
3. Discuss the statement: Life could not have formed in the modern atmosphere and living organisms could not survive in the primordial one.
4. Given your knowledge of the evolution of Earth's atmosphere, do you think that it is likely that there is life on other planets? Defend your position.
5. Imagine that enough matter vanished from the Earth's core so that the Earth's mass decreased by half. In what ways would the atmosphere change? Would normal pressure at sea level be affected? Would the thickness of the atmosphere change? Explain.
6. If gasoline produces only carbon dioxide and water when it burns completely, why is automobile exhaust a source of air pollution?
7. State which of the following processes are potential sources of gaseous air pollutants, particulate air pollutants, both, or neither: (a) Gravel is screened to separate sand, small stones, and large stones into different piles. (b) A factory stores drums of liquid chemicals outdoors. Some of the drums are not tightly closed, and others have rusted and are leaking. The exposed liquids evaporate. (c) A waterfall drives a turbine, which makes electricity. (d) Automobile bodies in an assembly plant are sprayed with paint. The automobile bodies then move through an oven that dries the paint. (e) A garbage dump catches fire.
8. How can sulfur in coal contribute to the acidity of rainwater? What happens in a furnace when the coal is burned? What happens in the outdoor atmosphere?
9. Gasoline vapor plus ultraviolet lamps do not produce the same smog symptoms as do automobile exhaust plus ultraviolet lamps. What is missing from gasoline vapor that helps to produce smog?

10. Imagine that someone planned to build a municipal garbage incinerator in your neighborhood. The facility would burn domestic trash and use the energy to generate electricity. Moreover, stringent air pollution controls would keep toxic emissions to very low levels. Discuss the environmental benefits and drawbacks of this proposed incinerator.

Earth Science ⊛ Now™

Assess your understanding of this chapter's topics with additional quizzing and comprehensive interactivities at **http://earthscience.brookscole.com/earthsci3e** as well as current and up-to-date weblinks, additional readings, and InfoTrac College Edition exercises.

Chapter 19

Moisture, Clouds, and Weather

An intense winter storm drove high waves over the sea wall in Winthrop, Massachusetts, Saturday, January 4, 2003. Roadways in several coastal communities from Marblehead to Scituate, Massachusetts, were closed, and several families were evacuated.

AP Photo./Michael Dwyer

Today's weather may be sunny and warm, a sharp contrast to yesterday, when it was rainy and cold. In New York City, a winter wind from the northwest brings cool air, but when a breeze blows from the southeast, the temperature rises and a storm develops as warm, moist maritime air flows into the city. Moisture, temperature, and wind combine to create the atmospheric conditions called weather.

The most severe weather, such as a winter blizzard or a hurricane, brings heavy precipitation and violent wind. The energy that drives these storms ultimately is derived from the Sun. In this chapter we will learn how the Sun's heat drives a blizzard that sweeps across the land with swirling snow and subzero temperatures, or a hurricane that blackens the sky and flattens houses.

Earth Science ⊛ Now™

This icon, appearing throughout the book, indicates an opportunity to explore interactive tutorials, animations, or practice problems available on the Earth ScienceNow Web site at **http://earthscience.brookscole.com/earthsci3e**

19.1 Moisture in Air

Precipitation occurs only when there is moisture in the air. Therefore to understand precipitation, we must first understand how moisture collects in the atmosphere and how it behaves.

Humidity

When water boils on a stove, a steamy mist rises above the pan, and then disappears into the air. The water molecules have not been lost, they have simply become invisible. In the pan, water is liquid, and in the mist above, the water exists as tiny droplets. These droplets then evaporate, and the invisible water vapor mixes with air. Water also evaporates into air from the seas, streams, and lakes, and from soil. Winds then distribute this moisture throughout the atmosphere. Thus, all air contains some water vapor, even over the driest deserts.

Humidity is the amount of water vapor in air. **Absolute humidity** is the mass of water vapor in a given volume of air, expressed in grams per cubic meter (g/m^3).

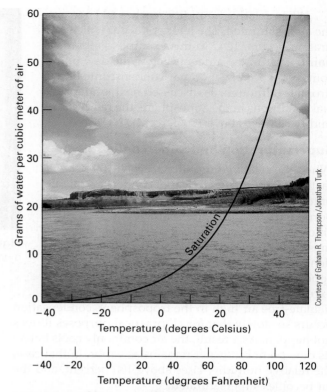

Earth Science ⊛ Now™ **ACTIVE FIGURE 19.1** Warm air can hold more water vapor than cold air.

Air can hold only a certain amount of water vapor, and warm air can hold more water vapor than cold air can. For example, air at 25°C can hold 23 g/m^3 of water vapor, but at 12°C, it can hold only half that quantity, 11.5 g/m^3 (Figure 19.1). **Relative humidity** is the amount of water vapor in air relative to the maximum it can hold at a given temperature. It is expressed as a percentage:

$$\text{Relative humidity (\%)} = \frac{\text{actual quantity of water per unit of air}}{\text{maximum quantity at the same temperature}} \times 100$$

If air contains half as much water vapor as it can hold, its relative humidity is 50 percent. Suppose that air at 25°C contains 11.5 g/m^3 of water vapor. Since air at that temperature can hold 23 g/m^3, it is carrying half of its maximum, and the relative humidity is 11.5 g/23 g × 100 = 50 percent.

Now let us take some of this air and cool it without adding or removing any water vapor. Because cold air holds less water vapor than warm air, the relative humidity increases even though the *amount* of water vapor remains constant. If the air cools to 12°C, and it still contains 11.5 g/m^3, the relative humidity reaches 100 percent because air at that temperature can hold only 11.5 g/m^3.

When relative humidity reaches 100 percent, the air is **saturated.** The temperature at which saturation occurs, 12°C in this example, is the **dew point.** If saturated air cools below the dew point, some of the water vapor may condense into liquid droplets (although, as discussed next, under special conditions in the atmosphere, the relative humidity can rise above 100 percent).

Supersaturation and Supercooling

When the relative humidity reaches 100 percent (at the dew point), water vapor condenses quickly onto solid surfaces such as rocks, soil, and airborne particles. Airborne particles such as dust, smoke, and pollen are abundant in the lower atmosphere. Consequently, water vapor may condense easily at the dew point in the lower atmosphere, and there, the relative humidity rarely exceeds 100 percent. However, in the clear, particulate-free air high in the troposphere, condensation occurs so slowly that for all practical purposes it does not happen. As a result, the air commonly cools below its dew point but water remains as vapor. In that case, the relative humidity rises above 100 percent, and the air becomes **supersaturated.**

Similarly, liquid water does not always freeze at its freezing point. Small droplets can remain liquid in a cloud even when the temperature is −40°C. Such water is **supercooled.**

Figure 19.2 Ice crystals condense on a window on a frosty morning.

19.2 Cooling and Condensation

As you have just learned, moisture condenses to form water droplets or ice crystals when moist air cools below its dew point. Clouds and fog are visible concentrations of this airborne water and ice. Three atmospheric processes cool air to its dew point and cause condensation: (1) Air cools when it loses heat by radiation. (2) Air cools by contact with a cool surface such as water, ice, rock, soil, or vegetation. (3) Air cools when it rises.

Radiation Cooling

As described in Chapter 18, the atmosphere, rocks, soil, and water absorb the Sun's heat during the day, and then radiate some of this heat back out toward space at night. As a result of heat lost by radiation, air, land, and water become cooler at night, and condensation may occur.

Contact Cooling—Dew and Frost

You can observe condensation on a cool surface with a simple demonstration. Heat water on a stove until it boils and then hold a cool drinking glass in the clear air just above the steam. Water droplets will condense on the surface of the glass because the glass cools the hot, moist air to its dew point. The same effect occurs in a house on a cold day. Water droplets or ice crystals appear on windows as warm, moist indoor air cools on the glass (Figure 19.2).

In some regions, the air on a typical summer evening is warm and humid. After the Sun sets, plants, houses, windows, and most other objects lose heat by radiation and therefore become cool. During the night, water vapor condenses on the cool objects. This condensation is called **dew.** If the dew point is below freezing, **frost** forms. Thus frost is not frozen dew, but ice crystals formed directly from vapor.

Cooling of Rising Air

Dew, frost, and some types of fog form by radiation and contact cooling close to the Earth's surface. However, clouds and precipitation normally form at higher elevations where the air is not cooled by direct contact with the ground. In contrast, almost all cloud formation and precipitation occurs when air cools as it rises (Figure 19.3).

Work and heat are both forms of energy. Work can be converted to heat or heat can be converted to work, but energy is never lost. If you pump up a bicycle tire you are performing work to compress the air. This energy is not lost; much of it converts to heat. Therefore, both the pump and the newly filled tire feel warm. Conversely, if you puncture a tire, the air rushes out. It must perform work to expand, so the air rushing from a punctured tire cools. Variations in temperature caused by compression and expansion of gas are called **adiabatic temperature changes.** Adiabatic means without gain or loss of heat. During adiabatic warming, air warms up because work is done on

Figure 19.3 Most clouds form as rising air cools. The cooling causes invisible water vapor to condense as visible water droplets or ice crystals, which we see as a cloud.

it, not because heat is added. During adiabatic cooling, air cools because it performs work, not because heat is removed.

As explained in Chapter 17, air pressure decreases with elevation. When dense surface air rises, it expands because the atmosphere around it is now of lower density, just as air expands when it rushes out of a punctured tire. Rising air performs work to expand, and therefore it cools adiabatically. Dry air cools by 10°C for every 1000 meters it rises (5.5°F/1000 ft). This cooling rate is called the **dry adiabatic lapse rate.** Thus, if dry air were to rise from sea level to 9000 meters (about the height of Mount Everest), it would cool by 90°C (162°F).

Almost all air contains some water vapor. As moist air rises and cools adiabatically, its temperature may eventually decrease to the dew point. At the dew point, moisture may condense as droplets, and a cloud forms. But recall that condensing vapor releases latent heat. As the air rises through the cloud, its temperature now is affected by two opposing processes. It cools adiabatically, but at the same time it is heated by the latent heat

released by condensation. However, the warming caused by latent heat is generally less than the amount of adiabatic cooling. The net result is that the rising air continues to cool, but more slowly than at the dry adiabatic lapse rate. The **wet adiabatic lapse rate** is the cooling rate after condensation has begun. It varies from 5°C/1000 m (2.7°F/1000 ft) for air with a high moisture content, to 9°C/1000 m (5°F/1000 ft) for relatively dry air (Figure 19.4). Thus, once clouds start to form, rising air no longer cools as rapidly as it did lower in the atmosphere. Rising air cools at the dry adiabatic lapse rate until it cools to its dew point and condensation begins. Then, as it continues to rise, it cools at the lesser wet adiabatic lapse rate as condensation continues.

On the other hand, sinking air becomes warmer because of adiabatic compression. Warm air can hold more water vapor than cool air. Consequently, water does not condense from sinking, warming air, and the latent heat of condensation does not affect the rate of temperature rise. As a result, sinking air always becomes warmer at the dry adiabatic rate.

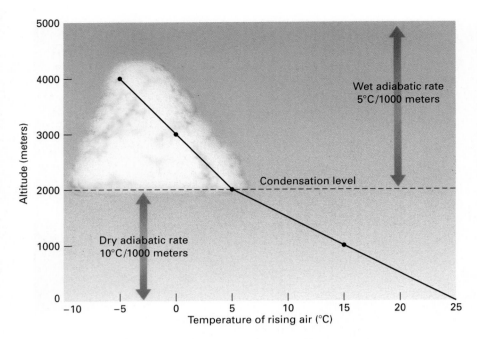

Earth Science ◉ Now™ ACTIVE
FIGURE 19.4 A rising air mass initially cools rapidly at the dry adiabatic lapse rate. Then, after condensation begins, it cools more slowly at the wet adiabatic lapse rate.

Interactive Question: From the graph, estimate the air temperature at an elevation of 500 meters? 1500 Meters? Calculate the dry adiabatic lapse rate from your estimates.

19.3 Rising Air and Precipitation

To summarize: When moist air rises, it cools and forms clouds. Three mechanisms cause air to rise (Figure 19.5):

Orographic Lifting

When air flows over mountains, it is forced to rise. This rising air frequently causes rain or snow over the mountains, as will be explained in Section 19.7.

Frontal Wedging

A moving mass of cool, dense air may encounter a mass of warm, less dense air. When this occurs, the cool, denser air slides under the warm air mass, forcing the warm air upward to create a weather front. We will discuss weather fronts in more detail later in this chapter.

Convection-Convergence

If one portion of the atmosphere becomes warmer than the surrounding air, the warm air expands, becomes less dense, and rises. Thus a hot air balloon rises because it contains air that is warmer and less dense than the air around it. If the Sun heats one parcel of air near the Earth's surface to a warmer temperature than that of surrounding air, the warm air will rise, just as the hot air balloon rises.

Convective Processes and Clouds

On some days clouds hang low over the land and obscure nearby hills. At other times clouds float high in the sky, well above the mountain peaks. What factors determine the height and shape of a cloud?

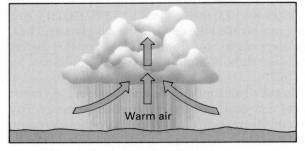

A   Orographic lifting

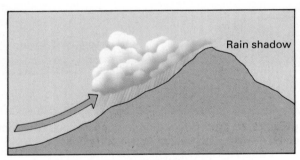

B   Frontal wedging

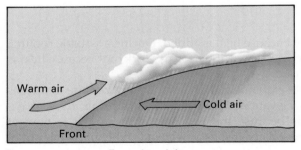

C   Convection–convergence

Figure 19.5 Three mechanisms cause air to rise and cool: (A) Orographic lifting, (B) Frontal wedging, and (C) Convection–convergence.

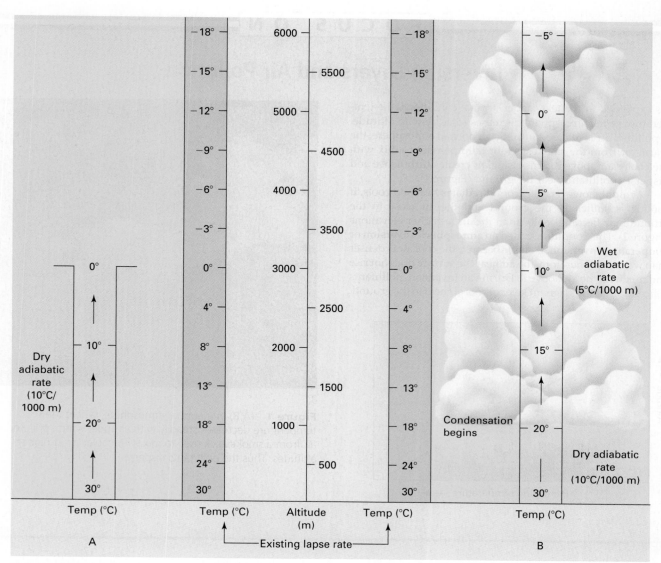

Figure 19.6 (A) As dry air rises, it expands and cools at the dry adiabatic lapse rate. Thus, it soon cools to the temperature of the surrounding air, and it stops rising. (B) As moist air rises, initially it cools at the dry adiabatic lapse rate. It soon cools to its dew point, and clouds form. Then, it cools more slowly at the wet adiabatic lapse rate. As a result, it remains warmer than surrounding air and continues to rise for thousands of meters. It stops rising when all moisture has condensed, and the air again cools at its dry adiabatic rate.

Interactive Question: How would cloud formation be affected if the wet adiabatic lapse rate were 8°C /1000 meters?

Recall that air is generally warmest at the Earth's surface and cools with elevation throughout the troposphere. The rate at which air that is neither rising nor falling cools with elevation is called the **normal lapse rate.** The average normal lapse rate is 6°C/1000 m (3.3°F/1000 ft), and thus is less than the dry adiabatic lapse rate. However, the normal lapse rate is variable. Typically, it is greatest near the Earth's surface, and decreases with altitude. The normal lapse rate also varies with latitude, the time of day, and the seasons. It is important to note that the normal lapse rate is simply the vertical temperature structure of the atmosphere. In contrast, *rising* air cools because of adiabatic cooling.

Figure 19.6 shows two rising warm air masses, one consisting of dry air and the other of moist air. The central part of the figure shows that the normal lapse rate is the same for both air masses: The temperature of the atmosphere decreases rapidly in the first few thousand meters, and then more slowly with increasing elevation. However, the two air masses behave differently because of their different moisture contents.

The dry air mass (A) rises and cools at the dry adiabatic lapse rate of 10°C/1000 m. As a result, in this example, its temperature and density become equal to that of surrounding air at an elevation of 3000 meters. Because the density of the rising air is the same as that

Inversion Layers and Air Pollution

As explained in the text, under normal conditions, the temperature of the atmosphere decreases steadily with altitude. If polluted air is released into such a normal atmosphere, the warm air from the smokestack or tailpipe rises to mix with the cooler air above it. This rising air creates turbulence and disperses pollutants near the ground (Figure 1).

At night, however, the ground radiates heat and cools. If cooling is sufficient, the ground and the air close to the ground may become cooler than the air at higher elevations (Figure 2). This condition, called an **atmospheric inversion** or **temperature inversion,** is stable because the cool air is denser than warm air. Therefore, the air near the surface does not rise and mix with the air above it. During an inversion, pollutants concentrate in the stagnant layer of cool air next to the ground.

B

Figure 1 (A,B) In a normal atmosphere, where the temperature decreases steadily with altitude, warm, polluted air from a smokestack rises to mix with cooler air at higher altitudes. Thus the pollutants disperse.

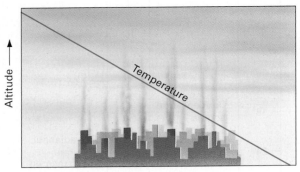

of the surrounding air, the rising air is no longer buoyant, and it stops rising. No clouds form because the air has not cooled to its dew point.

In (B), the rising moist air initially cools at the dry adiabatic rate of 10°C/1000 m, but only until the air cools to its dew point, at an elevation of 1000 meters. At that point, moisture begins to condense, and clouds form. But the condensing moisture releases latent heat of condensation. This additional heat causes the rising air to cool more slowly, at the wet adiabatic rate of 5°C/1000 m. As a result, the rising air remains warmer and more buoyant than surrounding air, and it continues to rise for thousands of meters, creating a towering, billowing cloud with the potential for heavy precipitation.

In simple terms, warm moist air is **unstable** because it rises rapidly, forming towering clouds and heavy rainfall. Also, as shown in Figure 19.5C, air rushes along the ground to replace the rising air, thus generating surface winds. Most of us have experienced a violent thunderstorm on a hot summer day. Puffy clouds seem to appear out of nowhere in a blue sky. These clouds grow vertically and darken as the afternoon progresses. Suddenly, gusts of wind race across the land and shortly thereafter, heavy rain falls. These events, to be described in more detail in Section 19.7, are all caused by unstable rising moist air.

In contrast, warm dry air doesn't rise rapidly, doesn't ascend to high elevations, and doesn't lead to cloud formation and precipitation. Thus warm dry air is said to be **stable.** Yet, convection is only one of the three processes that leads to rising air. Orographic lifting and frontal wedging also lead to rising air, cloud formation, and rain.

Usually, the morning Sun warms air near the ground and breaks the inversion. However, under some conditions, inversions last for days. For example, a large mass of warm air may move into a region at high altitude and float over the colder air near the ground, keeping the air over a city stagnant. Inversions are common along coastlines and large lakes, where the water cools surface air. In the Los Angeles basin, cool maritime air is often trapped beneath a warm subtropical air mass. The cool air cannot move eastward because of the mountains, and it cannot rise because it is too dense. Pollutants from the city's automobiles and factories then concentrate until the stagnant air becomes unhealthy.

Two types of weather changes can break up an inversion. If the Sun heats the Earth's surface sufficiently, the cool air near the ground warms and rises, dispersing the pollutants. Alternatively, storm winds may dissipate an inversion layer.

B

Figure 2 (A,B) During an inversion, when warm air lies on top of cooler air near the ground, warm, polluted air from a smokestack cannot rise above the inversion layer. In this photograph, taken in the Gdansk Shipyards in Poland, an early morning inversion layer concentrates clouds, steam, and pollutants close to the ground.

19.4 Types of Clouds

Even a casual observer of the daily weather will notice that clouds are quite different from day to day. Different meteorological conditions create the various cloud types and, in turn, a look at the clouds provides useful information about the daily weather.

Cirrus clouds are wispy clouds that look like hair blowing in the wind or feathers floating across the sky (from Latin: wisp of hair). Cirrus clouds form at high altitudes, 6000 to 15,000 meters (20,000 to 50,000 feet). The air is so cold at these elevations that cirrus clouds are composed of ice crystals rather than water droplets. High winds aloft blow them out into long, gently curved streamers (Figure 19.7).

Figure 19.7 Cirrus clouds are high, wispy clouds composed of ice crystals.

Figure 19.8 Stratus clouds spread out across the sky in a low, flat layer.

Figure 19.9 Cumulus clouds are fluffy white clouds with flat bottoms.

Stratus clouds are horizontally layered, sheet-like clouds (from Latin: layer). They form when condensation occurs at the same elevation at which air stops rising, and the clouds spread out into a broad sheet. Stratus clouds form the dark, dull gray, overcast skies that may persist for days and bring steady rain (Figure 19.8).

Cumulus clouds are fluffy white clouds that typically display flat bottoms and billowy tops (from Latin: heap or pile) (Figure 19.9). On a hot summer day the

top of a cumulus cloud may rise 10 kilometers or more above its base in cauliflower-like masses. The base of the cloud forms at the altitude at which the rising air cools to its dew point and condensation starts. However, in this situation the rising air remains warmer than the surrounding air and therefore continues to rise. As it rises, more vapor condenses, forming the billowing columns.

Other types of clouds are named by combining these three basic terms (Figure 19.10). **Stratocumulus**

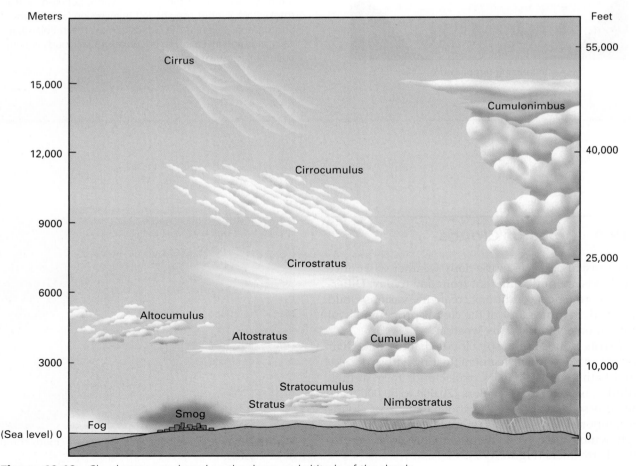

Figure 19.10 Cloud names are based on the shape and altitude of the clouds.

clouds are low sheet-like clouds with some vertical structure. The term *nimbo* refers to a cloud that precipitates. Thus a **cumulonimbus** cloud is a towering rain cloud. If you see one, you should seek shelter, because cumulonimbus clouds commonly produce intense rain, thunder, lightning, and sometimes hail. A **nimbostratus** cloud is a stratus cloud from which rain or snow falls. Other prefixes are also added. *Alti* is derived from the Latin root *altus*, meaning high. An **altostratus** cloud is simply a high stratus cloud.

Types of Precipitation

Rain

Why does rain fall from some clouds, whereas other clouds float across a blue sky on a sunny day and produce no rain? The droplets in a cloud are small, about 0.01 millimeter in diameter (about 1/7 the diameter of a human hair). In still air, such a droplet would require 48 hours to fall from a cloud 1000 meters above the Earth. But these tiny droplets never reach the Earth because they evaporate faster than they fall.

If the air temperature in a cloud is above freezing, the tiny droplets may collide and coalesce. You can observe similar behavior in droplets sliding down a window pane on a rainy day. If two droplets collide, they merge to become one large drop. If the droplets in a cloud grow large enough, they fall as drizzle (0.1 to 0.5 millimeter in diameter) or light rain (0.5 to 2 millimeters in diameter). About one million cloud droplets must combine to form an average-size raindrop.

In many clouds, however, water vapor initially forms ice crystals rather than condensing as tiny droplets of supercooled water. Part of the reason for this is that the temperature in clouds is commonly below freezing, but another factor also favors ice formation. At near- or below-freezing temperatures, air that is slightly undersaturated with respect to water is slightly supersaturated with respect to ice. For example, if the relative humidity of air is 95 percent with respect to water, it is about 105 percent with respect to ice. Thus, as air cools toward its dew point, all the vapor forms ice crystals rather than supercooled water droplets. The tiny ice crystals then grow larger as more water vapor condenses on them, until they are large enough to fall. The ice then melts to form raindrops as it falls through warmer layers of air.

If you have ever been caught in a thunderstorm, you may remember raindrops large enough to be painful as they struck your face or hands. Recall that a cumulus cloud forms from rising air and that its top may be several kilometers above its base. The temperature in the upper part of the cloud is commonly below freezing. As a result, ice crystals form, and begin to fall. Condensation continues as the crystal falls through the

Figure 19.11 Snow blankets the ground during the winter in temperate regions. Snow and ice cover the ground year-round in the high mountains and at the Poles.

towering cloud, and the crystal grows. If the lower atmosphere is warm enough, the ice melts before it reaches the surface. Raindrops formed in this manner may be 3 to 5 millimeters in diameter, large enough to hurt when they hit.

Snow, Sleet, and Glaze

As explained above, when the temperature in a cloud is below freezing, the cloud is composed of ice crystals rather than water droplets. If the temperature near the ground is also below freezing, the crystals remain frozen and fall as snow (Figure 19.11). In contrast, if raindrops form in a warm cloud and fall through a layer of cold air at lower elevation, the drops freeze and fall as small spheres of ice called **sleet**. Sometimes the freezing zone near the ground is so thin that raindrops do not have time to freeze before they reach the Earth. However, when they land on subfreezing surfaces, they form a coating of ice called **glaze** (Figure 19.12). Glaze can be heavy enough to break tree limbs and electrical transmission lines. It also coats highways with a dangerous icy veneer. In the winter of 1997–98,

Figure 19.12 Glaze forms when rain falls on a surface that is colder than the freezing temperature of water.

a sleet and glaze storm in eastern Canada and the northeastern United States caused billions of dollars in damage. The ice damaged so many electric lines and power poles that many people were without electricity for a few weeks.

Hail

Occasionally, precipitation takes the form of very large ice globules called **hail**. Hailstones vary from 5 millimeters in diameter to a record 14 centimeters in diameter, weighing 765 grams (more than 1.5 pounds), that fell in Kansas. A 500 gram (1-pound) hailstone crashing to Earth at 160 kilometers (100 miles) per hour can shatter windows, dent car roofs, and kill people and livestock. Even small hailstones can damage crops. Hail falls only from cumulonimbus clouds. Because cumulonimbus clouds form in columns with distinct boundaries, hailstorms occur in local, well-defined areas. Thus, one farmer may lose an entire crop while a neighbor is unaffected.

A hailstone consists of concentric shells of ice like the layers of an onion. Two mechanisms have been proposed for their formation. In one, turbulent winds blow falling ice crystals back upward in the cloud. New layers of ice accumulate as additional vapor condenses on the recirculating ice grain. An individual particle may rise and fall several times until it grows so large and heavy that it drops out of the cloud. In the second mechanism, hailstones form in a single pass through the cloud. During their descent, supercooled water freezes onto the ice crystals. The layering develops because different temperatures and amounts of supercooled water exist in different portions of the cloud, and each layer forms in a different part of the cloud.

19.5 Fog

Fog is a cloud that forms at or very close to ground level, although most fog forms by processes different from those that create higher-level clouds. **Advection fog** occurs when warm, moist air from the sea blows onto cooler land. The air cools to its dew point, and water vapor condenses at ground level. San Francisco, Seattle, and Vancouver, B.C., all experience foggy winters as warm, moist air from the Pacific Ocean is cooled first by the cold California current and then by land. The foggiest location in the United States is Cape Disappointment, Washington, where visibility is obscured by fog 29 percent of the time.

Radiation fog occurs when the Earth's surface and air near the surface cool by radiation during the night (Figure 19.13). Water vapor condenses as fog when the air cools below its dew point. Often the cool, dense foggy air settles into valleys. If you are driving late at night in hilly terrain, beware, because a sudden dip in the roadway may lead you into a thick fog where visibility is low. A ground fog of this type typically "burns off" in the morning. The rising Sun warms the land or water surface which, in turn, warms the low-lying air. As the air becomes warmer, its capacity to hold water vapor increases, and the fog droplets evaporate. Radiation fog is particularly common in areas where the air is polluted because water vapor condenses readily on the tiny particles suspended in the air.

Recall that vaporization of water absorbs heat, and therefore cools both the surface and the surrounding air. In addition, vaporization adds moisture to the air. The cooling and the addition of moisture combine to form conditions conducive to fog. **Evaporation fog** occurs when air is cooled by evaporation from a body of water, commonly a lake or river. Evaporation fogs are common in late fall and early winter, when the air has become cool but the water is still warm. The water evaporates, but the vapor cools and condenses to fog almost immediately upon contact with the cold air.

Upslope fog occurs when air cools as it rises along a land surface. Upslope fogs occur both on gradually

Figure 19.13 Radiation fog is seen as a morning mist in this field in Idaho.
Interactive Question: Why does fog of this type commonly concentrate in low places?

sloping plains and on steep mountains. For example, the Great Plains rise from sea level at the Mississippi Delta to 1500 meters (5000 feet) at the Rocky Mountain front. When humid air moves northwest from the Gulf of Mexico toward the Rockies, it rises and cools adiabatically to form upslope fog. The rapid rise at the mountain front also forms fog.

19.6 Pressure and Wind

Warm air is less dense than cold air. Thus warm air exerts a relatively low atmospheric pressure and cold air exerts a relatively high atmospheric pressure. Warm air rises because it is less dense than the surrounding cool air (Figure 19.14A). Air rises slowly above a typical low-pressure region, at a rate of about 1 kilometer per day. In contrast, if air in the upper atmosphere cools, it becomes denser than the air beneath it and sinks (Figure 19.14B).

Air must flow inward over the Earth's surface toward a low-pressure region to replace a rising air mass. But a sinking air mass displaces surface air, pushing it outward from a high-pressure region. Thus vertical air flow in both high- and low-pressure regions is accompanied by horizontal air flow, called **wind.** Winds near the Earth's surface always flow away from a region of high pressure and toward a low-pressure region. Ultimately, all wind is caused by the pressure differences

resulting from unequal heating of the Earth's atmosphere (Figure 19.15).

Pressure Gradient

Wind blows in response to *differences* in pressure. Imagine that you are sitting in a room and the air is still. Now you open a can of vacuum-packed coffee and hear the hissing as air rushes into the can. Because the pressure in the room is higher than that inside the coffee can, wind blows from the room into the can. But if you blow up a balloon, the air inside the balloon is at higher pressure than the air in the room. When the balloon is punctured, wind blows from the high-pressure zone of the balloon into the lower-pressure zone of the room (Figure 19.16).

Wind speed is determined by the magnitude of the pressure difference over distance, called the **pressure gradient.** Thus wind blows rapidly if a large pressure difference exists over a short distance. A steep pressure gradient is analogous to a steep hill. Just as a ball rolls quickly down a steep hill, wind flows rapidly across a steep pressure gradient. To create a pressure-gradient map, air pressure is measured at hundreds of different weather stations. Points of equal pressure are connected by map lines called **isobars.** A steep pressure gradient is shown by closely spaced isobars, whereas a weak pressure gradient is indicated by widely spaced isobars (Figure 19.17). Pressure gradients change daily, or sometimes hourly, as high- and low-pressure zones move. Therefore, maps are updated frequently.

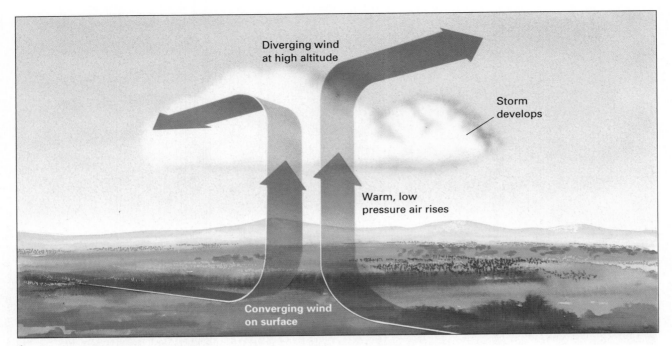

Diverging wind
at high altitude

Storm
develops

Warm, low
pressure air rises

Converging wind
on surface

A

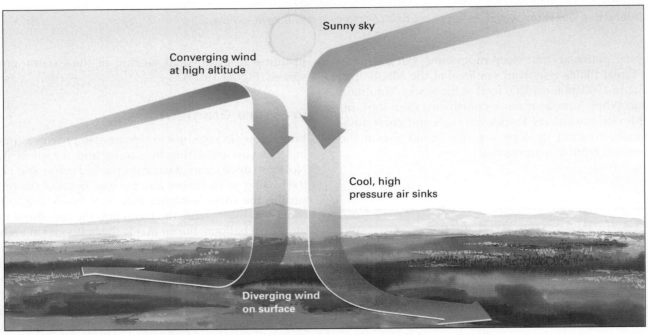

Sunny sky

Converging wind
at high altitude

Cool, high
pressure air sinks

Diverging wind
on surface

B

Figure 19.14 (A) Rising low-pressure air creates clouds and precipitation. Air flows inward toward the low-pressure zone, creating surface winds. (B) Sinking high pressure air creates clear skies. Air flows outward from the high-pressure zone, and also creates surface winds.

Figure 19.15 Winds vary from gentle zephyrs that cool bathers on a hot summer day to hurricanes and tornadoes that sink ships and destroy homes.

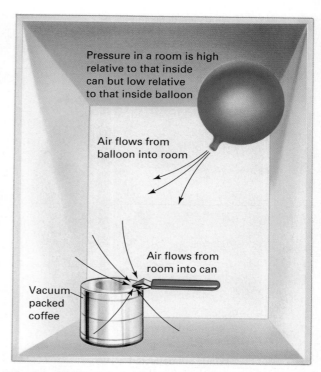

Figure 19.16 Winds blow in response to differences in pressure.

Pressure in a room is high relative to that inside can but low relative to that inside balloon

Air flows from balloon into room

Air flows from room into can

Vacuum packed coffee

Figure 19.17 Pressure map and winds at 5000 feet in North America on February 3, 1992. High-altitude data are shown because the winds are not affected by surface topography and thus the effect of pressure gradient is well illustrated. Note that in the northeast and northwest, steep pressure gradients, shown by closely spaced isobars, cause high winds that spiral counterclockwise into the low-pressure zones. Widely spaced isobars around high-pressure zones in the central United States cause weaker winds.

Interactive Question: Where on this map would you expect stormy conditions? Where would you expect fair weather?

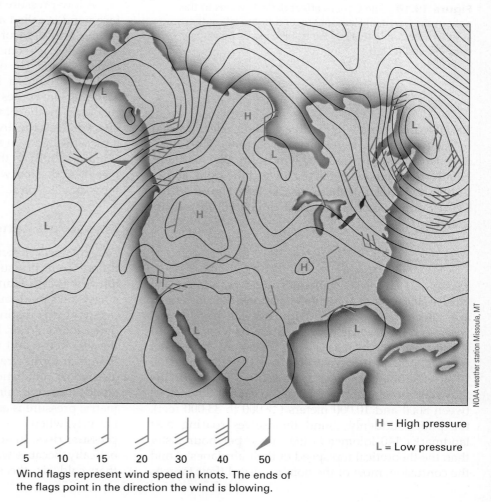

| 5 | 10 | 15 | 20 | 30 | 40 | 50 |

Wind flags represent wind speed in knots. The ends of the flags point in the direction the wind is blowing.

H = High pressure

L = Low pressure

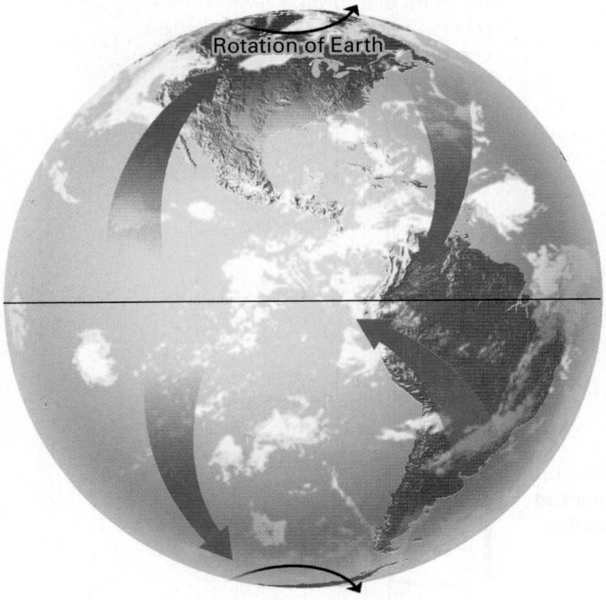

Winds are deflected
to the right in the
Northern Hemisphere

Rotation of Earth

Winds are deflected
to the left in the
Southern Hemisphere

Figure 19.18 The Coriolis effect deflects winds to the right in the Northern Hemisphere, and to the left in the Southern Hemisphere. Only winds blowing due east or west are unaffected.

Coriolis Effect

Recall from Chapter 16 that the Coriolis effect, caused by the Earth's spin, deflects ocean currents. The Coriolis effect similarly deflects winds. In the Northern Hemisphere wind is deflected toward the right, and in the Southern Hemisphere, to the left (Figure 19.18). The Coriolis effect alters wind direction, but not its speed.

Friction

Rising and falling air generates wind both along the Earth's surface and at higher elevations. Surface winds are affected by friction with the Earth's surface, whereas high-altitude winds are not. As a result, wind speed normally increases with elevation. This effect was first noted during World War II. On November 24, 1944, U.S. bombers were approaching Tokyo for the first mass bombing of the Japanese capital. Flying between 8000 and 10,000 meters (27,000 to 33,000 feet), the pilots suddenly found themselves roaring past landmarks 140 kilometers (90 miles) per hour faster than the theoretical top speed of their airplanes! Amid the confusion, most of the bombs missed their targets,

and the mission was a military failure. However, this experience introduced meteorologists to **jet streams,** narrow bands of high-altitude wind. The jet stream in the Northern Hemisphere flows from west to east at speeds between 120 and 240 kilometers per hour (75 and 150 mph). As a comparison, surface winds attain such velocities only in hurricanes and tornadoes. Airplane pilots traveling from Los Angeles to New York fly with the jet stream to gain speed and save fuel, whereas pilots moving from east to west try to avoid it.

Jet stream influence on weather and climate will be discussed in more detail later in this chapter and in Chapter 20.

Cyclones and Anticyclones

Figure 19.19A shows the movement of air in the Northern Hemisphere as it converges toward a low-pressure area. If the Earth did not spin, wind would flow directly across the isobars, as shown by the black arrows. However, the Earth does spin, and the Coriolis effect deflects wind to the right, as shown by the small red arrows. This rightward deflection creates a counterclockwise vortex near the center of the low-pressure region, as shown by the large magenta arrows.

A low-pressure region with its accompanying surface wind is called a **cyclone.** In this usage, "cyclone" means a system of rotating winds, not the violent storms that are sometimes called cyclones, hurricanes, and typhoons. The opposite mechanism forms an **anticyclone** around a high-pressure region. When descending air reaches the surface, it spreads out in all directions. In the Northern Hemisphere, the Coriolis effect deflects the diverging winds to the right, forming a pinwheel pattern with the wind spiraling clockwise (Figure 19.19B). In the Southern Hemisphere, the Coriolis effect deflects winds leftward, and creates a counterclockwise spiral.

Pressure Changes and Weather

As explained earlier, wind blows in response to any difference in pressure. However, low pressure generally brings clouds and precipitation with the wind, and sunny days predominate during high pressure. To understand this distinction, recall that warm air is less dense than cold air. If warm and cold air are in contact, the less dense and therefore buoyant warm air rises. Rising air forms a region of low pressure. But rising air also cools adiabatically. If the cooling is sufficient, clouds form and rain or snow may fall. Thus, low barometric pressure is an indication of wet weather. Alternatively, when cool air sinks, it is compressed and the pressure rises. In addition, sinking air is heated adiabatically. Because warm air can hold more water vapor than cold air, the sinking air absorbs moisture and

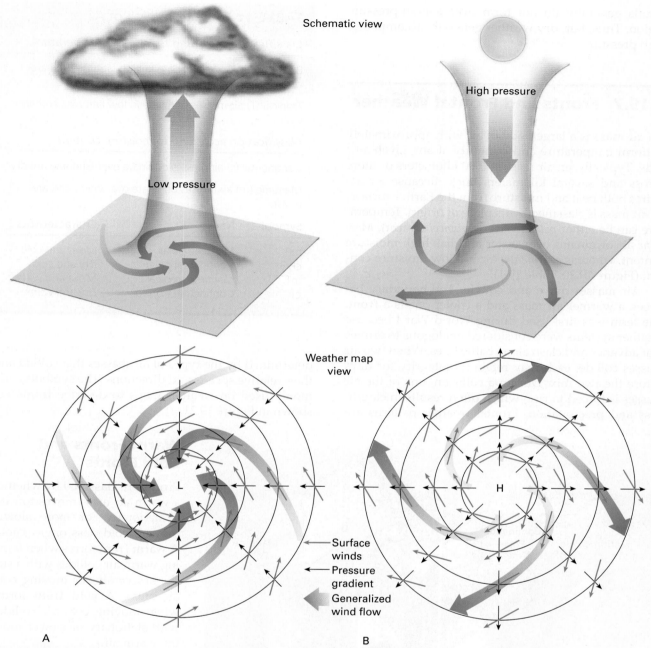

Schematic view

Low pressure

High pressure

Weather map view

Surface winds

Pressure gradient

Generalized wind flow

A

B

Figure 19.19 (A) In the Northern Hemisphere, a cyclone consists of winds spiraling counterclockwise into a low pressure region. (B) An anticyclone consists of winds spiraling clockwise out from a high-pressure zone.

Interactive Question: Redraw this figure showing cyclones and anticyclones in the Southern Hemisphere.

clouds generally do not form over a high-pressure region. Thus, fair, dry weather generally accompanies high pressure.

19.7 Fronts and Frontal Weather

An **air mass** is a large body of air with approximately uniform temperature and humidity at any given altitude. Typically, an air mass is 1500 kilometers or more across and several kilometers thick. Because air acquires both heat and moisture from the Earth's surface, an air mass is classified by its place of origin. Temperature can be either *polar* (cold) or *tropical* (warm). *Maritime* air originates over water and has high moisture content, whereas *continental* air has low moisture content (Figure 19.20, Table 19.1).

Air masses move and collide. The boundary between a warmer air mass and a cooler one is a **front.** The term was first used during World War I because weather systems were considered analogous to armies that advance and clash along battle lines. When two air masses collide, each may retain its integrity for days before the two mix. During a collision, one of the air masses is forced to rise, which often results in cloudiness and precipitation. Frontal weather patterns are

TABLE 19.1 Classification of Air Masses

Classification according to latitude (temperature):

Polar (P) air masses originate in high latitudes and are cold.

Tropical (T) air masses originate in low latitudes and are warm.

Classification according to moisture content:

Continental (c) air masses originate over land and are dry.

Maritime (m) air masses originate over water and are moist.

Symbol	Name	Characteristics
mP	Maritime polar	Moist and cold
cP	Continental polar	Dry and cold
mT	Maritime tropical	Moist and warm
cT	Continental tropical	Dry and warm

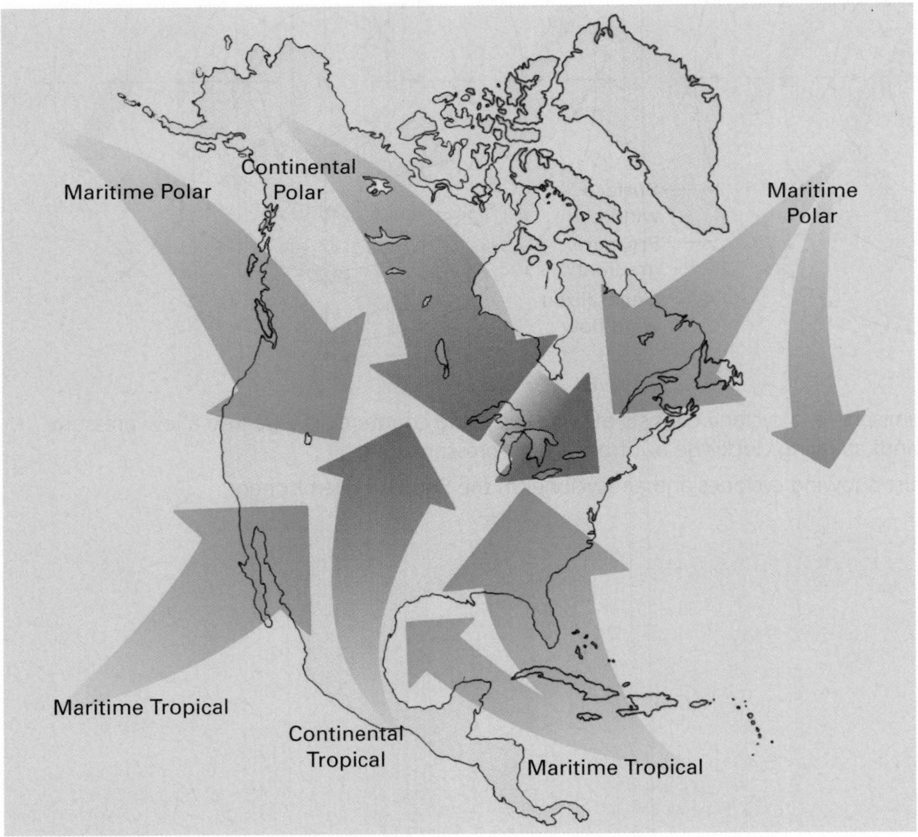

determined by the types of air masses that collide and their relative speeds and directions. The symbols commonly used on weather maps to describe fronts are shown in Figure 19.21.

Warm Fronts and Cold Fronts

Fronts are classified by whether a warm air mass moves toward a stationary (or more slowly moving) cold mass, or vice versa. A **warm front** forms when moving warm air collides with a stationary or slower moving cold air mass. A **cold front** forms when moving cold air collides with stationary or slower moving warm air.

In a warm front, the moving warm air rises over the denser cold air as the two masses collide (Figure 19.22). The rising warm air cools adiabatically and the cooling generates clouds and precipitation. Precipitation is generally light because the air rises slowly along the gently sloping frontal boundary. Figure 19.22 shows that a characteristic sequence of clouds accompanies a warm front. High, wispy cirrus and cirrostratus clouds develop near the leading

Figure 19.20 Air masses are classified by their source regions.

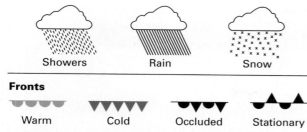

Fronts

Warm | Cold | Occluded | Stationary

Figure 19.21 Symbols commonly used in weather maps. "Warm" and "cold" are relative terms. Air over the central plains of Montana at a temperature of 0°C may be warm relative to polar air above northern Canada but cold relative to a 20°C air mass over the southeastern United States.

edge of the rising warm air. These high clouds commonly precede a storm. They form as much as 1000 kilometers ahead of an advancing band of precipitation that falls from thick, low-lying nimbostratus and stratus clouds near the trailing edge of the front. The cloudy weather may last for several days because of the gentle slope and broad extent of the frontal boundary.

A cold front forms when faster-moving cold air overtakes and displaces warm air. The dense, cold air distorts into a blunt wedge and pushes under the warmer air (Figure 19.23). Thus the leading edge of a cold front is much steeper than that of a warm front. The steep contact between the two air masses causes

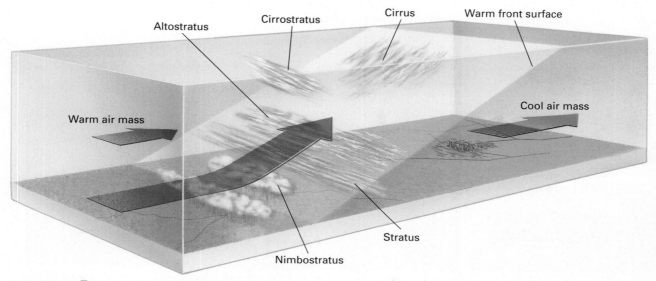

Earth Science ⊕ Now™ **ACTIVE FIGURE 19.22** In a warm front, moving warm air rises gradually over cold air.

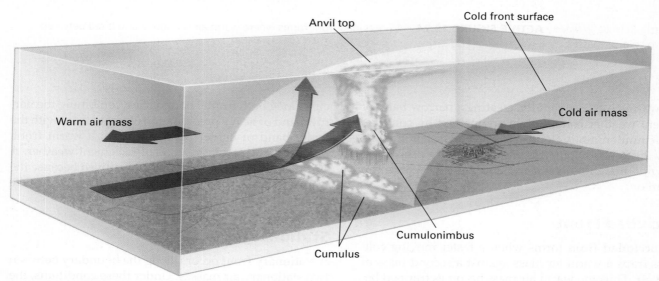

Earth Science ⊕ Now™ **ACTIVE FIGURE 19.23** In a cold front, moving cold air slides abruptly beneath warm air, forcing it steeply upward.

Interactive Question: Explain why the surface of the warm front rises gradually with elevation, while the cold front rises much more steeply.

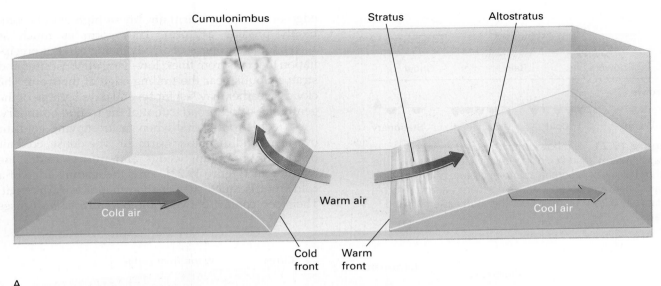

Cumulonimbus   Stratus   Altostratus

Warm air

Cold air   Cool air

Cold front   Warm front

A

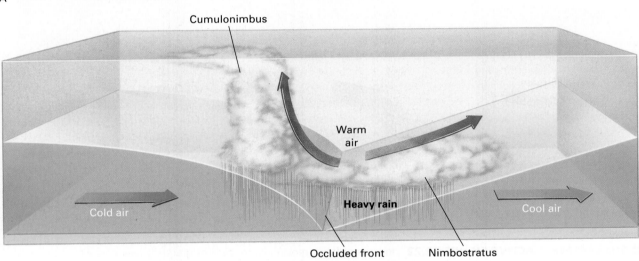

Cumulonimbus

Warm air

Cold air   Heavy rain   Cool air

Occluded front   Nimbostratus

B

Earth Science ⊛ Now™   **ACTIVE FIGURE 19.24**   An occluded front forms where warm air is trapped and lifted between two cold air masses.

the warm air to rise rapidly, creating a narrow band of violent weather commonly accompanied by cumulus and cumulonimbus clouds. The storm system may be only 25 to 100 kilometers wide, but within this zone downpours, thunderstorms, and violent winds are common.

Occluded Front

An **occluded front** forms when a faster moving cold mass traps a warm air mass against a second mass of cold air. Thus the warm air mass becomes trapped between two colder air masses (Figure 19.24). The faster-moving cold air mass then slides beneath the warm air, lifting it completely off the ground. Precipitation oc-

curs along both frontal boundaries, combining the narrow band of heavy precipitation of a cold front with the wider band of lighter precipitation of a warm front. The net result is a large zone of inclement weather. A storm of this type is commonly short-lived because the warm air mass is cut off from its supply of moisture evaporating from the Earth's surface.

Stationary Front

A **stationary front** occurs along the boundary between two stationary air masses. Under these conditions, the front can remain over an area for several days. Warm air rises, forming conditions similar to those in a warm front. As a result, rain, drizzle, and fog may occur.

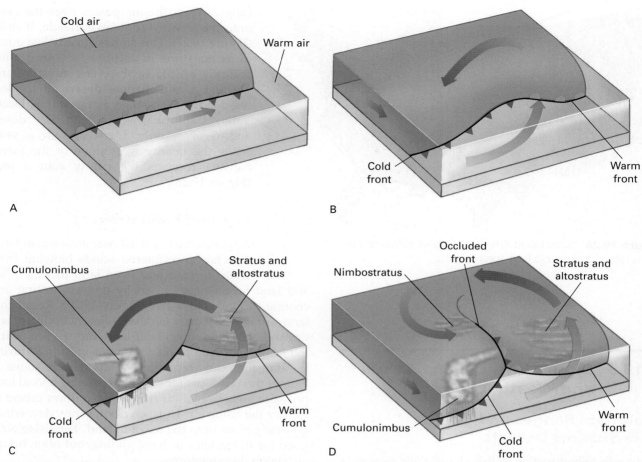

Earth Science ⊛ Now™ **ACTIVE FIGURE 19.25** A mid-latitude cyclone develops along a front between polar air and a tropical air mass. (A) A front develops. (B) Some small disturbance creates a kink in the front. (C) A low-pressure region and cyclonic circulation develop. (D) An occluded front forms.

The Life Cycle of a Middle-Latitude Cyclone

Most low-pressure cyclones in the middle latitudes of the Northern Hemisphere develop along a front between polar and tropical air masses. The storm often starts with winds blowing in opposite directions along a stationary front between the two air masses (Figure 19.25A). In this figure, a warm air mass was moving northward, and was deflected to the east by the Coriolis force. At the same time, a cold air mass traveling southward was deflected to the west.

In Figure 19.25B, the cold, polar air continues to push southward, creating a cold front and lifting the warm air off the ground. Then, some small disturbance deforms the straight frontal boundary, forming a wave-like kink in the front. This disturbance may be a topographic feature such as a mountain range, air flow from a local storm, or a local temperature variation. Once the

kink forms, the winds on both sides are deflected to strike the front at an angle. Thus, a warm front forms to the east and a cold front forms to the west.

Rising warm air then forms a low-pressure region near the kink (Figure 19.25C). In the Northern Hemisphere, the Coriolis effect causes the winds to circulate counterclockwise around the kink, as explained in Section 19.6. To the west the cold front advances southward, and to the east the warm front advances northward. At the same time, rain or snow falls from the rising warm air (Figure 19.25D). Over a period of one to three days, the air rushing into the low-pressure region equalizes pressure differences, and the storm dissipates. Many of the pinwheel-shaped storms seen on weather maps are cyclones of this type. In North America, the jet stream and other prevailing upper-level westerly winds generally move cyclones from west to east along the same paths, called **storm tracks** (Figure 19.26).

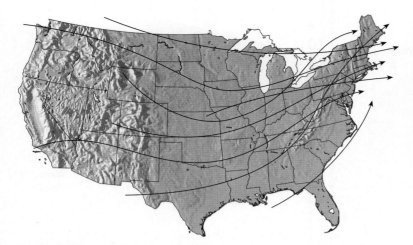

Figure 19.26 Most North American cyclones follow certain paths called storm tracks from west to east.

range. When the air passes over the crest onto the leeward (downwind) side, it sinks (Figure 19.27). This air has already lost much of its moisture. In addition, it warms adiabatically as it falls, absorbing moisture and creating a **rain-shadow desert** on the leeward side of the range. For example, Death Valley, California, is a rain-shadow desert and receives only 5 cm of rain a year, while the nearby west slope of the Sierra Nevada receives 178 cm of rain a year (Figure 19.28).

Sea and Land Breezes

Anyone who has lived near an ocean or large lake has encountered winds blowing from water to land and from land to water. Sea and land breezes are caused by uneven heating and cooling of land and water (Figure 19.29). Recall that land surfaces heat up faster than adjacent bodies of water, and cool more quickly. If land and sea are nearly the same temperature on a summer morning, during the day the land warms and heats the air above it. Hot air then rises over the land, producing a local low-pressure area. Cooler air from the sea flows inland to replace the rising air. Thus, on a hot, sunny day, winds generally blow from the sea onto land. The rising air is good for flying kites or hang gliding, but often brings afternoon thunderstorms.

At night the reverse process occurs. The land cools faster than the sea, and descending air creates a local high pressure area over the land. Then the winds reverse, and breezes blow from the shore out toward the sea.

19.8 Mountains, Oceans, Lakes, and Weather

Mountain Ranges and Rain-Shadow Deserts

As we described earlier in this chapter, air rises in a process called orographic lifting when it flows over a mountain range. As the air rises, it cools adiabatically, and water vapor may condense into clouds that produce rain or snow. These conditions create abundant precipitation on the windward side and the crest of the

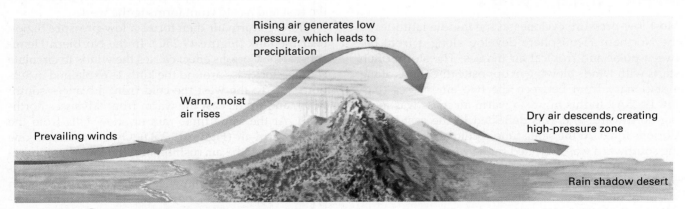

Earth Science ⊛ Now™ ACTIVE FIGURE 19.27 A rain-shadow desert forms where moist air rises over a mountain range and precipitates most of its moisture on the windward side and crest of the range. The dry, descending air on the lee side absorbs moisture, forming a desert.

Figure 19.28 Rain-shadow deserts lie east of the California mountain ranges. Rainfall is shown in centimeters per year.

Monsoons

A **monsoon** is a seasonal wind and weather system caused by uneven heating and cooling of continents and oceans. Just as sea and land breezes reverse direction with day and night, monsoons reverse direction with the seasons. In the summertime the continents become warmer than the sea. Warm air rises over land, creating a large low-pressure area and drawing moisture-laden maritime air inland. When the moist air rises as it flows over the land, clouds form and heavy monsoon rains fall. In winter the process is reversed. The land cools below the sea temperature, and as a result, air descends over land, producing dry continental high pressure. At the same time air rises over the ocean and the prevailing winds blow from land to sea. More than half of the inhabitants of the Earth depend on monsoons because the predictable heavy summer rains bring water to the fields of Africa and Asia. If the monsoons fail to arrive, crops cannot grow and people starve.

Figure 19.29 (A) Sea breezes blow inland during the day, and (B) land breezes blow out to sea at night.

A

B

19.9 Thunderstorms

An estimated 16 million thunderstorms occur every year, and at any given moment about 2000 thunderstorms are in progress over different parts of the Earth. A single bolt of lightning can involve several hundred million volts of energy and for a few seconds produces as much power as a nuclear power plant. It heats the surrounding air to 25,000°C or more, much hotter than the surface of the Sun. The heated air expands instantaneously to create a shock wave that we hear as thunder.

Despite their violence, thunderstorms are local systems, often too small to be included on national weather maps. A typical thunderstorm forms and then dissipates in a few hours and covers from about ten to a few hundred square kilometers. It is not unusual to stand on a hilltop in the sunshine and watch rain squalls and lightning a few kilometers away. All thunderstorms develop when warm, moist air rises, forming cumulus clouds that develop into towering cumulonimbus clouds. Different conditions cause these local regions of rising air.

1. **Wind convergence** Central Florida is the most active thunderstorm region in the United States. As the subtropical Sun heats the Florida peninsula, rising air draws moist air from both the east and west coasts. Where the two air masses converge, the moist air rises rapidly to create a thunderstorm. Thunderstorms also occur in other environments where moist air masses converge.

2. **Convection** Thunderstorms also form in continental interiors during the spring or summer, when afternoon sunshine heats the ground and generates cells of rising moist air.

3. **Orographic Lifting** Moist air rises as it flows over hills and mountain ranges, commonly generating mountain thunderstorms.

4. **Frontal thunderstorms** Thunderstorms commonly occur along frontal boundaries, particularly at cold fronts.

A typical thunderstorm occurs in three stages. In the initial stage, moisture in rising air condenses, forming a cumulus cloud (Figure 19.30A). As the cloud forms, the condensing vapor releases latent heat. In an average thunderstorm, 400,000 tons of water vapor condenses within the cloud, and the energy released by the condensation is equivalent to the explosion of 12 atomic bombs the size of the one dropped on Hiroshima during World War II. This heat warms air in the cloud, and fuels the violent convection characteris-

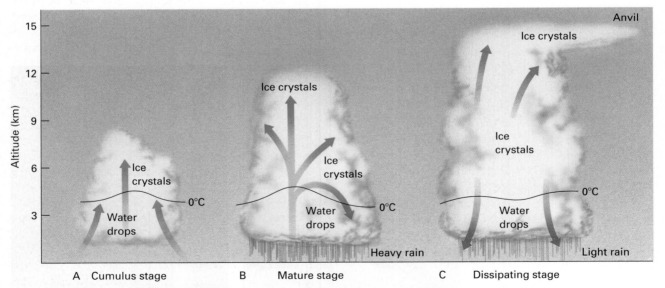

Earth Science ⊛ Now™ ACTIVE FIGURE 19.30 A typical thunderstorm develops in three stages. (A) Air rises, cools, and condenses, creating a cumulus cloud. (B) Latent heat of condensation energizes the storm, forming heavy rain and violent wind. (C) The cloud cools, convection weakens, and the storm wanes.

Interactive Question: Why does hail fall only from cumulonimbus clouds?

tic of thunderstorms. Large droplets or ice crystals develop within the cloud at this stage, but the rising air keeps them in suspension, and no precipitation falls to the ground.

Eventually, water droplets or hailstones become so heavy that updrafts can no longer support them, and they fall as rain or hail. During this stage, warm air continues to rise and may attain velocities of over 300 kilometers per hour in the central and upper portions of the cloud. The cloud may double its height in minutes. At the same time, ice falling through the cloud chills the lower regions and this cool air sinks, creating a downdraft. Thus, air currents rise and fall simultaneously within the same cloud. These conditions, known as **wind shear,** are dangerous for aircraft, and pilots avoid large thunderheads (Figure 19.30B).

As explained earlier, rainfall from a cumulonimbus cloud can be unusually heavy. In one extreme example in 1976, a sequence of thunderstorms dropped 25 centimeters of rain in about 4 hours over Big Thompson Canyon on the eastern edge of the Colorado Rockies. The river flooded the narrow canyon, killing 139 people.

The mature stage of a thunderstorm, with rain or hail and lightning, usually lasts for about 15 to 30 minutes and seldom longer than an hour. The cool downdraft reduces the temperature in the lower regions of the cloud. As the temperature drops, convection weakens and warm, moist air is no longer drawn into the cloud (Figure 19.30C). Once the water supply is cut off, condensation ceases, and the storm loses it source of latent heat. Within minutes the rapid vertical air motion dies and the storm dissipates. Although a single thundercloud dissipates rapidly, new thunderheads can build in the same region, causing disasters such as that at Big Thompson Canyon.

In 1996, a group of climbers were slowly approaching the summit of Mount Everest. Below them, fluffy white clouds began to obscure the lower peaks. Most of the climbers thought that the clouds were benign and continued on toward the summit. But one of the climbers was an airplane pilot and realized that the view from 8500 meters was analogous to a view from an airplane and not the perspective that we are normally accustomed to. To his trained eye, the clouds were the tops of rising thunderheads. Realizing that dangerous strong winds and heavy precipitation accompany a thunderstorm, he abandoned his summit attempt and retreated. The others pushed onward. A few hours later the intense storm engulfed the summit ridge and six climbers perished.

Lightning is an intense discharge of electricity that occurs when the buildup of static electricity overwhelms the insulating properties of air (Figure 19.31). If you walk across a carpet on a dry day, the friction be-

Figure 19.31 Time-lapse photo captures multiple ground-to-ground lightning strikes during a nighttime thunderstorm in Norman, Oklahoma, March 1978.

tween your feet and the rug shears electrons off the atoms on the rug. The electrons migrate into your body, and concentrate there. If you then touch a metal doorknob, a spark consisting of many electrons jumps from your finger to the metal knob.

In 1752 Benjamin Franklin showed that lightning is an electrical spark. He suggested that charges separate within cumulonimbus clouds and build until a bolt of lightning jumps from the cloud. In the 250 years since Franklin, atmospheric physicists have been unable to agree upon the exact mechanism of lightning. According to one hypothesis, friction between the intense winds and moving ice crystals in a cumulonimbus cloud generates both positive and negative electrical charges in the cloud, and the two types of charges become physically separated. The positive charges tend to accumulate in the upper portion of the cloud, and the negative charges build up in the lower reaches of the cloud. When enough charge accumulates, the electrical potential exceeds the insulating properties of air, and a spark jumps from the cloud to the ground, from the ground to the cloud, or from one cloud to another.

Another hypothesis suggests that cosmic rays bombarding the cloud from outer space produce ions at the top of the cloud. Other ions form on the ground as winds blow over the Earth's surface. The electrical discharge occurs when the potential difference between the two groups of electrical charges exceeds the insulating properties of air (Figure 19.32A, B). Perhaps neither hypothesis is entirely correct and some combination of the mechanisms causes lightning.

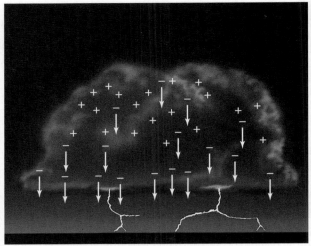

A

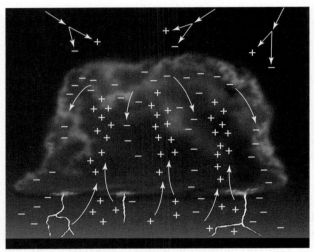

B

Earth Science⊛Now™ **ACTIVE FIGURE 19.32** Two hypotheses for the origin of lightning. (A) Friction between intense winds and ice particles generates charge separation. (B) Charged particles are produced from above by cosmic rays and below by interactions with the ground. The particles are then distributed by convection currents.

19.10 Tornadoes and Tropical Cyclones

Tornadoes and tropical cyclones are both intense low-pressure centers. Strong winds follow the steep pressure gradients and spiral inward toward a central column of rising air.

Tornadoes

A **tornado** is a small, short-lived, funnel-shaped storm that protrudes from the base of a cumulonimbus cloud (Figure 19.33). The base of the funnel can be from

A

B

Figure 19.33 (A) The dark funnel cloud of a tornado descends on Dimmit, Texas, on June 2, 1995. (B) Tornadoes that accompanied Hurricane Andrew added to the terror and confusion at La Place, Louisiana, where two people died and many homes were destroyed.

2 meters to 3 kilometers in diameter. Some tornadoes remain suspended in air while others touch the ground. After a tornado touches ground, it may travel for a few meters to a few hundred kilometers across the surface. The funnel travels from 40 to 65 kilometers per hour, and in some cases, as much as 110 kilometers per hour, but the spiraling winds within the funnel are much faster. Few direct measurements have been made of pressure and wind speed inside a tornado. However, we know that a large pressure difference occurs over a very short distance. Meteorologists estimate that winds in tornadoes may reach 500 kilometers per hour or greater. These winds rush into the narrow low-pressure zone and then spiral upward. After a few seconds to a few hours, the tornado lifts off the ground and dissipates.

Tornadoes are the most violent of all storms. One tornado in 1910 lifted a team of horses and then deposited it, unhurt, several hundred meters away. They were lucky. In the past, an average of 120 Americans were killed every year by these storms, and property damage costs millions of dollars. The death toll has decreased in recent years because effective warning systems allow people to seek shelter, but the property damage has continued to increase (Figure 19.33B). Tornado winds can lift the roof off a house and then flatten the walls. Flying debris kills people and livestock caught in the open. Even so, the total destruction from tornadoes is not as great as that from hurricanes because the path of a tornado is narrow and its duration short.

Although tornadoes can occur anywhere in the world, 75 percent of the world's twisters concentrate in the Great Plains, east of the Rocky Mountains. Approximately 700 to 1000 tornadoes occur in the United States each year. They frequently form in the spring or early summer. At that time, continental polar (dry, cold) air from Canada collides with maritime tropical (warm, moist) air from the Gulf of Mexico. As explained previously, these conditions commonly create thunderstorms. Meteorologists cannot explain why most thunderstorms dissipate harmlessly but a few develop tornadoes. However, one fact is apparent: Tornadoes are most likely to occur when large differences in temperature and moisture exist between the two air masses and the boundary between them is sharp.

The probability that any particular place will be struck by a tornado is small. Nevertheless, Codell, Kansas, was struck three years in a row—in 1916, 1917, and 1918—and each time the disaster occurred on May 20! During a two-day period in 1974, 148 tornadoes occurred in 13 states.

Tropical Cyclones

A **tropical cyclone** (called a *hurricane* in North America and the Caribbean, a *typhoon* in the western Pacific, and a *cyclone* in the Indian Ocean) is less intense than a tornado but much larger and longer-lived (Table 19.2).

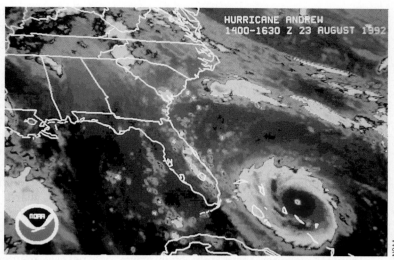

Figure 19.34 A color-enhanced satellite image of Hurricane Andrew as it approached the Florida Coast in 1992.

Tropical cyclones are circular storms that average 600 kilometers in diameter and persist for days or weeks (Figure 19.34). Intense low pressure in the center of a hurricane generates wind that varies from 120 to more than 300 kilometers per hour.

The low atmospheric pressure created by a tropical cyclone can raise the sea surface by several meters. Often, as a tropical cyclone strikes shore, strong onshore winds combine with the abnormally high water level created by low pressure to create a **storm surge** that floods coastal areas. In 1969 during Hurricane Camille, sea level rose more than 8 meters above normal on the Gulf Coast as a result of a storm surge.

The deadliest hurricane in the United States struck Galveston, Texas, in September 1900. Eight thousand people died and millions of dollars of damage occurred. One reason the death toll was so high was that the population was caught unaware. A tropical cyclone has a sharp boundary, and even a few hundred kilometers outside that boundary, fluffy white clouds may

TABLE 19.2 Comparison of Tornadoes and Tropical Cyclones

Feature	Range	
	Tornado	Tropical Cyclone
Diameter	2–3 km	400–800 km
Path length (distance traveled across terrain)	A few meters to hundreds of kilometers	A few hundred to a few thousand kilometers
Duration	A few seconds to a few hours	A few days to a week
Wind speed	300–800 km/hr	120–250 km/hr
Speed of motion	0–70 km/hr	20–30 km/hr
Pressure fall	20–200 mb	20–60 mb

be floating in a blue sky. Today, in the United States, hurricanes are detected by satellite and people are evacuated from coastal areas well in advance of oncoming storms. Warning cannot eliminate property damage, however. When Hurricane Hugo struck the North Carolina coast in 1989 with 220-kilometer-per-hour winds, waves flooded coastal areas, destroying 1900 homes and killing 40 people. Property damage totaled $3 billion.

In the spring of 1991, more than 100,000 people were killed when a cyclone sent 7-meter waves across the heavily populated, low-lying coast of Bangladesh. Although meteorologists had been tracking the storm, communication was so poor and transportation facilities so inadequate that people were not evacuated in time.

Tropical cyclones form only over warm oceans, never over cold oceans or land. Thus, moist warm air is crucial to development of this type of storm. Recall that a mid-latitude cyclone develops when a small disturbance produces a wave-like kink in a previously linear front. A similar mechanism initiates a tropical cyclone. In late summer, the Sun warms tropical air. The rising hot air creates a belt of low pressure that encircles the globe over the tropics. In addition, many local low-pressure disturbances move across the tropical oceans at this time of year. If a local disturbance intersects the global tropical low, it creates a bulge in the isobars. Winds are deflected by the bulge and, directed by the Coriolis effect, begin to spiral inward. Warm, moist air rises from the low. Water vapor condenses from the rising air, and the latent heat warms the air further, which causes even more air to rise. As the low pressure becomes more intense, strong surface winds blow inward to replace the rising air. This surface air also rises, and more condensation and precipitation occur. But the additional condensation releases more heat, which continues to add energy to the storm.

The center of the storm is a region of vertical airflow, called the eye. In the outer, and larger part of the eye, the air that has been rushing inward spirals upward. In the inner eye, air sinks. Thus, the horizontal wind speed in the eye is reduced to near zero (Figure 19.35). Survivors who have been in the eye of a hurricane report an eerie calm. Rain stops, and the Sun may even shine weakly through scattered clouds. But this is only a momentary reprieve. A typical eye is only 20 kilometers in diameter, and after it passes the hurricane rages again in full intensity.

Once a hurricane develops, it is powered by the latent heat released by continuing condensation. The entire storm is pushed by prevailing winds, and its path is deflected by the Coriolis effect. It dissipates after it reaches land or passes over colder water because the supply of moist, warm air is cut off. Condensing water vapor in a single tropical cyclone releases as much latent heat energy as that produced by all the electric generators in the United States in a six month period.

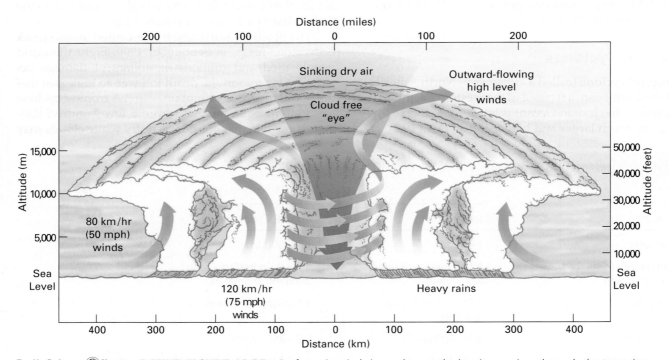

Earth Science ⊛ **Now**™ **ACTIVE FIGURE 19.35** Surface air spirals inward toward a hurricane, rises through the towering wall of clouds, and then flows outward above the storm. Falling air near the storm's center creates the eerie calm in the eye of the hurricane.

TABLE 19.3 Damage Normalized to 1995 Dollars, Caused by the Ten Most Destructive Hurricanes in United States History

Rank	Hurricane	Year	Category	Damage (billion $)
1.	SE Florida, Alabama	1926	4	$72.303
2.	*Andrew* (SE Florida, Louisiana)	1992	4	$33.094
3.	SW Florida	1944	3	$16.864
4.	New England	1938	3	$16.629
5.	SE Florida, Lake Okeechobee	1928	4	$13.795
6.	*Betsy* (SE Florida, Louisiana)	1965	3	$12.434
7.	*Donna* (Florida, E. United States)	1960	4	$12.048
8.	*Camille* (Mississippi, Louisiana, Virginia)	1969	5	$10.965
9.	*Agnes* (NW Florida, NE United States)	1972	1	$10.705
10.	*Diane* (NE United States)	1955	1	$10.232

Source: National Center for Atmospheric Research

TABLE 19.4 The Saffir–Simpson Hurricane Damage Potential Scale

Type	Category	Damage	Pressure (millibar)	Winds (km/h)	Storm surge (m)
Depression				>56	
Tropical Storm				63–117	
Hurricane	1	minimal	980	119–152	1.2–1.5
Hurricane	2	moderate	965–979	154–179	1.8–2.4
Hurricane	3	extensive	945–964	179–209	2.7–3.7
Hurricane	4	extreme	920–944	211–249	4–5.5
Hurricane	5	catastrophic	<920	>249	>5.5

Tropical Cyclones in the United States

Three tropical cyclones, or hurricanes, that struck the United States between 1989 and 1995, Opal (1995), Andrew (1992), and Hugo (1989), caused a total of more than $40 billion in damage. The record-high dollar value of damage from these and other recent hurricanes has led a variety of sources, ranging from *Newsweek* magazine to the United States Senate, to link global warming to increasing hurricane damage.

However, a recent study[1] indicates that hurricane frequency and intensity have actually been lower during the past decade than the average for the past century. The increased dollar value of damage occurred because: (1) More Americans lived near the Atlantic and Gulf coasts in the late 1990s than earlier in the century; (2) Inflation increased the dollar value of homes and other structures; and (3) Americans now own more things than ever before and consequently, the dollar value of their possessions is at an all-time high.

[1] Roger Pielke and Christopher Landsea, "Normalized Hurricane Damage in the United States: 1925–1995," *Proceedings of the Twenty-Second Conference on Hurricanes and Tropical Meteorology,* American Meteorological Society, May 1997.

The results show that Andrew was not the most damaging hurricane in history. An unnamed tropical cyclone that struck Florida and Alabama in 1926 would have more than doubled Andrew's monetary damage if it had occurred in 1995. Table 19.3 shows the top ten most destructive hurricanes, normalized to 1995 dollars by population increase, inflation, and personal property increases.

This study indicates that, although the non-normalized dollar value of damage done by tropical cyclones during the past decade reached a record high, the high-dollar value resulted from cultural changes. In fact, the frequency and intensity of hurricanes during that time was lower than normal. Americans living in Florida and Gulf Coast coastal areas should expect even greater financial losses when the frequency and intensity of tropical cyclones returns to normal. Some meteorologists predict that it is only a matter of time before a single $50 billion hurricane strikes Florida or the Gulf Coast.

The numerical "category" of tropical cyclones given in Table 19.3 is based on a rating scheme called the Saffir–Simpson scale, after its developers (Table 19.4). This scale, commonly mentioned in weather reports, rates the damage potential of a hurricane or other tropical storm, and typical values of atmospheric pressure, wind speed, and height of storm surge associated with storms of increasing intensity.

19.11 El Niño

Hurricanes are common in the southeastern United States and on the Gulf Coast, but they rarely strike California. Consequently, Californians were taken by surprise in late September of 1997 when Hurricane Nora ravaged Baja California and then, somewhat diminished by landfall, struck San Diego and Los Angeles. The storm brought the first rain to Los Angeles after a record 219 days of drought, then spread eastward to flood parts of Arizona where it caused the evacuation of 1000 people.

Other parts of the world also experienced unusual weather during the autumn of 1997. In Indonesia and Malaysia, fall monsoon rains normally douse fires intentionally set in late summer to clear the rainforest. The rains were delayed for two months in 1997, and, as a result, the fires raged out of control, filling cities with such dense smoke that visibility at times was no more than a few meters. Even an airliner crash was attributed to the smoke. Severe drought in nearby Australia caused ranchers to slaughter entire herds of cattle for

lack of water and feed. At the same time, far fewer hurricanes than usual threatened Florida and the U.S. Gulf Coast. Floods soaked northern Chile's Atacama Desert, a region that commonly receives no rain at all for a decade at a time, record snowfalls blanketed the Andes, and heavy rains caused floods in Peru and Ecuador.

All of these weather anomalies have been attributed to **El Niño,** an ocean current that brings unusually warm water to the west coast of South America. But the current does not flow every year; instead, it occurs about every 3 to 7 years, and its effects last for about a year before conditions return to normal. Although meteorologists paid little attention to the phenomenon until the El Niño year of 1982–83, many now think that El Niño affects weather patterns for nearly three quarters of the Earth.

Meteorologists first began recording El Niños in 1982–83, although they were known to Peruvian fishermen much earlier because they warm coastal waters and diminish fish harvests. The fishermen called the warming events "El Niño" because they commonly occur around Christmas, the birthday of El Niño—the Christ Child.

To understand the El Niño effects, first consider interactions between southern Pacific sea currents and weather in a normal, non-El Niño year (Figure 19.36). Normally in fall and winter, strong trade winds blow westward from South America across the Pacific Ocean. The winds drag the warm, tropical surface wa-

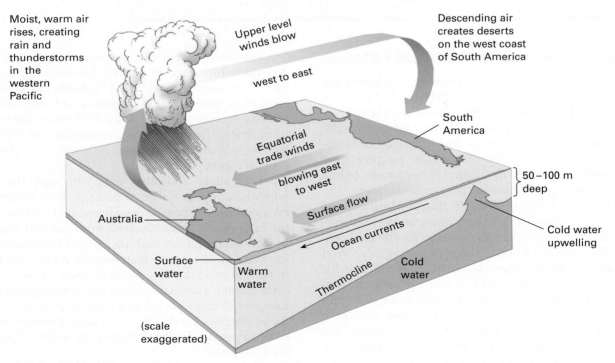

Figure 19.36 In a normal year, trade winds drag warm surface water westward across the Pacific and pile it up in a low mound near Indonesia and Australia, where the warm water causes rain. The surface flow creates upwelling of cold, deep, nutrient-rich waters along the coast of South America.

ter away from Peru and Chile, and pile it up in the western Pacific near Indonesia and Australia. In the western Pacific, the warm water forms a low mound thousands of kilometers across. The water is up to 10°C warmer and as much as 60 centimeters higher than the surface of the ocean near Peru and Chile.

As the wind-driven surface water flows away from the South American coast, cold, nutrient-rich water rises from the depths to replace the surface water. The nutrients support a thriving fishing industry along the coasts of Peru and Chile.

Abundant moisture evaporates from the surface of a warm ocean. In a normal year, much of this water condenses to bring rain to Australia, Indonesia, and other lands in the southwestern Pacific, which are adjacent to the mound of warm water. On the eastern side of the Pacific, the cold upwelling ocean currents cool the air above the coasts of Peru and northern Chile. This cool air becomes warmer as it flows over land. The warming lowers the relative humidity and creates the coastal Atacama Desert.

In an El Niño year, for reasons poorly understood by meteorologists, the trade winds slacken (Figure 19.37). The mound of warm water near Indonesia and Australia then flows downslope—eastward across the Pacific Ocean toward Peru and Chile. The anomalous accumulation of warm water off South America causes unusual rains in normally dry coastal regions,

and heavy snowfall in the Andes. At the same time, the cooler water near Indonesia, Australia, and nearby regions causes drought. The mass of warm water that caused the 1997−98 El Niño was about the size of the United States, and caused one of the strongest El Niño weather disturbances in history.

El Niño has global effects that go far beyond regional rainfall patterns. For example, El Niño deflects the jet stream from its normal path as it flows over North America, directing one branch northward over Canada, and the other across southern California and Arizona. Consequently, those regions receive more winter precipitation and storms than usual, while fewer storms and warmer winter temperatures affect the Pacific Northwest, the northern plains, the Ohio River valley, the mid-Atlantic states, and New England. Southern Africa experiences drought, while Ecuador, Peru, Chile, southern Brazil, and Argentina receive more rain than usual.

Altered weather patterns created by El Niño wreak havoc. Globally, 2000 deaths and more than $13 billion in damage are attributed to the 1982−83 El Niño effects. In the United States alone, more than 160 deaths and $2 billion in damage, mostly from storm and flood damage, occurred. In southern Africa, economic losses of $1 billion and uncounted deaths due to disease and starvation have been attributed to the 1982−83 El Niño.

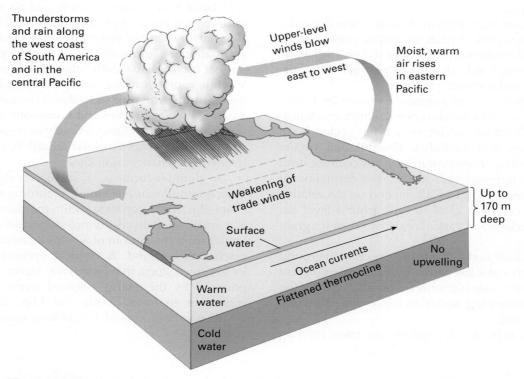

Figure 19.37 In an El Niño year, the trade winds slacken and the warm water flows eastward toward South America, causing the storms and rain to move over South America, and diminishing the upwelling currents.

Summary

Absolute humidity is the mass of water vapor in a given volume of air. **Relative humidity** is the amount of water vapor in air compared to the amount the air could hold at that temperature. Condensation occurs when moist air becomes **saturated** because it cools below its **dew point.** Air becomes **supersaturated** when water remains vapor at a temperature below the dew point. Similarly, **supercooled** water remains liquid below its freezing point.

Three atmospheric processes cool air to its dew point and cause condensation: (1) radiation, (2) contact with a cool surface, and (3) adiabatic cooling of rising air. Dew, frost, and some types of fog form by radiation and contact cooling. However, clouds and precipitation normally form as a result of the cooling that occurs when air rises.

When warm air rises, it performs work and therefore cools **adiabatically.** The **dry adiabatic lapse rate** is the cooling rate of rising dry air. The **wet adiabatic lapse rate** is the cooling rate of moist air after condensation has begun. Sinking air becomes warmer because of adiabatic compression.

A cloud is a visible concentration of water droplets or ice crystals in air. Almost all cloud formation and precipitation occur when air rises. Three mechanisms cause air to rise: **convection, orographic lifting,** and **frontal wedging.**

As moist air rises, initially it cools at the dry adiabatic lapse rate. Once it cools to its dew point, clouds form. Then, it cools more slowly at the wet adiabatic lapse rate. As a result, it remains warmer than surrounding air and continues to rise.

The characteristics of a cloud depend on the height to which air rises and the elevation at which condensation occurs. The three fundamental types of clouds are **cirrus, stratus,** and **cumulus.** Precipitation occurs when small water droplets or ice crystals coalesce until they become large enough to fall. The formation of rain, snow, **sleet,** and **glaze** all depend on the relative temperature of upper level air and ground level air. **Hail** forms as layers of vapor condense on an ice grain in a cloud.

Fog is a cloud that forms at or very close to ground level although most fog forms by processes different from those that create higher-level clouds. Types of fog include: **advection fog, radiation fog, evaporation fog,** and **upslope fog.**

When air is heated, it expands and rises, creating low pressure. Cool air sinks, exerting a downward force and forming high-pressure. Uneven heating of the Earth's surface causes pressure differences which, in turn cause **wind.** Wind speed is determined by the **pressure gradient.** Winds are deflected by the Coriolis effect. **Jet streams** are high altitude winds that move rapidly because they are not slowed by friction with the Earth.

Cyclones and **anticyclones** are low-pressure and high-pressure zones, respectively. Winds spiral into a cyclone, and outward from an anticyclone.

When air is heated, it expands and rises, creating low pressure. The rising air cools adiabatically often causing cloud formation and precipitation. Thus low barometric pressure is an indication of wet weather. Alternatively, when air is cooled, it sinks and the barometric pressure rises. This falling air is compressed and heated adiabatically. The sinking air absorbs moisture and clouds generally do not form over a high-pressure region. Thus fair, dry weather generally accompanies high pressure.

When two **air masses** collide, the warmer air rises along the **front,** forming clouds and often precipitation. A **warm front** forms when moving warm air collides with a stationary or slower moving cold air mass. Warm fronts often bring several days of wet weather. A **cold front** forms when moving cold air collides with stationary or slower moving warm air. Cold fronts create a narrow band of violent weather. **Occluded fronts** and **stationary fronts** also affect weather patterns.

Air cools adiabatically when it rises over a mountain range, often causing precipitation. A **rain-shadow desert** forms where air sinks down the leeward side of a mountain. Sea breezes and **monsoons** arise because ocean temperature changes slowly in response to daily and seasonal changes in solar radiation, whereas land temperature changes quickly.

A thunderstorm is a small, short-lived storm from a cumulonimbus cloud. Lightning occurs when charged particles separate within the cloud. A **tornado** is a small, short-lived, funnel-shaped storm that protrudes from the bottom of a cumulonimbus cloud and reaches the ground. A **tropical cyclone** is a larger, longer-lived storm that forms over warm oceans and is powered by the energy released when water vapor condenses to form clouds and rain. **El Niño** is a weather pattern caused by shifting motion of ocean currents.

Earth Systems Interactions

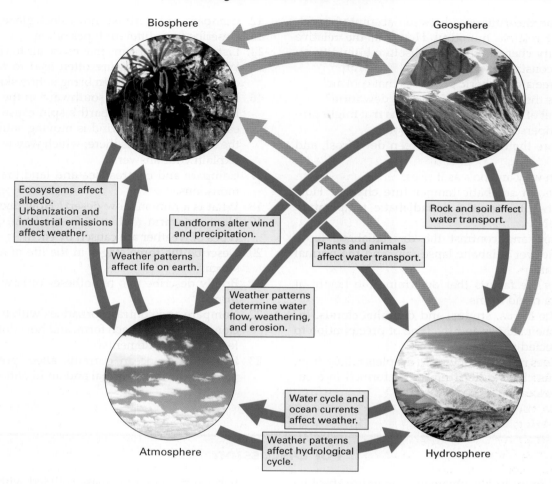

Biosphere

Geosphere

Ecosystems affect albedo. Urbanization and industrial emissions affect weather.

Landforms alter wind and precipitation.

Rock and soil affect water transport.

Weather patterns affect life on earth.

Plants and animals affect water transport.

Weather patterns determine water flow, weathering, and erosion.

Atmosphere

Water cycle and ocean currents affect weather.

Weather patterns affect hydrological cycle.

Hydrosphere

Key Terms

humidity 447
absolute humidity 447
relative humidity 447
saturation 447
dew point 447
supersaturation 448
supercooling 448
dew 448
frost 448
adiabatic temperature
    changes 448
dry adiabatic lapse
    rate 449
wet adiabatic lapse
    rate 449
orographic lifting 450

frontal wedging 450
convection-
    convergence 450
normal lapse rate 451
atmospheric inversion 452
temperature inversion 452
unstable air 452
stable air 452
cirrus cloud 453
stratus cloud 454
cumulus cloud 454
stratocumulus
    cloud 454
cumulonimbus
    cloud 455
nimbostratus cloud 455

altostratus cloud 455
sleet 455
glaze 455
hail 456
advection fog 456
radiation fog 456
evaporation fog 456
upslope fog 456
wind 457
pressure gradient 457
isobar 457
jet stream 460
cyclone 460
anticyclone 460
air mass 462
front 462

warm front 462
cold front 462
occluded front 464
stationary front 464
storm tracks 465
rain-shadow desert 466
monsoon 467
wind shear 469
tornado 470
tropical cyclone 471
storm surge 471
El Niño 474

For Review

1. Describe the difference between absolute humidity and relative humidity. How can the relative humidity change while the absolute humidity remains constant?
2. List three atmospheric processes that cool air.
3. What is the dew point? How does dew form?
4. List a set of atmospheric conditions that might produce supersaturation or supercooling.
5. What are the differences between dew, frost, and fog?
6. Explain why air cools as it rises.
7. What is an adiabatic temperature change? How does it differ from a nonadiabatic temperature change?
8. Compare and contrast the dry adiabatic lapse rate, the wet adiabatic lapse rate, and the normal lapse rate.
9. Discuss the factors that determine the height at which a cloud forms.
10. Describe cirrus, stratus, and cumulus clouds. Include their shapes and the type of precipitation to be expected from each.
11. How does rain form? How do droplets falling from a stratus cloud differ from those formed in a cumulus cloud?
12. Compare and contrast snow, sleet, glaze, and hail.
13. Describe four different types of fog.
14. List three mechanisms that cause air to rise.
15. Why does low pressure often lead to rain? Why does high pressure often bring sunny skies?
16. If the wind is blowing southward in the Northern Hemisphere, will the Earth's spin cause it to veer east or west? If the wind is moving southward in the Southern Hemisphere, which way will it veer? Explain your answer.
17. Compare and contrast sea and land breezes with monsoons.
18. What is a rain-shadow desert? How does it form?
19. How do warm and cold fronts form, and what types of weather are caused by each?
20. Describe the three stages in the life of a thunderstorm.
21. Briefly describe two hypotheses of how lightning forms.
22. Compare and contrast tornadoes with tropical cyclones. How does each form, and how does each affect human settlements?
23. Explain how ocean currents affect precipitation patterns during a normal and an El Niño year.

For Discussion

1. Using Figure 19.1, estimate the maximum absolute humidity at 0°C, 10°C, 20°C, and 40°C. Estimate the quantity of water in air, at 50 percent relative humidity, at each of the above temperatures.
2. Explain why frost forms on the inside of a refrigerator (assuming it is an old-fashioned one and not a modern frost-free unit). Would more frost tend to form in (a) summer or winter, and (b) in a dry desert region or a humid one? Explain.
3. Which of the following conditions produces frost? Which produces dew? Explain. (a) A constant temperature throughout the day. (b) A warm summer day followed by a cool night. (c) A cool fall afternoon followed by freezing temperature at night.
4. Draw a chart showing temperatures at cloud level, between the cloud and the ground, and at ground level that will cause condensing water vapor to fall as rain, snow, sleet, and glaze.
5. What is the energy source that powers the wind?
6. Are sea breezes more likely to be strong on an overcast day or on a bright sunny one? Explain.
7. What is an air mass? Describe what would likely happen if a polar air mass collided with a humid subtropical air mass.
8. Study the weather map in today's newspaper, and predict the weather two days from now in your area, Salt Lake City, Chicago, and New York City. Defend your prediction. Check the paper in two days to see if you were right or wrong.
9. Compare the annual precipitation in the place where you live with precipitation patterns in adjacent regions at the same latitude. Explain any differences you observe.
10. Give an example of how the geosphere, the hydrosphere, and the biosphere affect, and are affected by weather.

Earth Science ⊕ Now™

Assess your understanding of this chapter's topics with additional quizzing and comprehensive interactivities at **http://earthscience.brookscole.com/earthsci3e** as well as current and up-to-date weblinks, additional readings, and InfoTrac College Edition exercises.

Chapter 21

Climate Change

© Ron Watts/CORBIS

Climate change has occurred through Earth history and continues to occur today. In recent decades, many plants, animals, and people have died as a result of intense drought in the Sahel of North Africa.

In March 2000, an 11,000-square kilometer iceberg as large as the state of Connecticut broke free from the Ross Ice Shelf in Antarctica and drifted north, where it melted in warmer water. Two months later, a massive chunk of ice cracked off the nearby Ronne Ice Shelf. In September, a second Connecticut-sized chunk of the Ross Ice Shelf disintegrated. Then in January of 2002, a Rhode Island-sized section of the Larsen Ice Shelf splintered into millions of small fragments (Figure 21.1). Since the height of the last Ice Age, 18,000 years ago, the Ross Ice Shelf has receded 700 kilometers, shedding 5.3 million cubic kilometers of ice. And, as evidenced by the recent disintegration, the process continues to this day.

During the past 100 years, the average temperature of the Earth's atmosphere has risen by about 0.6°C. It is tempting to make the seemingly obvious conclusion that warm air has melted sections of the Antarctic ice, causing ice-shelf collapse. But this conclusion may not be correct. The Earth's climate system is complicated by so many opposing processes, threshold effects, and feedback mechanisms that even the most obvious-seeming inferences must be scrutinized closely.

In order to have a balanced perspective on what is happening today, we must first study historical climate

January 31, 2002

Figure 21.1 The Larsen B ice shelf rims a small portion of the eastern coastline of the Antarctic Peninsula. Between January 31 and March 5 of 2002, 3250 square kilometers of ice, about the size of the state of Rhode Island, broke off the ice shelf and floated northward.

February 23, 2002

March 5, 2002

National Snow and Ice Data Center

change. The geological record in almost every locality on Earth provides evidence that past regional climates were different from modern climates. Geologists have discovered sand dunes beneath prairie grasslands near Denver, Colorado, indicating that this semiarid region was recently desert. Moraines on Long Island, New York, tell us that this temperate region was once glaciated. Fossil ferns in nearby Connecticut indicate that, before the glaciers, the northeastern United States was warm and wet.

Many of these regional climatic fluctuations resulted from global climate change. Thus, 18,000 years ago, the Earth was cooler than it is today and glaciers descended to lower latitudes and altitudes. During Mississippian time, from 360 to 325 million years ago, the Earth was warmer than it is today. Vegetation grew abundantly and some of it collected in huge swamps to form coal.

During the past 10,000 years, global climate has been mild and stable as compared with the preceding 100,000 years. During this time, humans have developed from widely separated bands of hunter-gatherers, to agrarian farmers, and then to crowded communities living in huge industrial megalopolises. Today, with a global population of over 6 billion, people have stressed the food-producing capabilities of the planet. If temperature or rainfall patterns were to change, even slightly, crop failures could lead to famines. In addition, cities and farmlands on low-lying coasts could be flooded under rising sea level. As a result, climate change may be one of the most important issues that we face in the twenty-first century.

Earth Science ⊕ Now™

This icon, appearing throughout the book, indicates an opportunity to explore interactive tutorials, animations, or practice problems available on the Earth ScienceNow Web site at **http://earthscience.brookscole.com/earthsci3e**

21.1 Climate Change in Earth History

Recall from Chapter 17 that the Earth's primordial atmosphere contained high concentrations of carbon dioxide (CO_2) and water vapor (H_2O). Both of these greenhouse gases absorb infrared radiation in the atmosphere. Astronomers have calculated that the Sun was 20 to 30 percent fainter early in Earth history than it is today. Yet oceans did not freeze. The high concentrations of atmospheric carbon dioxide and water vapor retained enough of the Sun's lesser radiation to warm Earth's atmosphere and surface to temperatures that kept the oceans liquid. Luckily for us, the concentration of carbon dioxide and water in the atmosphere declined gradually as the Sun warmed.

Figure 21.2 is a graph of mean global temperature and precipitation throughout Earth history. Note, for example, that the planet plunged into the deep-freeze on at least five occasions. There is evidence that the cold periods 700 to 600 million years ago were so extreme that the oceans froze from pole to pole, accompanied by near-total land coverage of glaciers, leading to a "Snowball Earth," described in Chapter 13. In contrast, our planet was relatively warm for 248 million years from the start of the Mesozoic era almost to the present. The last 2 million years have witnessed the most recent ice age. According to many climatologists, the current period is an interglacial warming episode and the ice sheets are likely to return in the geologically near future.

Many additional climate changes occurred during Earth history, but they were of too short a duration to be apparent on this graph. For example, ice core records from Greenland, Antarctica, and alpine glaciers show that between 110,000 and 10,000 years ago the mean annual global temperature changed frequently and dramatically. Figure 21.3 gives a close look at a portion of this temperature data. The graph shows that the atmospheric temperature in Greenland changed several times by 5 to 10°C within five to ten years. Many of the cold intervals persisted for 1000 years or more. As mentioned above, the past 10,000 years, during which civilization developed, witnessed anomalously stable climate.

Figure 21.4 gives us an even more detailed look at a 100-year span from 1880 to 2001. This time period encompasses recent times so the temperature data were largely obtained by direct measurement. In this small interval of time, the temperature has risen by 0.6°C.

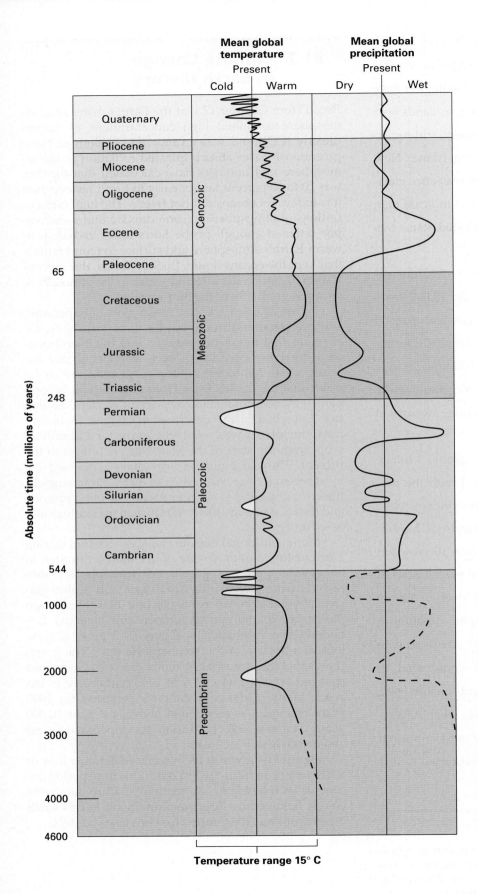

Figure 21.2 Mean global temperature and precipitation have both fluctuated throughout Earth history. *Source:* Redrawn from L. A. Frakes, *Climates throughout Geologic Time,* New York: Elsevier Scientific Publishing, 1989, 310 pages.

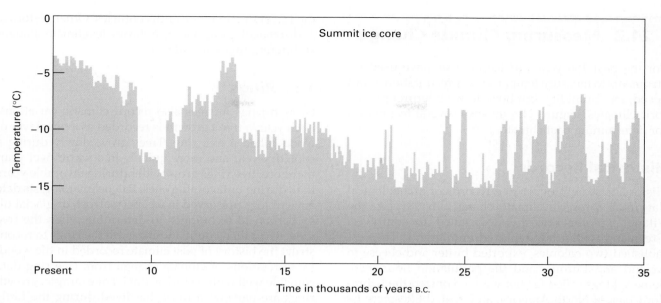

Figure 21.3 Atmospheric temperature fluctuations during the past 35,000 years in Greenland. The data were collected by the Greenland Ice Core Project.

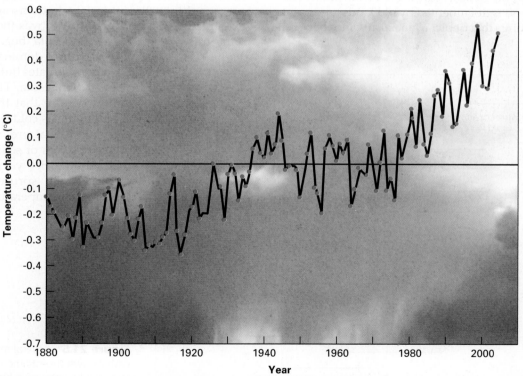

Figure 21.4 Mean global temperature changes from 1880 to 2002. The zero line represents the average from 1951 to 1980, and plus or minus values represent deviations from the average.

Interactive Question: Compare the magnitudes of some of the large temperature changes in Figure 21.3 with the temperature change shown in Figure 21.4. Discuss the comparative magnitudes of possible human-induced climate change during the past century with past examples of natural climate change.

21.2 Measuring Climate Change

For the past 100 years, meteorologists have used instruments to measure temperature, precipitation, wind speed, and humidity. But how do we interpret prehistoric climates? Figure 21.5 reviews several techniques for determining past climate.

Historical Records

Historians search for written records or archeological data that chronicle climate change. In 985 C.E. the Viking explorer Eric the Red sailed to southwest Greenland with a few hundred immigrants. They established two colonies, exported butter and cheese to Iceland and Europe, and the population flourished. Some Vikings sailed farther west, colonized the Labrador Coast of North America, and visited Ellesmere Island, near 80° north latitude. Then within three to four hundred years, the colonies vanished. Sagas tell of heavy sea ice in summer, crop failures, starvation, and death.

During the same time, European glaciers descended into lowland valleys. This period of global cooling, called the *Little Ice Age,* lasted from about 1450 to 1850 C.E., and is documented by old landscape paintings and writings that depict a glacial advance between the fifteenth and nineteenth centuries. Other historical and archaeological evidence chronicles climate changes at different times and places.

Tree Rings

Growth rings in trees also record climatic variations. Each year, a tree's growth is recorded as a new layer of wood called a tree ring. Trees grow slowly during a cool, dry year and more quickly in a warm, wet year; therefore, tree rings grow wider during favorable years than during unfavorable ones. Paleoclimatologists date ancient logs preserved in ice, permafrost, or glacial till by carbon-14 techniques to determine when the tree died. They then count and measure the rings to reconstruct the history of past climate recorded in the wood. Interpretations of climate change from tree ring data coincide well with historical data. For example, growth rings are narrow in trees that lived during the Little Ice Age.

Plant Pollen

Plant pollen is widely distributed by wind and is coated with a hard waxy cover that resists decomposition. As a result, pollen grains are abundant and well preserved in sediment in lake bottoms and bogs. For example, 11,000 years ago, spruce was the most abundant tree species in a Minnesota bog. In modern forests, spruce dominates in colder Canadian climates but is less abundant in Minnesota. Therefore, scientists deduce that the climate in Minnesota was colder 11,000 years ago than it is at present. Pollen in younger layers of sediment shows that about 10,500 years ago, pines displaced the spruce, indicating that the temperature became warmer.

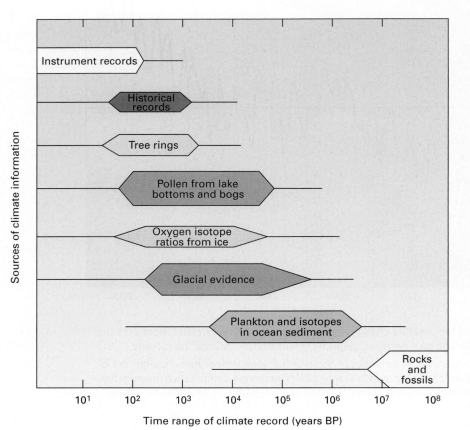

Figure 21.5 Several methods, each with its own useful time range, allow scientists to determine historical and ancient climates. *Source:* Adapted from T. Webb III, J. Kutzbach, and F. A. Street-Perrott in *Global Change,* T. F. Malone and J. D. Roederer, eds., pp. 212–218. Copyright 1985 by Cambridge University Press, U.K., with the permission of Cambridge University Press.

Figure 21.6 Scientists remove an ice core from a glacier in Greenland. Studies of ancient ice provide information about past climate.

Oxygen Isotope Ratios in Glacial Ice

Oxygen consists mainly of two isotopes, abundant ^{16}O and rare ^{18}O. Both isotopes are incorporated into water, H_2O. Water molecules containing ^{16}O are lighter and evaporate more easily than those containing ^{18}O. At high temperature, however, evaporating water vapor contains a higher proportion of ^{18}O than it does at lower temperatures. Therefore, the ratio of $^{18}O/^{16}O$ in vapor from warm water is higher than that from cool water. Some of the water vapor condenses as snow, which accumulates in glaciers. Thus the $^{18}O/^{16}O$ ratios in glacial ice reflect water temperature at the time the water evaporated. Because most of the atmospheric water vapor that falls as snow originated from evaporation of ocean water, scientists then use the $^{18}O/^{16}O$ data from glacial ice to estimate mean ocean surface temperatures. Because the sea surface and the atmosphere are in close contact, mean ocean surface temperature reflects mean global atmospheric temperature.

Geologists have drilled deep into Greenland and Antarctic glaciers, where the ice is up to 110,000 years old, and have carefully removed ice cores (Figure 21.6). The age of the ice at any depth is determined by counting annual ice deposition layers or by carbon-14 dating of windblown pollen within the glacier. The oxygen isotope ratios in each layer reflect the air temperature at the time the snow fell. The temperature data in Figure 21.3 were obtained from Greenland ice cores.

Glacial Evidence

Erosional and depositional features created by glaciers, such as the tills, tillites, and glacial striations described in Chapter 13, are evidence of the growth and retreat of alpine glaciers and ice sheets, which in turn reflect climate. The timing of recent glacial advances can be determined by several methods. One effective technique is carbon-14 dating of logs preserved in glacial till.

Plankton and Isotopes in Ocean Sediment

In a technique that parallels pollen studies, scientists estimate climate by studying fossils in deep sea sediment. The dominant life forms in the ocean are microscopic plankton that float near the sea surface. Just as pollen ratios change with air temperature, plankton species ratios change with sea surface temperature. Thus, fossil plankton assemblages found in sediment cores reflect sea surface temperature.

Most hard tissues formed by animals and plants, such as shells, exoskeletons, teeth, and bone contain oxygen. Many organisms absorb a high ratio of $^{18}O/^{16}O$ at low temperatures, but the ratio decreases with increasing temperature. For example, foraminifera are tiny marine organisms. During a time of Pleistocene cooling and glacial growth, their shells contain an average of 2 percent more ^{18}O than similar shells formed during a warm interglacial interval. Thus, just as scientists estimate paleoclimate by measuring oxygen isotope ratios in glacial ice, they can estimate ancient climate by measuring oxygen isotope ratios in fossil corals, plankton, teeth, and the remains of other organisms. Oxygen is also incorporated into soil minerals so isotope ratios in soil and sea-floor sediment also reflect paleoclimate.

The Rock and Fossil Record

Fossils are abundant in many sedimentary rocks of Cambrian age and younger. Geologists can approximate climate in ancient ecosystems by comparing fossils with modern relatives of the ancient organisms (Figure 21.7). For example, modern coral reefs grow only in tropical water. Therefore, we infer that fossil reefs also formed in the tropics. Coal deposits and ferns formed in moist tropical environments; cactus indicate that the region was once desert.

Looking backward even farther—into the Proterozoic era, before life became abundant—it is difficult to measure climate with fossils. Thus, geologists search for clues in rocks. Tillite is a sedimentary rock formed from glacial debris, and thus indicates a cold climate. Lithified dunes formed in deserts or along coasts.

Sedimentary rocks form in water, so their existence tells us that the temperature was above freezing and below boiling. Carbonate rocks precipitate from carbon dioxide dissolved in sea water. Geochemists know the chemical conditions under which carbon dioxide dissolves and precipitates, so they can calculate a range of atmospheric and oceanic compositions and temperatures that would have produced limestone and other carbonate rocks. Most thick limestones formed in warm, shallow seas. Some ancient mineral deposits such as the banded iron deposits described in Chapter 17 also reflect the chemistry of the ancient atmosphere.

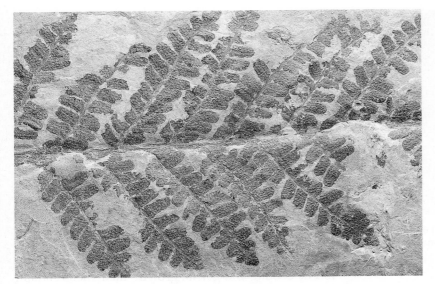

A

B

Figure 21.7 (A) A fossil fern indicated that a region was wet and warm at the time the fern grew. (B) These fossil sand dune cross-beds indicate that this region was dry at the time the dunes formed.

After scientists learned that climates have changed, they began to search further to understand how climates change. In the following four sections, we will discuss natural mechanisms of climate change. The final three sections will focus on climate change caused by humans, and its possible consequences:

21.3 Astronomical Causes of Climate Change

Recall from Chapter 13 that variations in the Earth's orbit and rotational pattern may have caused the climate fluctuations responsible for the glacial advances and retreats of the Pleistocene Ice Age. Other astronomical factors may also cause climate change.

Changes in Solar Radiation

A star the size of our Sun produces energy by hydrogen fusion for about 10 billion years. During this time, its energy output increases slowly. As mentioned above, solar output has increased by 20 to 30 percent during Earth history. This slow evolution has influenced climate over long expanses of geologic time. Fortunately for us, the atmospheric carbon dioxide concentration was high during the Earth's early history, so temperature was relatively warm even though solar output was low.

Within the past few hundred million years, solar output has changed by only one fifty-millionth of one percent per century and therefore the variation had no measurable influence on climate change over thousands to even millions of years. Over shorter periods of time, solar magnetic storms, sunspots, and anomalous variations cause fluctuations in solar output that may affect the Earth's climate. Magnetic storms on the Sun create dark, cool regions on the solar surface called sunspots. Sunspot activity alternates dramatically on an 11-year cycle and on longer cycles spanning hundreds of years. During periods of high sunspot activity, the Sun is slightly cooler than during periods of low activity. Several studies show that changes in global temperatures coincide with changes in sunspot activity (Figure 21.8). Critics argue that the correlation must be a statistical coincidence because differences in solar output resulting from sunspot cycles are too small to alter the Earth's temperature. Proponents counter that a feedback mechanism must be involved. Perhaps changes in solar radiation affect the stratospheric ozone concentration, which alters heat transfer mechanisms between the stratosphere and the troposphere. The issue remains unresolved.

In March, 2003, Richard Wilson of Columbia University reported that over the past 24 years solar output has increased by 0.05 percent per decade. He further claims that this increase could account for the current warming trend. This issue will be discussed further in section 21.7.

Bolide Impacts

Recall that the evidence strongly suggests that a bolide crashed to Earth about 65 million years ago. The impact blasted enough rock and dust into the sky to block out sunlight and cool the planet. According to one current hypothesis, this cooling led to the extinction of the dinosaurs. Other bolide impacts may have caused rapid and catastrophic climate changes throughout Earth history.

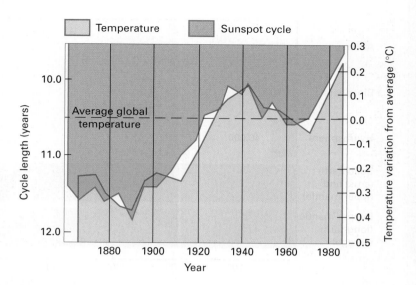

Figure 21.8 Times of maximum sunspot abundance (blue curve) correlate closely to mean global atmospheric temperature (brown curve) between 1860 and 1990. Global temperature is expressed as change from the average annual temperature in the years 1951 to 1980. *Source:* E. Friis-Christensen and K. Lassen, "Length of the Solar Cycle: An Indicator of Solar Activity Closely Associated with Climate," *Science* 254, Nov. 1, 1991, 698f.

21.4 Water and Climate

Recall that water is abundant in all four Earth spheres. It occurs in rocks and soil of the geosphere, comprises over 90 percent of the living organisms of the biosphere, constitutes essentially the entire hydrosphere, and exists in the atmosphere as vapor, liquid droplets, and solid crystals of snow and ice. Moreover, water moves freely from one system to another. As a result, "water acts as the venetian blind of our planet, as its central heating system, and as its refrigerator, all at the same time."[1] We have already discussed many of the components of the complex and often conflicting relationship between water and climate. As a brief review:

- Water vapor is the most abundant greenhouse gas. Thus it warms the atmosphere and the Earth's surface.
- Clouds reflect sunlight and therefore cool the atmosphere and the Earth's surface. But clouds also absorb heat radiating from the Earth's surface. Thus, water in the atmosphere causes both warming and cooling.
- Glaciers and snowfields have a high albedo (80 to 90 percent); they reflect sunlight and also cool the Earth's climate. On the other hand, surface water has a very low albedo, only about 5 percent. As a result, any change from surface water to glaciers, or vice versa can have dramatic effect on the planet's albedo and temperature.
- When water evaporates from the ocean surface, solar energy is stored as latent heat of the resultant vapor. The vapor moves vast distances, transporting this heat. The heat is then released when the water vapor condenses to form rain or snow.

- Similarly, heat is released when water freezes to form snow and ice. But once a glacier forms or a portion of the Earth's surface is snow-covered, a lot of heat is required to melt the ice.
- Flowing water weathers rocks and initiates chemical reactions that alter the carbon dioxide concentration in the atmosphere. Carbon dioxide is a greenhouse gas that warms the Earth's surface.
- Ocean currents move heat to and from the polar regions. But, because more currents flow from the equator toward the poles than the other way around, there is a net transport of heat toward the polar regions. This polar warming effect is counterbalanced by the fact that currents also transport moisture. When the moisture falls as snow, the increased albedo cools the polar regions.

Climate models attempt to quantify all of these factors, but clearly the balances are delicate to unravel. For this reason, it is difficult to predict climate changes.

21.5 The Natural Carbon Cycle and Climate

Carbon circulates among the atmosphere, the hydrosphere, the biosphere, and the geosphere and is stored in each of these reservoirs (Figure 21.9).

Carbon in the Atmosphere

As explained in Chapter 17, oxygen and nitrogen, the most abundant gases in the atmosphere, are transparent to infrared radiation and are not greenhouse gases. Carbon exists in the atmosphere mostly as carbon dioxide (CO_2), and in smaller amounts as methane (CH_4). Although only 0.1 percent of the total carbon near the Earth's surface is in the atmosphere, this reservoir

[1] Thomas Karl, Neville Nichols, and Jonathan Gregory, "The Coming Climate," *Scientific American* (May 1997): 79ff.

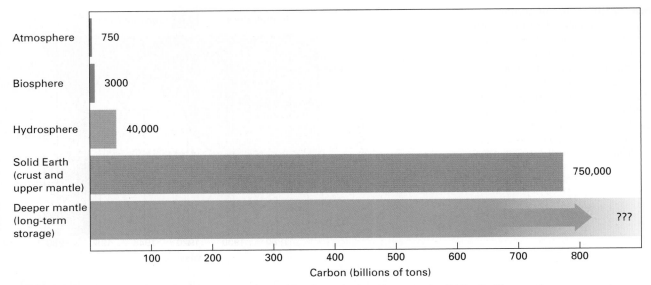

Figure 21.9 Carbon reservoirs in the atmosphere, biosphere, hydrosphere, and solid Earth. The numbers represent billions of tons of carbon. *Source:* Wilfred M. Post et al., "The Global Carbon Cycle." *The American Scientist,* 78, July–August 1990, p. 310.

Interactive Question: How would the amount of carbon in the atmosphere be affected if 1 percent of the carbon dissolved in sea water were released into the atmosphere?

plays an important role in controlling atmospheric temperature because carbon dioxide and methane are greenhouse gases; they absorb infrared radiation and heat the lower atmosphere. If either of these compounds is removed from the atmosphere, the atmosphere cools; if they are released into the atmosphere, the air becomes warmer.

Carbon in the Biosphere

Carbon is the fundamental building block for all organic tissue. Plants extract carbon dioxide from the atmosphere and build their body parts predominantly of carbon. This process occurs both on land and in the sea. Most of the aquatic fixation of carbon is conducted by microscopic photoplankton. Therefore, healthy terrestrial and aquatic ecosystems play a vital role in removing carbon from the atmosphere.

Most of the carbon is released back into the atmosphere by natural processes, such as respiration, fire, or rotting (Figure 21.10). However at certain times and places, organic material does not decompose completely and is stored as fossil fuels—coal, oil, and gas (see Chapter 5). Thus, plants transfer carbon from the biosphere to rocks of the upper crust.

Carbon in the Hydrosphere

Carbon dioxide dissolves in sea water. Most of it then reacts to form bicarbonate, HCO_3^- (commonly found in your kitchen as baking soda or bicarbonate of soda), and carbonate $(CO_3)^{2-}$.

The amount of carbon dioxide dissolved in the oceans depends in part on the temperature of the atmosphere and the oceans. When sea water warms, it releases dissolved carbon dioxide into the atmosphere, causing greenhouse warming. In turn, greenhouse warming further heats the oceans, causing more carbon dioxide to escape. Warmth evaporates sea water as well, and water vapor also absorbs infrared radiation. Clearly, such a feedback mechanism can escalate. A runaway greenhouse effect may be responsible for the high temperature on Venus.

Carbon in the Crust and Upper Mantle

As shown in Figure 21.9, the atmosphere contains about 750 billion tons of carbon. In contrast, the crust and upper mantle contain 1,000 times as much, or 750 trillion tons of carbon. The upper geosphere, combined with the hydrosphere, and biosphere contain almost 800 trillion tons of carbon. Thus, if only a minute portion of the carbon in the geosphere, hydrosphere, and biosphere is released, the atmospheric concentration of carbon dioxide can change dramatically, with a draconian effect on climate.

Carbonate Rocks

Marine organisms absorb calcium and carbonate ions from sea water and convert them into calcium carbonate $(CaCO_3)$ in shells and other hard parts. This process removes carbon from sea water and causes more atmospheric carbon dioxide to dissolve into the sea water. Thus, formation of shells removes carbon dioxide from

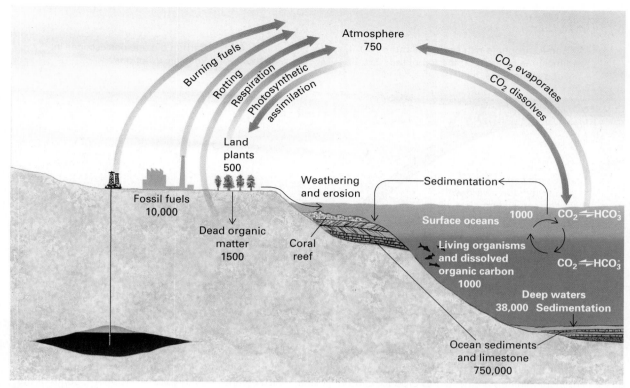

Figure 21.10 The carbon cycle. The numbers show the size of the reservoirs and represent billions of tons of carbon.
Source: Data taken from U. Siegenthaler and J. L. Sarmiento, "Atmospheric Carbon Dioxide and the Ocean." *Nature,* 365, September 9, 1993, p. 119.

the atmosphere. The shells and skeletons of these organisms gradually collect to form limestone.

When sea level falls or tectonic processes raise portions of the sea floor above sea level, limestone and silicate rocks weather by processes that extract additional carbon dioxide from the atmosphere.[2]

Carbon in Fossil Fuels

Carbon is stored in fossil fuels and carbon dioxide is released when these fuels are burned. Recoverable fossil fuels contain about 4 trillion tons of carbon, five times the amount in the atmosphere today. For this reason, scientists are concerned that burning fossil fuels will raise atmospheric carbon dioxide levels. This topic is discussed in Section 21.5.

Methane in Sea-Floor Sediment

When organic material falls to the sea floor and is buried with mud, bacteria decompose it, releasing methane, commonly called natural gas. Between a depth of about 500 meters and 1 kilometer the temperature of water-saturated mud on continental shelves is

[2]The complete reaction is

$$CaCO_3 + CO_2 + H_2O \rightarrow Ca(HCO_3)_2$$

limestone   carbon dioxide   water   calcium bicarbonate (soluble)

low enough and the pressure is favorable to convert methane gas to a frozen solid called methane hydrate. Methane hydrate then gradually collects in mud on the continental shelves. After studying both drill samples and seismic data, geochemist Keith Kvenvolden of the United States Geological Survey estimates that methane hydrate deposits hold twice as much carbon as all conventional fossil fuels—10 times more than is in the atmosphere.

At present, commercial extraction of methane hydrates to produce natural gas is impractical. It is expensive to drill in deep water, and a thin layer spread throughout the continental shelves would be prohibitively expensive to exploit. However, scientists are studying links between methane hydrates and climate. Tectonic activity at subduction zones or landslides on continental slopes could release methane from hydrate deposits. Changes in bottom temperatures on continental shelves resulting from warming of sea water could also release methane from the frozen hydrates. In turn, increased atmospheric methane could trigger greenhouse warming. Ice core studies show that global atmospheric methane concentration has changed rapidly in the past, perhaps by sudden releases of oceanic methane hydrates.

About 55 million years ago, near the end of the Paleocene epoch, climate suddenly warmed and many

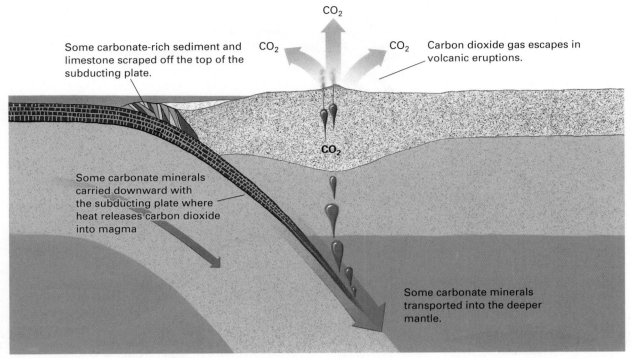

Figure 21.11 A subducting oceanic plate carries limestone and other carbonate-rich sediment into the mantle. Some of the carbonate minerals are heated to produce carbon dioxide, which escapes during volcanic eruptions. Some of the carbonate minerals may be stored in the mantle.

Labels in figure:
Some carbonate-rich sediment and limestone scraped off the top of the subducting plate.

CO_2 Carbon dioxide gas escapes in volcanic eruptions.

Some carbonate minerals carried downward with the subducting plate where heat releases carbon dioxide into magma

Some carbonate minerals transported into the deeper mantle.

aquatic and terrestrial species became extinct. According to one model, a change in sea surface circulation caused equatorial waters to remain in low latitudes. High equatorial temperatures evaporated enough water to increase the salinity of the sea surface. When the salinity reached a threshold value where the surface water was denser than the cold deep water, the warm, salty water sank. The warm, sinking water melted the methane hydrates and released the methane. Aquatic species were poisoned by the methane in the water and many terrestrial species succumbed to the rapid greenhouse warming.[3]

Carbon in the Deeper Mantle

During subduction, oceanic crust sinks into the mantle (Figure 21.11). The descending plate may carry carbonate rocks and sediment. As this material sinks to greater depths, the carbonate minerals become hot and release carbon dioxide, which is carried back to the surface by volcanic eruptions. Some carbonate rock may be carried into deeper regions of the mantle during subduction, although geologists are uncertain how much. Large quantities of carbon were trapped within the Earth during its formation. Much of this carbon escaped early in Earth History, but some remains in the deep mantle and may rise from the mantle to the surface during volcanic eruptions. Carbon exchanges between the deep mantle and the surface are an important topic of current research.

21.6 Tectonics and Climate Change

Positions of the Continents

A map of Pangea shows that 200 million years ago, Africa, South America, India, and Australia were all clustered near the South Pole (Figure 21.12). Because climate is colder at high latitudes than near the equator, continental position alters continental climate.

In addition, continental interiors generally experience colder winters and hotter summers than coastal areas. When all the continents were joined into a supercontinent, the continental interior was huge, and regional climates were different from the climates on many smaller continents with extensive coastlines.

The positions of the continents also influence wind and sea currents, which, in turn, affect climate. For example, today the Arctic Ocean is nearly landlocked, with three straits connecting it with the Atlantic and Pacific Oceans (Figure 21.13). The Bering Strait between Alaska and Siberia is 80 kilometers across, Kennedy Channel between Ellesmere and Greenland is only 40 kilometers across, and a third, wider seaway

[3]Gerald Dickens et al., "A Blast of Gas in the Latest Paleocene; Simulating First-Order Effects of Massive Dissociation of Oceanic Methane Hydrate," *Geology* (March 1997): 259–262.

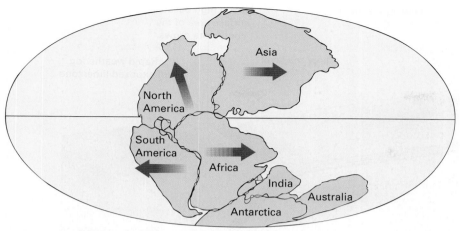

Earth Science ⊕Now™ **ACTIVE FIGURE 21.12** Two hundred million years ago, when the Pangea supercontinent was assembled, Africa, South America, India, and Australia were all positioned close to the South Pole.

NASA/JPL

Figure 21.13 With the modern distribution of continents, the Arctic Ocean is nearly landlocked. Most of this sea water is covered with ice for most of the year, as indicated by the white zone in this photograph. When the continents move sufficiently to open or close the narrow straits connecting the Arctic Ocean to more southern waters, currents and global heat transfer will be affected.

runs along the east coast of Greenland. Presently, cold currents run southward through Kennedy Channel and the Bering Strait, and the North Atlantic drift carries warm water northward along the coast of Norway. If any of these straits were to widen or close, global heat transfer would be affected. Deep-sea currents also transport heat and are affected by continental positions.

Tectonic plates move from 1 to 16 centimeters per year. A plate that moves 5 centimeters per year travels 50 kilometers in a million years. Thus continental motion can change global climate within a geologically short period of time by opening or closing a crucial strait. (However, even this "geologically short period of time" is extremely long when compared with the rise of human civilization.) Much longer times are required to modify climate by altering the proximity of a continent to the poles or by creating a supercontinent.

Mountains and Climate

Global cooling during the past 40 million years coincided with the formation of the Himalayas and the North American Cordillera.[4] Mountains interrupt airflow, altering regional winds. Air cools as it rises and passes over high, snow-covered peaks. However, it is unclear whether this regional cooling could account for the global cooling that accompanied this episode of mountain formation.

Large portions of the Himalayas and the North American Cordillera are composed of marine limestone. Recall from the previous section that when marine limestone weathers, carbon dioxide is removed from the atmosphere. When sea-floor rocks are thrust upward to form mountains, they become exposed to the air. Rapid weathering then may remove enough atmospheric carbon dioxide to cause global cooling.

Volcanoes and Climate

Recall from Chapter 8 that volcanoes emit ash and sulfur compounds that reflect sunlight and cool the atmosphere. For two years after Mt. Pinatubo erupted in 1991, the Earth cooled by a few tenths of a degree Celsius. Temperature rose again in 1994 after the ash and sulfur settled out.

[4]William F. Ruddiman and John Kutzbach, "Plateau Uplift and Climatic Change," *Scientific American* (March 1991): 66ff.

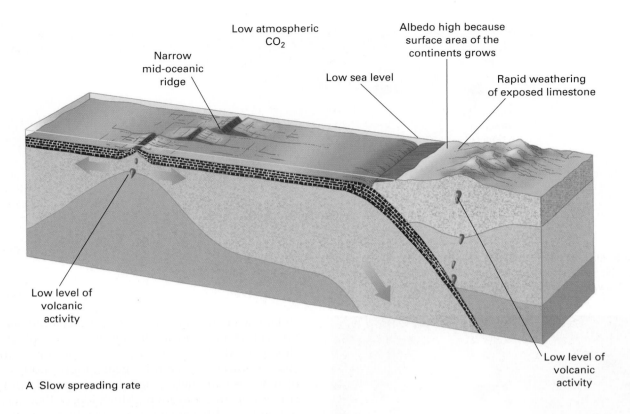

Low atmospheric
CO$_2$

Narrow
mid-oceanic
ridge

Albedo high because
surface area of the
continents grows

Low sea level

Rapid weathering
of exposed limestone

Low level of
volcanic
activity

Low level of
volcanic
activity

A Slow spreading rate

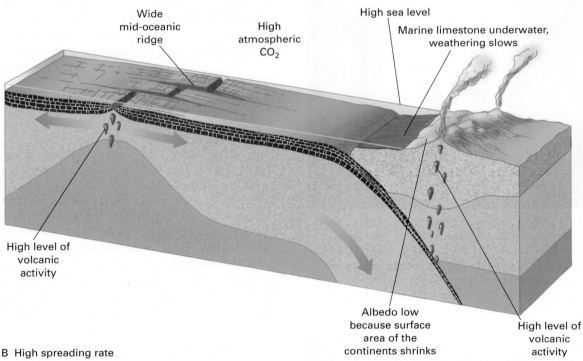

Wide
mid-oceanic
ridge

High
atmospheric
CO$_2$

High sea level

Marine limestone underwater,
weathering slows

High level of
volcanic
activity

Albedo low
because surface
area of the
continents shrinks

High level of
volcanic
activity

B High spreading rate

Figure 21.14 (A) When subduction is slow, the Mid-Oceanic Ridge is narrow. As a result, sea level is low, exposing marine limestone to weathering. Volcanic activity is also low. The atmospheric carbon dioxide concentration is low because of rapid weathering and low volcanic activity. Also, global albedo is high because the surface of the continents grows at the expense of shrinking oceans. All of these factors cool the Earth. (B) When subduction is fast, the Mid-Oceanic Ridge is wide. As a result, sea level is high, flooding coastal regions. Volcanic activity is also high. The atmospheric carbon dioxide concentration is high because weathering is slow and volcanic activity is high. Also, global albedo is low because of the low surface area of the continents and greater surface area of the seas. All of these factors warm the Earth.

Volcanoes also emit carbon dioxide that warms the atmosphere by absorbing infrared radiation. The net result—warming or cooling—depends on the size of the eruption, its violence, and the proportion of solids and gases released. Some scientists believe that a great eruption in Siberia 250 million years ago cooled the atmosphere enough to cause or contribute to the Permian extinction. A huge sequence of eruptions called the mid-Cretaceous superplume, 120 million years ago, may have emitted enough carbon dioxide to warm the atmosphere by 7 to 10°C. Dinosaurs flourished in huge swamps, and some of the abundant vegetation collected to form massive coal deposits.

How Tectonics, Sea Level, Volcanoes, and Weathering Interact to Regulate Climate

Tectonics, sea level, volcanoes, and weathering are all part of a tightly interconnected Earth system that affects both global and regional climate. When tectonic plates spread slowly, the Mid-Oceanic Ridge system is so narrow that it displaces relatively small amounts of sea water. As a result, sea level falls. When sea level falls, large marine limestone deposits on the continental shelves are exposed as dry land. The limestone weathers. Weathering of limestone removes carbon dioxide from the atmosphere, leading to global cooling. At the same time, when sea-floor spreading is slow, subduction is also slow. Volcanic activity at both the spreading centers and the subduction zones slows down, so relatively small amounts of carbon dioxide are emitted. With small additions of carbon dioxide from volcanic eruptions and removal of atmospheric carbon dioxide by weathering, the atmospheric carbon dioxide concentration decreases and the global temperature cools. In addition, dropping sea level decreases the surface area of the oceans and increases the surface area of the higher-albedo continents. This results in an increase of average global albedo, and, consequently, reinforces the global cooling (Figure 21.14A). These conditions may have caused the cooling at the end of the Carboniferous period shown in Figure 21.2.

In contrast, during periods of rapid sea-floor spreading, a high-volume Mid-Oceanic Ridge system raises sea level. Marine limestone beds are submerged, weathering slows down, and weathering removes less carbon dioxide from the atmosphere. Volcanic activity is high during periods of rapid plate movement, so large amounts of carbon dioxide are released into the atmosphere. Rising sea level decreases continental area, and therefore decreases the average global albedo. All of these factors lead to global warming (Figure 21.14B). But rapid spreading also coincides with rapid subduction and accelerated mountain-building leading to accelerated weathering on the continents,

which consumes carbon dioxide. Once again, climate systems are driven by so many opposing mechanisms that it is often difficult to determine which will prevail.

21.7 Humans, the Carbon Cycle, and Climate

We have learned that the amount of carbon in the atmosphere is determined by many natural factors, including rates of plant growth, mixing of surface ocean water and deep ocean water, growth rates of marine organisms, weathering, the movement of tectonic plates, and volcanic activity. Within the past few hundred years, humans have become an important part of the carbon cycle. Modern industry releases four greenhouse gases—carbon dioxide, methane, chlorofluorocarbons (CFCs), and nitrogen oxides.

People release carbon dioxide when they burn fossil fuels. Logging also frees carbon dioxide because stems and leaves are frequently burned and forest litter rots more quickly when it is disturbed by heavy machinery. The recent rise in the concentration of atmospheric carbon dioxide has attracted considerable attention because it is the most abundant industrial greenhouse gas (Figure 21.15).

In addition, several other greenhouse gases are released by modern agriculture and industry. Small amounts of methane are released during some industrial processes. Larger amounts are released from the guts of cows, other animals, and termites, and from rotting that occurs in rice paddies. Today, industry and agriculture combined add about 37×10^{12} grams of methane into the atmosphere every year. Chlorofluorocarbons, were, until recently, used as refrigerants and as propellants in aerosol cans. This source is rapidly diminishing because international treaties have banned CFC production. N_2O, yet another greenhouse gas, is released from the manufacture and use of nitrogen fertilizer, some industrial chemical syntheses, and from the exhaust of high-flying jet aircraft.

With this background, let us ask two simple and related questions: Has the human release of greenhouse gases caused a warming of the Earth over the past century? Is this trend likely to continue?

Let us first summarize the data:

Human activities release greenhouse gases.
The concentration of these gases in the atmosphere has risen in the past 100 years.
Greenhouse gases absorb infrared radiation and trap heat.
The atmosphere has warmed by 0.6°C during the last century.

Starting with these observations, and using computer models to test their hypotheses, most atmospheric

Figure 21.15 Atmospheric carbon dioxide concentration has risen by about 17 percent within the past century. The short-term fluctuations are caused by seasonal changes in carbon dioxide absorption by plants.

scientists conclude that rising atmospheric concentrations of industrial greenhouse gases have caused the recent global temperature rise. Furthermore, climate models predict that the mean global temperature will increase by 1 to 3.5°C during the next century.

However, not all scientists agree. Some argue that these observations do not prove that industrial greenhouse gases are responsible for the observed global warming. Climate has changed frequently and drastically throughout Earth history. Therefore modern global warming may just be a natural event, not a result of industrial greenhouse gas emissions. Earlier in this chapter we explained that the Sun has warmed slightly over the past few decades. This increase of solar output is one of many possible mechanisms that may contribute to the current observed warming.

The debate over the causes of global warming has been long, often acrimonious, and frequently political. Clearly many factors— natural and anthropogenic— may be operating simultaneously. Yet, most climatologists agree that industrial carbon emissions are primarily responsible for the observed climate change.

Consequences of Greenhouse Warming

Many people ask, "What's the big deal? What difference will it make if the planet is a few degrees warmer than it is today?" Figure 21.16 summarizes the major predicted consequences of global warming.

Temperature Effects on Agriculture

A warmer global climate would mean a longer frost-free period in the high latitudes, which would benefit agriculture. In parts of North America, the growing season is now a week longer than it was a few decades ago. Snowfall in the midlatitudes would diminish, decreasing the winter and spring albedo, which could lead to further warming. On the negative side, warmth would also improve conditions for plant pathogens and parasites, which could decrease crop yields.

Perhaps an even greater concern is that climate change could cause a shift in the major atmospheric convection cells that regulate global climate. If climate belts shifted, the current patterns of productive agricultural zones and deserts could be altered, with serious worldwide consequences.

Precipitation and Soil Moisture Effects on Agriculture

In a warmer world, both precipitation and evaporation would increase. Computer models show that the effects would differ from region to region. Between 1900 and 2000, rainfall increased in the great grain-growing regions in North America and Russia. On the other hand, parts of North Africa, India, and Southeast Asia received less rainfall over the same time. The resulting drought has led to famine during recent decades.

In a hotter world, more soil moisture will evaporate. As mentioned above, in the Northern Hemi-

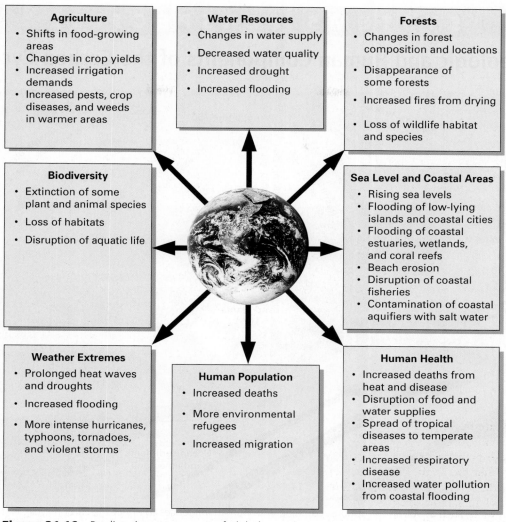

Agriculture
- Shifts in food-growing areas
- Changes in crop yields
- Increased irrigation demands
- Increased pests, crop diseases, and weeds in warmer areas

Water Resources
- Changes in water supply
- Decreased water quality
- Increased drought
- Increased flooding

Forests
- Changes in forest composition and locations
- Disappearance of some forests
- Increased fires from drying
- Loss of wildlife habitat and species

Biodiversity
- Extinction of some plant and animal species
- Loss of habitats
- Disruption of aquatic life

Sea Level and Coastal Areas
- Rising sea levels
- Flooding of low-lying islands and coastal cities
- Flooding of coastal estuaries, wetlands, and coral reefs
- Beach erosion
- Disruption of coastal fisheries
- Contamination of coastal aquifers with salt water

Weather Extremes
- Prolonged heat waves and droughts
- Increased flooding
- More intense hurricanes, typhoons, tornadoes, and violent storms

Human Population
- Increased deaths
- More environmental refugees
- Increased migration

Human Health
- Increased deaths from heat and disease
- Disruption of food and water supplies
- Spread of tropical diseases to temperate areas
- Increased respiratory disease
- Increased water pollution from coastal flooding

Figure 21.16 Predicted consequences of global warming.

sphere, scientists predict that global warming will lead to increased rainfall, adding moisture to the soil. At the same time, warming will increase evaporation that removes soil moisture. Most computer models forecast a net loss of soil moisture and depletion of ground water, despite the prediction that rainfall will increase. Drought and soil moisture depletion would increase demands for irrigation. But, as documented in Chapter 12, irrigation systems are already stressing global water resources, causing both shortages and political instability in many parts of the world. As a result of all these factors, most scientists predict that higher mean global temperature would decrease global food production, perhaps dramatically.

Extreme Weather Events

Computer models predict that weather extremes, such as intense rainstorms, flooding, heat waves, prolonged droughts, and violent storms such as hurricanes, typhoons, and tornados will become more common in a warmer, wetter world. In the United States, the number of heavy downpours (defined as 5 centimeters or 2 inches of rain in a single day) increased by 25 percent from 1900 to 2000. Worldwide, there were ten times as many catastrophic floods in the decade from 1990 to 2000 as there were in an average decade between 1950 and 1985. Thus, we face the paradox of *both* more floods and more droughts.

Changes in Biodiversity

According to a study by the World Wildlife Fund in 2000, global warming could alter one third of the world's wildlife habitats by 2100. In some northern latitude regions, 70 percent of habitats would be significantly affected. As soil moisture decreases, trees would die and wildfires would become more common, further reducing forest cover. Species that could not adapt might become extinct. Undoubtedly, others would flourish. Ecological systems would change, but it is important to remember that terrestrial ecosystems have adjusted to far greater perturbations than we are experiencing today.

Geologic and Human Components of the Carbon Cycle

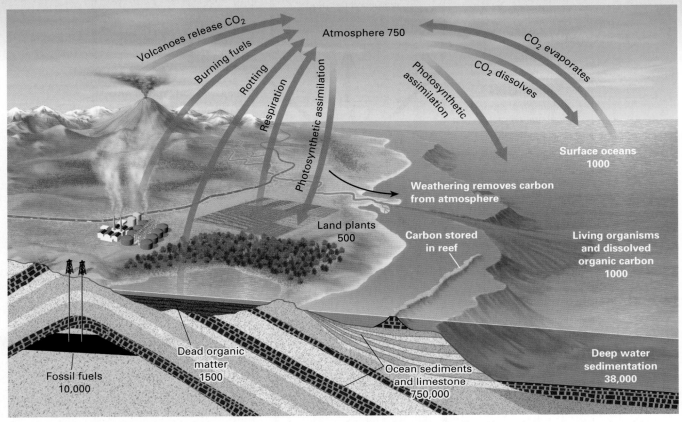

Natural geologic events, such as volcanic eruptions, combine with human influences to affect the carbon cycle. Note that this figure is an amalgam of Figures 21.10 and 21.11. The figure is schematic because all of the pictured reservoirs and mechanisms do not usually appear in a single landscape.

Sea-Level Change

When water is warmed, it expands slightly. From 1900 to 2000, mean global sea level rose 10 to 25 centimeters, or roughly the thickness of a dime every year. Oceanographers suggest that even this modest rise may be affecting coastal estuaries, wetlands, and coral reefs. However, sea-level rise could increase dramatically if the polar ice sheets of Antarctica and Greenland melt at an accelerated rate. This effect will be discussed further in the following section (Figure 21.17).

Effects on People

Humans evolved during a period of rapid climate change in the savannas and forests of Africa. In fact, many anthropologists argue that we flourished be-cause we adapted to climate change faster and more efficiently than other species in the African ecosystem. A few million years later, we survived the Pleistocene Ice Age. We are a clever and resourceful species. Yet the consequences of global warming could be severe. In a warmer world, tropical diseases such as malaria have been spreading to higher latitudes. But the biggest problem arises because expanding human population is already stressing global systems. As a result, small shifts in food production or water availability could lead to mass starvation, water scarcity, and political instability. In addition, rising sea level could flood coastal cities and farmlands, causing trillions of dollars worth of damage throughout the world.

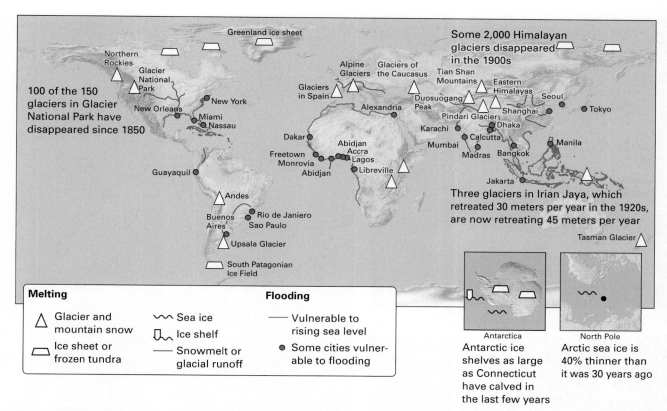

Figure 21.17 Global changes resulting from melting glaciers and polar ice caps. *Source:* Adapted from Newsweek—Begley, Sharon, "Mercury's Rising," December 4, 2000, p. 52. © 2000 Newsweek, Inc. All rights reserved. Reprinted by permission.

21.8 Feedback and Threshold Mechanisms in Climate Change

In a linear relationship, if you raise the concentration of greenhouse gases a small amount, the mean global temperature will rise by a small amount, and further small increases of greenhouse gas concentrations will cause additional small temperature increases, and so on. However, many scientists argue that climate change does not necessarily follow linear relationships.

In Chapter 1 we mentioned that the melting of ice is a *threshold phenomenon*. If the air above a glacier warms from –1.5 to –0.5°C, the ice does not melt and the warming may cause only minimal environmental change. However, if the air warms another degree to +0.5°C, the ice warms beyond the threshold defined by its melting point. Melting ice can cause sea level rise and a host of cascading effects.

Recall that a *feedback mechanism* occurs when a small initial perturbation affects another component of

the Earth systems, which amplifies the original effect, which perturbs the system even more, which leads to a greater effect, and so on. The Antarctic ice shelf collapse discussed in the introduction to this chapter could initiate a catastrophic feedback mechanism. Glacial ice in western Antarctica occupies three different environments. Continental glaciers rest on solid ground that lies above sea level. Grounded ice rests on the continental shelf below sea level. Floating ice is attached to grounded ice but is floating on the ocean surface.

Within the past few decades, some process has caused the grounded ice to become thinner. As a result, some of this ice has lifted off the bottom and started to float. In turn, large chunks of the floating ice have broken up and drifted away. Scientists do not know why the grounded ice has thinned. Much of Antarctic has actually become *cooler* in recent decades. Even in the Antarctic Peninsula, where slight warming has occurred, the temperature is usually so far below freezing that a small warming would not melt the ice.

When scientists study sea floor sediments, they find evidence for earlier oscillations in the Antarctic

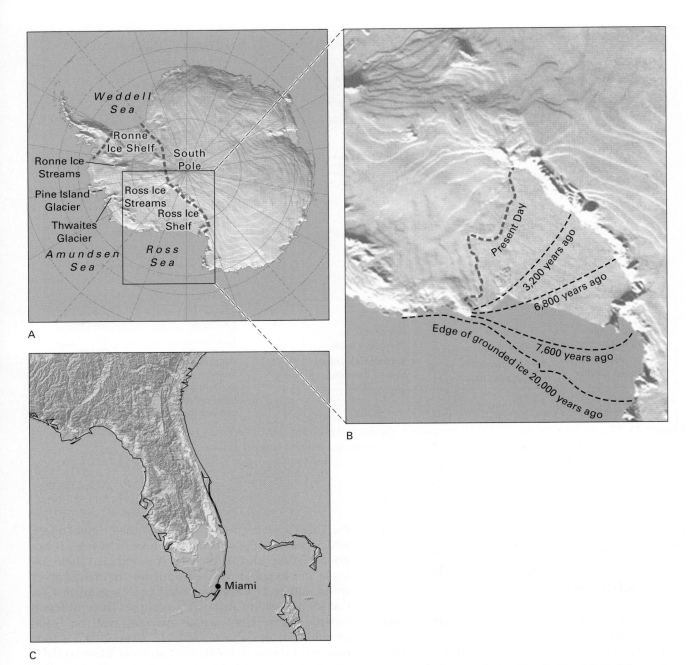

Figure 21.18 (A) Antarctica is surrounded by ice shelves, which are particularly extensive on the western edge of the continent. (B) About 5.3 million cubic kilometers of ice has broken free and floated into the ocean since the last ice age maximum about 20,000 years ago. The Ross Ice Shelf has retreated up to 900 km and retreat has accelerated in the past decade. (C) A complete collapse of the West Antarctic Ice Sheet would raise global sea level by five meters and drown low-lying regions such as south Florida. *Source:* Ross Ice Shelf. *Scientific American,* Dec. 2002, p. 101.

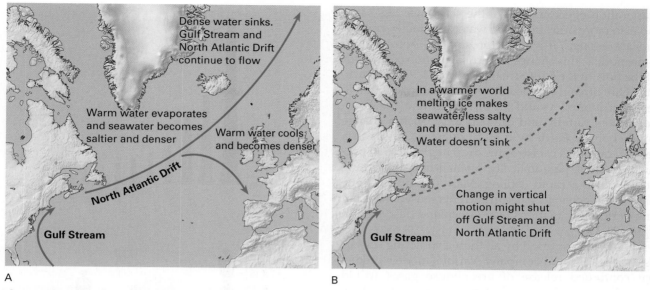

A   B

Figure 21.19 Some climate models indicate that warmer temperatures may shut off the Gulf Stream and North Atlantic drift, which could result in subsequent global cooling.

ice shelves. Thus, the changes occurring today are not unusual. Even though we do not know *why* the ice shelves have been disintegrating, it is important to study the effects of this break-up.

Recall from Chapter 13, that glaciers flow slowly downslope, and large ones spread outward under their own weight. As grounded ice begins to float, sea water creeps beneath the glacier and saturates the bottom mud. Wet mud is an ideal lubricant, so the glacier flows faster. As flow increases, more ice pushes out into the sea, breaks off and floats away. But the grounded ice had been acting as a barrier that reduced the flow of the part of the ice that rested on land. When the grounded ice barrier begins to float and flow faster, the land-based portion of the ice then is not held back effectively and it too may speed up.

If this process accelerates, enough ice may spill into the ocean to cause a significant rise in sea level. Oceans have a lower albedo than land. Therefore, if sea level rises and floods low-lying land, the oceans would increase in surface area. Average global albedo would decrease and both the oceans and the atmosphere would become warmer. This would lead to further break-up of the West Antarctic Ice Sheet and more sea-level rise. Also, as the oceans warm, the warm surface water releases additional carbon dioxide and water vapor leading to even greater warming. According to this scenario, climate would spiral out of control. Thus the break-up of the West Antarctic Ice Sheet could eventually lead to rising sea level and flooding of coastal cities and farmlands (Figure 21.18).

How Global Warming Could Cause Global Cooling

Paradoxically, some scientists have calculated that a small initial global warming could lead to an eventual global cooling. Warm air increases evaporation from the oceans and also carries more water vapor than cooler air. Therefore, if the Earth were to become warmer, more water vapor from the tropics would be transported to the polar areas, where it would fall as snow. Thus, according to this scenario, in a warmer world, glaciers and snowfields would *grow*. Albedo would increase, sea level would fall, and the Earth would cool.

Another scenario is even more dramatic and draconian. In Chapter 16 we learned that the Gulf Stream and the North Atlantic Drift flow from the tropical Atlantic Ocean northward toward northern Europe. This surface water becomes saltier as it approaches the high latitudes because the warm water evaporates. As the water reaches the coast of Greenland, it cools. Cooling and increased salt content make the water denser, so it sinks. According to some models this sinking is essential in maintaining the conveyor-belt flow of the Gulf Stream (Figure 21.19A).

Now, what would happen if the air and the water surface were to become warmer? Warm water is more buoyant than cold water. Warming would increase evaporation, but it would also melt portions of the Greenland Ice Cap. Abundant fresh water flowing onto the surface of the North Atlantic would overwhelm the evaporation effect and make the sea water less salty, and also more buoyant. If the water became warm and buoyant enough, it would stop sinking. According to some models, this change in vertical motion could shut off the flow of the Gulf Stream (Figure 21.19B). In turn, if the Gulf Stream stopped or veered southward, global heat distribution would be disrupted and the Earth would cool rapidly and dramatically.[5] Such a change could cool the Earth by 5 to 10 degrees Celsius in a decade, causing a catastrophic drop in global food production. Thus, paradoxically, a small initial warming would cause a rapid cooling. Many scientists argue that a similar change in ocean currents caused the rapid temperature fluctuations over Greenland described in Figure 21.3.

If you are confused by all these conflicting scenarios, you are in good company. Various models predict that continued release of greenhouse gases would cause slow warming, rapid warming, or rapid cooling. All we know for certain is that the Earth's climate has changed significantly in the past, and that by introducing greenhouse gases into the atmosphere, we are becoming an agent for future change.

21.9 The Kyoto Treaty on Greenhouse Warming

In December of 1997, representatives from 160 nations met in Kyoto, Japan, to discuss global climate change. The major issues were: How seriously are humans altering climate? How will climate change affect humans and global ecosystems? Can the nations of the world cooperate to reduce carbon emissions and defuse the problem?

One significant argument at the 1997 Kyoto conference concerned the relative amounts of greenhouse gases produced by the wealthy industrial nations and the less wealthy, developing nations. As an example, China has a population of 1.2 billion, a little over four times that of the United States, which has a population of 280 million. Each person in the United States releases about eight times as much carbon dioxide as the average Chinese person (Figure 21.20). The net result is that people in the United States emit twice as much carbon dioxide as do people in China.

At the Kyoto conference, the United States argued that all countries must decrease emission of greenhouse gases by the same proportion. However, repre-

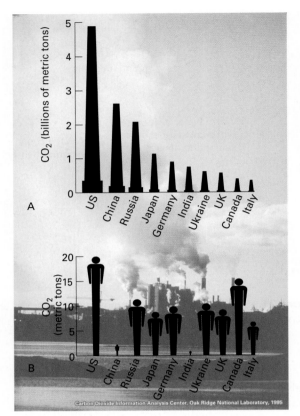

Figure 21.20 (A) Carbon dioxide emissions from the top ten emitting countries in 1994. (B) Per capita carbon dioxide emissions from the top ten emitting countries in 1994.

sentatives of developing nations, including China, argued that the United States' position is unfair because it condemns people in developing nations to continued poverty. They reasoned that the world's poor people should be allowed to raise their standard of living first, before they worry about global warming. The United States countered that because of the great number of people in China and the rest of the developing world, even a small per capita increase in fossil fuel use would lead to an unacceptably large increase in total carbon dioxide emissions.

In the final treaty, the United States agreed to reduce greenhouse emissions by 7 percent, the European Union by 8 percent, and Japan by 6 percent from 1990 levels. These targets were scheduled to be reached between 2008 and 2012. The developing countries, including China, did not agree to any emissions reductions.

After a treaty is signed, it must be ratified by each signature country. The Kyoto Treaty was scheduled to become compulsory for all nations when it is ratified by 55 countries accounting for 55 percent of 1990 in-

[5] Wallace C. Broecker, "Thermohaline Circulation, the Achilles Heel of our Climate System: Will Man-Made CO_2 Upset the Current Balance?" *Science* 278 (November 28, 1997): 1582.

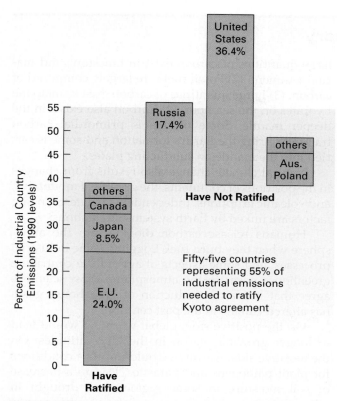

Figure 21.21 Fifty-five nations representing 55 percent of all industrial carbon dioxide emissions are needed to ratify the Kyoto Protocol.

dustrial country carbon emissions. By the end of 2002, 99 countries with 39 percent of industrial country emissions had approved the treaty (Figure 21.21). After several years of conflicting policy statements, in December, 2003, Russia announced that it would not ratify the Kyoto Protocol. The Kremlin claimed that the treaty "places significant limitations on the economic growth of Russia . . . Of course this protocol can't be ratified." Without Russia and the United States, the treaty is dead, even if every other undecided country ratified.

President George W. Bush has argued that he will never sign the Kyoto Treaty because emissions reduction would harm the U.S. economy. Furthermore, the administration stresses that no one has proven that global warming would have adverse economic effects.

In rebuttal, supporters of the Kyoto Treaty argue the following:

- Wealth is not necessarily dependent on profligate fuel consumption. For example, Japan is a wealthy industrial nation, yet Japanese emit less than half the carbon per capita as the average American.
- Furthermore, reduction of fuel consumption and carbon emissions could actually help the economy. People save money when they use less fuel. Moreover, if individuals and businesses shifted to the more fuel-efficient technologies that were discussed in Chapter 5, the massive implementation of new infrastructure would be a boon to the economy.
- Computer models show that the longer we procrastinate and fail to decrease emissions, the longer it will take the system to recover, once emissions are reduced.
- Finally, the argument continues, the alternative—climate change—could possibly initiate runaway feedback mechanisms that would spiral out of control. Global food production could be disrupted, leading to mass starvation and global political unrest. Therefore, on the grounds that it is better to be "safe than sorry," we should reduce emissions now.

Summary

Global climate has changed throughout Earth history from extreme cold with extensive glaciation, to a 243-million-year warm period from the start of the Mesozoic era almost to the present. During the last 100,000 years, the mean annual global temperature has changed frequently and dramatically, although the past 10,000 years, during which civilization developed, witnessed anomalously stable climate.

Past climates are measured by historical records, tree rings, pollen assemblages, oxygen isotope ratios in glacial ice, glacial evidence, plankton assemblages and isotope studies in ocean sediment, and fossils in sedimentary rocks.

Astronomical causes of climate change include the variations in the Earth's orbit and the tilt of its axis, changes in solar radiation, and bolide impacts.

Water, in its various forms can cause warming or cooling. Water vapor warms the atmosphere, but clouds can cause warming or cooling. Glaciers and snowfields reflect sunlight and cause cooling. Evaporation is a cooling process; while condensation releases heat. The evaporation/condensation cycle transports heat from the equatorial regions to the poles. Weathering alters the carbon dioxide concentration in the atmosphere. Ocean currents transport heat and moisture.

Carbon circulates among all four of the Earth's realms. Carbon dioxide is a greenhouse gas that warms the atmosphere. Carbon exists in the biosphere as the fundamental building block for organic tissue. Carbon dioxide gas dissolves in sea water to form bicarbonate and carbonate ions. Carbon exists in the crust and mantle in several forms. (1) Marine organisms absorb calcium and carbonate ions and convert them to solid calcium carbonate (shells and skeletons). As a result, large quantities of carbon exist in limestone and marine sediment. (2) Fossil fuels are largely composed of carbon. (3) Large quantities of carbon exist as methane hydrates on the sea floor. (4) Carbon also exists in the deeper mantle. Some of this is primordial carbon trapped during the Earth's formation and some is carried into the mantle on subducting plates.

Natural climate change also results from changes in the positions of continents, the growth of mountains, and volcanic eruptions. Independent climate-changing factors are linked by Earth systems interactions.

Humans release carbon dioxide into the atmosphere when they burn fuel. Logging, some industrial processes, and some aspects of agriculture contribute greenhouse gases to the atmosphere. Most scientists agree that human introduction of greenhouse gases has altered climate in the past century.

On the positive side, global warming would lead to longer growing season in the high latitudes. On the negative side, warming would improve conditions for plant pathogens and parasites, lead to a decrease of soil moisture in some regions and drought in other regions, cause more catastrophic weather events, and encourage the spread of certain diseases, such as malaria.

The collapse of the West Antarctic Ice Sheet could lead to rising sea level and further global warming. Alternatively, some scientists have calculated that slight global warming could disrupt the vertical flow of water in the North Atlantic, leading to global cooling.

The United States has not signed the Kyoto Treaty. Proponents of the treaty argue that the economic downside would be minimal whereas the possible effects of global warming could be catastrophic.

Earth Systems Interactions

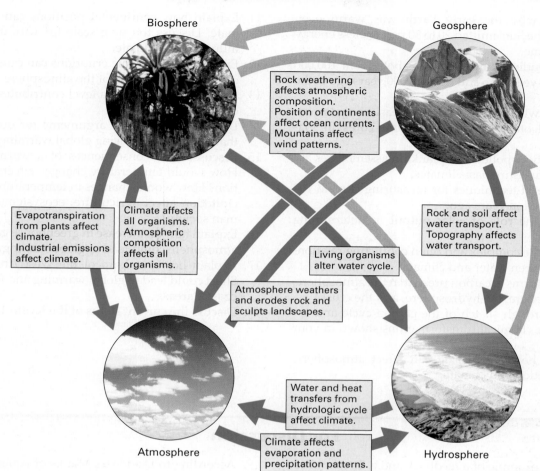

Biosphere

Geosphere

Rock weathering affects atmospheric composition.
Position of continents affect ocean currents.
Mountains affect wind patterns.

Evapotranspiration from plants affect climate.
Industrial emissions affect climate.

Climate affects all organisms.
Atmospheric composition affects all organisms.

Rock and soil affect water transport.
Topography affects water transport.

Living organisms alter water cycle.

Atmosphere weathers and erodes rock and sculpts landscapes.

Water and heat transfers from hydrologic cycle affect climate.

Climate affects evaporation and precipitation patterns.

Atmosphere

Hydrosphere

For Review

1. Explain why the early Earth was warm even though the Sun emitted 20 to 30 percent less energy at that time.
2. Briefly outline climate changes both from 100,000 to 10,000 years ago and from 10,000 years ago to the present.
3. Explain why oxygen isotope measurements provide paleotemperature data from cores in glacial ice.
4. Explain how pollen and plankton assemblages are used to measure past climates.
5. List several techniques for measuring climate 100 to 500 million years ago.
6. Discuss the role of solar output in determining climate.
7. Outline the complex and often conflicting relationship between water and climate.
8. In what forms is carbon present in the atmosphere, the biosphere, the hydrosphere, and the crust?
9. Draw a rough sketch of the carbon cycle and explain the chemical transformations shown in your cycle.
10. Explain how weathering can affect atmospheric composition and climate.
11. Explain how continental positions can affect climate. Discuss the time scale for various tectonic influences on climate.
12. Explain how volcanic eruptions can cause either a cooling or a warming of the atmosphere.
13. Explain why falling sea level contributes to global cooling.
14. Discuss the scientific arguments for our concern that humans are causing global warming.
15. Discusses the consequences of a warmer Earth. How would temperature changes affect precipitation? How would changes in temperature and precipitation affect agriculture, ecosystems, and human society?
16. Explain how an increase in greenhouse gases in the atmosphere could lead to global cooling.
17. Explain how break-up of the West Antarctic Ice Sheet could lead to global warming and flooding of coastal areas.
18. Discuss the current status of the Kyoto Treaty.

For Discussion

1. Give an example of a feedback and a threshold effect in a science other than Earth science (such as psychology, political science, or any other science).
2. Based on Figure 21.4, list the useful time ranges for historical records, pollen, and plankton as indicators of paleoclimates. Explain why each of these techniques is not useful farther back in time.
3. Discuss the difficulties and costs involved in reducing carbon dioxide emissions.
4. Explain why a small change in average global temperatures can have environmental, economic, and political effects.
5. Do you feel that the United States should ratify the Kyoto treaty? Defend your answer.
6. Stephen Jay Gould wrote, "During most of the past 600 million years, the Earth has been sufficiently warm so that even the bottom of an orbital cycle produced no ice caps." (*Natural History*, May 1991, p. 18.) Explain this statement in your own words.
7. According to David des Marais of Ames Research Center, about 2.2 billion years ago, rapid plate motion led to rapid rise of mountains throughout the world. As the mountains rose, large quantities of organic-rich sediment eroded and were transported into the sea, where they were buried. Predict how this burial might alter atmospheric composition.

Earth Science ⊕ Now™

Assess your understanding of this chapter's topics with additional quizzing and comprehensive interactivities at **http://earthscience.brookscole.com/earthsci3e** as well as current and up-to-date weblinks, additional readings, and InfoTrac College Edition exercises.